MATH SENSE

Skills, Problem Solving, Tools, and Applications

Measurement and Data Analysis

Robert P. Mitchell

New Readers Press

Acknowledgments

Advisers

Connie Eichhorn
Supervisor of Transitional Services
Omaha Public Schools
Omaha, NE

Lois Kasper
Instructional Facilitator
N.Y. Board of Education
New York, NY

Jan Phillips
Assistant Professor
William Rainey Harper College
Palatine, IL

Mary B. Puleo
Assistant Director
Sarasota County Adult and
Community Education
Sarasota, FL

Margaret Rogers
Coordinator
San Juan Unified Adult Education
Sacramento, CA

Consultant/Field-Test Adviser

Ernest Kettenring
Teacher, Teacher-Advisor, and Learning Center Coordinator
Wilson-Lincoln Community Adult School
Los Angeles Unified School District

Instructor
Pasadena City College Community Skills Center

Math Sense®: Measurements and Data Analysis
ISBN 1-56420-382-4
Copyright © 2003, 1996 New Readers Press
New Readers Press
Division of ProLiteracy Worldwide
1320 Jamesville Avenue, Syracuse, New York 13210
www.newreaderspress.com

Printed in the United States of America
9 8 7 6 5 4 3 2

All proceeds from the sale of New Readers Press materials support literacy programs in the United States and worldwide.

Developer: Learning Unlimited, Oak Park, IL
Content Editor: Sybil M. Sosin Publishing Services
Photo Illustrations: Mary McConnell
Series Editor: Judi Lauber
Production Director: Heather Witt
Illustrations: Linda Tiff, James P. Wallace
Production Specialist: Jeffrey R. Smith
Cover Design: Kimbrly Koennecke

Casio *fx*-260 image courtesy of Casio, Inc.

Contents

Introduction

Math skills play an increasingly vital role in today's world. Everyone needs to work confidently with numbers to solve problems on the job and in other areas of daily life.

This book and the others in the *Math Sense* series can help you meet your everyday math needs. Each unit is organized around four key areas that will build your competence and self-confidence.

- **Skills** pages present instruction and practice with both computation and word problems.

- **Tools** pages provide insight on how to use mathematical devices (such as rulers) and to apply key ideas (such as estimation) to solve math problems. Throughout the book, these pages also focus on filling in **answer grids** similar to the ones used on many standardized tests.

- **Problem Solver** pages provide key strategies to help you become a successful problem solver.

- **Application** pages are real-life topics that require mathematics.

Key Features

Skill Preview: You can use the Skill Preview to determine what skills you already have and what you need to concentrate on.

Talk About It: At the beginning of each unit, you will have a topic to discuss with classmates. Talking about mathematics is key to building your understanding.

Key Concepts: Throughout the book, you will see this symbol ▶, which indicates key math concepts and rules.

Making Connections: Throughout each unit, you will work with topics that connect math ideas to various interest areas and to other math concepts.

Special Problems: These specially labeled problems require an in-depth exploration of math ideas. You may be asked to explain or draw or to do something else that demonstrates your math skills.

Working Together: At the end of each unit, you will work with a partner or small group to apply your math skills.

Mixed and Unit Reviews: Periodic checkups will help you see how well you understand the material and can apply what you have learned.

Posttest: At the end of the book, you will find a test that combines all of the book's topics. You can use this final review to judge how well you have mastered the book's skills and strategies.

Glossary: Use this list of terms to learn or review key math words and ideas.

Tool Kit: You can refer to these resource pages as you work through the book.

Skill Preview

This survey of math skills will help you and your teacher decide what you need to study to get the most out of this book. It will show you how much you already know and what you need to learn in the areas of measurement and data analysis.

Do as much as you can of each section below. If you can't do all of the problems in a section, go ahead to the next section and do all that you can.

Part 1: Distance, Space, and Time

Change each quantity to the unit(s) indicated.

1. 46 in. = _____ ft. _____ in.   **2.** $2\frac{1}{3}$ yd. = _____ ft.   **3.** 135 cm = _____ m _____ cm

Perform the indicated operation. Simplify answers if possible.

4.   3 yd. 2 ft.
    + 1 yd. 2 ft.

5.   4 m 25 cm
    − 2 m 50 cm

6. $2\overline{)5\text{ ft. }4\text{ in.}}$

Solve each problem.

7. Tia uses gold chain to make doll jewelry. If she wants to make 8 bracelets that are each 7 cm 7 mm long, *about* how much chain will Tia need? Express your answer to the nearest centimeter.

|← — — — 7 cm 7 mm — — — →|

8. What are the perimeter and area of the rug shown below? (*Perimeter* is distance around; *area* is amount of surface.)

Perimeter: _____   Area: _____

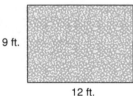

9 ft.

12 ft.

9. Determine the volume of the storage shed pictured below. (*Volume* is the amount of space enclosed by the shed walls.)

8 ft.

15 ft.

10 ft.

10. According to her schedule, Anne's bus will arrive at the stop at 10:45 A.M.

a. According to the clock shown at right, what is the time now?

b. How long must Anne wait before the bus arrives?

6

Part 2: Capacity, Weight, and Temperature

Change each quantity to the units indicated.

11. 39 fl. oz. = _____ qt. _____ fl. oz.

12. 1,250 ml = _____ liter(s) _____ ml

13. 24 oz. = _____ lb. _____ oz.

Perform the indicated operation. Simplify answers if possible.

14.   3 qt. 2 c.
        + 1 qt. 3 c.

15.   4 lb. 10 oz.
        − 1 lb. 15 oz.

16.   6.48 kg
        + 2.5 kg

Solve each problem.

17. How much milk is contained in the measuring cup below? Write your answer in two ways: as a fraction of a cup *and* as a number of fluid ounces.

_____ c. = _____ fl. oz.

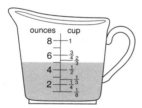

18. What metric unit is most closely equal to each of these English units?

  a. quart: _____

  b. pound: _____

19. What weight of apples is shown on the metric scale below? Express your answer both as a decimal number of kilograms *and* as a number of kilograms and grams.

__.__ kg = _____ kg _____ g

Kilogram Scale

20. What temperature does the thermometer below show?

Fahrenheit

Part 3: Organizing and Summarizing Data

Problems 21 and 22 are based on the *tally*.

21. How many shoppers took part in the poll?

22. How many more shoppers pay by check than pay by cash?

Home Foods Shoppers Poll	
Number of shoppers who:	
pay by cash	*pay by check*
~~HHT~~ ~~HHT~~ ~~HHT~~ ~~HHT~~ ~~HHT~~ ~~HHT~~ IIII	~~HHT~~ ~~HHT~~ ~~HHT~~ ~~HHT~~ ~~HHT~~ ~~HHT~~ ~~HHT~~ III

Problems 23 and 24 are based on the *line plot*.

23. How many apartments rent in the $501–$550 price range?

24. Do most of the apartments shown rent for more or less than $500?

Apartment Rental Prices in Oakwood

		X		
		X	X	X
	X	X	X	X
X	X	X	X	X
X	X	X	X	X
$401–$450	$451–$500	$501–$550	$551–$600	$601–$650

Problems 25–27 are based on the table.

25. Which listed school has the greatest *number* of male teachers?

26. Which listed school has the highest *percent* of male teachers?

27. For the schools listed, what is the *mean* (average) number of male teachers?

Name of School	Male Teachers	Total Teachers
Springfield School	5	15
Washington Center	10	40
Western College	7	35
Hillary Academy	6	20

Part 4: Displaying Data on a Graph

Problems 28 and 29 are based on the *pictograph*.

28. Approximately how many Wave Buster Ski Boats did the Newton Company sell during spring?

29. During spring, which model sold about twice as well as the All Pro model?

Spring Sales of Newton Ski Boats

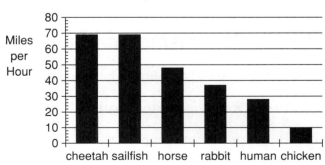

Problems 30 and 31 are based on the *bar graph*.

30. What is the *approximate* maximum speed in miles per hour of a horse?

31. Which animal has a maximum speed of *about* 10 miles per hour?

Maximum Speed of Selected Animals

Problems 32–34 are based on the *circle graph*.

32. Out of every 100 people polled, how many more gave the answer For than gave the answer Against?

33. What percent should be written on the graph in the section labeled Undecided?

34. If 440 people participated in the poll, *about* how many answered Against?

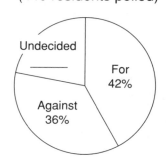

City Poll on Proposed School Tax
(440 residents polled)

Part 5: Analyzing Data

Problems 35–37 are based on the *line graph*.

35. What is the *approximate* gas mileage of the tested car at 25 miles per hour?

36. Does the graph show *positive* or *negative* correlation between mileage and speeds between 10 and 40 miles per hour?

37. What more do you need to know to be able to determine what *maximum* distance the test car can be driven on a full tank of gas?

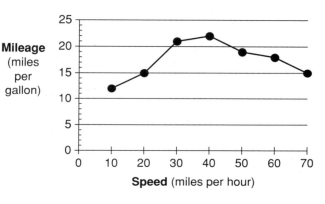

The Effect of Car Speed on Gas Mileage

Problems 38–40 refer to the spinner. Assume that the pointer will not stop on a line that separates two sections.

38. If you spin the spinner, what is the probability that the pointer will stop on a *shaded* section?

39. If you spin the spinner twice in a row, what is the probability that the pointer will stop on an *unshaded* section both times?

40. If you spin the spinner 50 times, *about* how many times will the pointer probably stop on a *shaded* section?

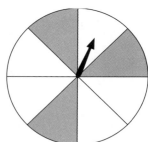

Answers start on next page.

1. 46 in. = **3 ft. 10 in.**
   $46 \div 12 = 3\,R10$

2. $2\frac{1}{3}$ yd. = **7 ft.**
   $2\frac{1}{3} \times 3 = 7$

3. 135 cm = **1 m 35 cm**
   100 cm = 1 m

4. **5 yd. 1 ft.**
   4 yd. 4 ft.; 4 ft. = 1 yd. 1 ft.

5. **1 m 75 cm**

4 m 25 cm	3 m 125 cm
− 2 m 50 cm =	− 2 m 50 cm
	1 m 75 cm

6. **2 ft. 8 in.**

   ```
        2 ft.     8 in.
      ┌──────────────────
    2 │ 5 ft.     4 in.
      − 4
      ──────────
        1 ft. =  12 in.
                 16 in.
               − 16 in.
               ─────────
   ```

7. **62 cm**
   7 cm 7 mm = 7.7 cm
   $\times 8$
   61.6 cm ≈ 62 cm

8. **Perimeter = 42 ft.; Area = 108 sq. ft.**
   perimeter = 12 + 9 + 12 + 9 = 42 ft.
   area = $l \times w$ = 12 × 9 = 108 sq. ft.

9. **1,200 cu. ft.**
   volume = 15 × 10 × 8 = 1,200 cu. ft.

10. **a.** 10:35   **b.** 10 minutes

11. 39 fl. oz. = **1 qt. 7 fl. oz.**
    1 qt. = 32 fl. oz.

12. 1,250 ml = **1 liter 250 ml**
    1,000 ml = 1 liter

13. 24 oz. = **1 lb. 8 oz.**
    1 lb. = 16 oz.

14. **5 qt. 1 c.**
    1 qt. = 4 c.

15. **2 lb. 11 oz.**

4 lb. 10 oz. =	3 lb. 26 oz.
− 1 lb. 15 oz.	− 1 lb. 15 oz.
	2 lb. 11 oz.

16. 8.98 kg *or* 8 kg 980 g

17. $\frac{5}{8}$ **c. = 5 fl. oz.**
    1 c. = 8 fl. oz.

18. **a.** liter   **b.** kilogram

19. **2.3 kg = 2 kg 300 g**
    1 kg = 1,000 g

20. 99.8°F

21. **79 shoppers**
    ||||| = 5 shoppers

22. **7**
    43 − 36 = 7

23. **5**
    Count the *X*s above the $501–$550 category.

24. **more than $500**
    There are many more *X*s in the three higher rent categories than in the lower two that represent apartments renting for $500 or less.

25. **Washington Center**
    10 male teachers

26. **Springfield School**
    $33\frac{1}{3}\%$ male teachers compared to 25% for Washington Center, 20% for Western College, and 30% for Hillary Academy

27. **7**
    (5 + 10 + 7 + 6) ÷ 4

28. **130**
    $6\frac{1}{2}$ symbols times 20

29. **Blue Dolphin**
    about 100 Blue Dolphin models sold, twice the number (50) of All Pro models

30. a little less than 50 miles per hour

31. chicken

32. **6**
    42 − 36 = 6; Each percent represents 1 person out of 100.

33. **22%**
    The three percents on the graph should add to 100%.

34. **about 158**
    36% of 440 = 0.36 × 440 = 158.4

35. about 18 miles per gallon

about halfway between the 20 miles per hour reading of 15 miles per gallon and the 30 miles per hour reading of about 21 miles per gallon

36. *positive* correlation

Between 10 and 40 miles per hour, mileage increases as speed increases.

37. the capacity of the gas tank (the number of gallons the tank holds when full)

To find maximum distance, you multiply the tank's capacity by 22, the car's maximum mileage rating.

38. $\frac{3}{8}$ *or* 37.5% *or* 3 chances out of 8

Probability can be expressed in any of these three ways.

39. $\frac{25}{64}$ *or* about 39%

$\frac{5}{8} \times \frac{5}{8} = \frac{25}{64} \approx 39\%$

The probability of the pointer stopping on an unshaded section each time is $\frac{5}{8}$. The probability of the pointer stopping on an unshaded section twice in a row is $\frac{5}{8} \times \frac{5}{8}$.

40. about 19 times

$50 \times \frac{3}{8} = \frac{150}{8} = 18\frac{6}{8} \approx 19$

Skill Preview Diagnostic Chart

Make note of any problems you answered incorrectly. Notice the skill area for each problem you missed. As you work through this book, be sure to focus on these skill areas.

Problem Number	Skill Area	Unit
1, 2, 3	Converting lengths	1
4, 5	Adding and subtracting lengths	1
6, 7	Multiplying and dividing lengths	1
8	Finding perimeter and area	1
9	Finding volume	1
10	Measuring time	1
11, 12	Converting capacity	2
13	Converting weight	2
14	Adding capacity	2
15, 16	Adding and subtracting weight	2
17	Using a measuring cup	2
18	Relating English and metric units	2
19	Using a metric scale	2
20	Using a clinical thermometer	2
21, 22	Using a tally sheet	3
23, 24	Reading a line plot	3
25, 26	Comparing sets of data	3
27	Calculating the mean	3
28, 29	Reading a pictograph	4
30, 31	Reading a bar graph	4
32, 33, 34	Reading a circle graph	4
35	Interpolating	5
36	Understanding correlation	5
37	Identifying needed information	5
38	Finding the probability of a single event	5
39	Finding the probability of successive events	5
40	Using probability for prediction	5

Distance, Space, and Time

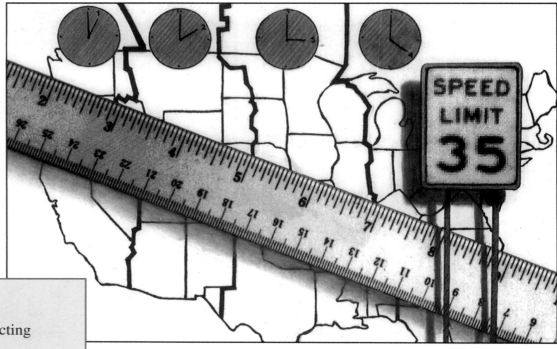

Measuring is a skill that each of us uses daily, often without even thinking about it. You probably deal often with measurements of distance, space, and time.

You measure distance each time you

- find the length of an object
- determine the distance between points

You're interested in space when you

- ask about the area of a rug
- determine the size of a table top
- compare the sizes of two freezers

You think about time when you

- use a microwave oven to cook a meal
- plan to meet a friend later that day
- use a calendar to plan a vacation

In this chapter, you'll learn the basic facts of measuring distance, space, and time. You'll use these skills in a wide range of problems.

When Is Measuring Important to Me?

When have you thought about distance, space, or time? Check the sentences that apply to you.

☐ I have measured the area of a floor to determine its size.

☐ I know about how far I live from the nearest school.

☐ I can tell if one room in a house is larger than another.

☐ I know about how long it takes to get to my favorite restaurant.

☐ I use an alarm clock to wake up in the morning.

☐ I use a microwave oven to warm leftover pizza.

To begin this unit, describe some situations in which distance, space, and time have been important to you.

1. Describe a recent time when you measured or needed to know the distance between two places.

   _____

   _____

2. Describe a time when you wanted to know the area of a table top, a floor, or some other surface. How did you find the size?

   _____

   _____

3. Describe two things for which volume, such as the amount of space inside a refrigerator, is an important selling point. (*Hint:* Think of two other things that involve storage.)

   a. _____

   b. _____

   Throughout this unit, you may use a calculator wherever that would be useful. Information about using a calculator appears on page 219.

Talk About It

Talk with other students about different ways you measure or keep track of time. Do you wear a watch or do you rely on various clocks? Tell of ways you estimate time when you aren't sure what time it is. Do you know how to use the Sun's position in the sky or the length of shadows to estimate time? Discuss any unusual methods you use.

English Units of Length

The measuring system most often used in the United States is called the **English system.** English units of length are shown below.

Unit	Sample Use	Abbreviation	Comparing Units
inch	7 inches	7 in. or 7"	$1 \text{ in.} = \frac{1}{12} \text{ ft.}$
foot	60 feet	60 ft. or 60'	$1 \text{ ft.} = 12 \text{ in.}$ $1 \text{ ft.} = \frac{1}{3} \text{ yd.}$
yard	120 yards	120 yd.	$1 \text{ yd.} = 3 \text{ ft.}$ $1 \text{ yd.} = 36 \text{ in.}$
mile	Buford · · Egan 235 miles	235 mi.	$1 \text{ mi.} = 1{,}760 \text{ yd.}$ $1 \text{ mi.} = 5{,}280 \text{ ft.}$

Converting to Larger Units

Sometimes **lengths** (distances) need to be written in larger units. To change to a larger unit of length, *divide by the number of smaller units* in the larger unit. Since the units are larger, your answer will show *fewer* units. Estimate first.

Example: Lynn bought a piece of ribbon 63 in. long. She wants to put this length into feet and inches.

Step 1	Step 2	Step 3	Step 4
Set up the problem.	Estimate first.	Divide 63 by 12. (12 in. = 1 ft.)	Write the whole number (5) as feet and the remainder (3) as inches.
63 in. = ___ ft. ___ in.	$63 \div 12 \approx$* $60 \div 12 = 5$ ft.	$63 \div 12 = 5 \text{ R}3$	63 in. = 5 ft. 3 in.

* The symbol $\approx$ means "is approximately equal to."

Your answer of **5 ft. 3 in.** is close to the estimate of 5 ft.

A. Change each length to the larger unit indicated. Estimate first.

1. 19 in. ≈ _____ ft.

19 in. = _____ ft. _____ in.
Hint: 1 foot = ? inches

39 in. ≈ _____ yd.

39 in. = _____ yd. _____ in.
Hint: 1 yard = ? inches

8 ft. ≈ _____ yd.

8 ft. = _____ yd. _____ ft.
Hint: 1 yard = ? feet

2. 53" ≈ _____ '

53" = _____ ' _____ "

92 in. ≈ _____ yd.

92 in. = _____ yd. _____ in.

17 ft. ≈ _____ yd.

17 ft. = _____ yd. _____ ft.

Converting to Smaller Units

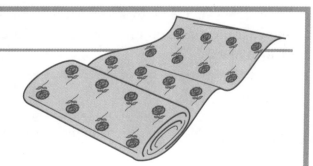

To change a larger unit to a smaller unit, *multiply by the number of smaller units* in the larger unit.

Example: Lynn also bought $2\frac{3}{4}$ yd. of fabric. She now wants to write this length in inches.

Step 1
Set up the problem.

$2\frac{3}{4}$ yd. = _____ in.

Step 2
Estimate first.

$2\frac{3}{4} \approx 3$

$3 \times 36 = 108$ in.

Step 3
Multiply $2\frac{3}{4}$ by 36. (1 yd. = 36 in.)

$2\frac{3}{4} \times 36 = \frac{11}{4} \times \frac{36}{1} = $ **99 in.**

B. Change each length to the smaller unit indicated. Estimate first.

3. 4' ≈ _____ "

4' = _____ "
Hint: 1 ft. = ? in.

$3\frac{2}{3}$ yd. ≈ _____ ft.

$3\frac{2}{3}$ yd. = _____ ft.
Hint: 1 yd. = ? ft.

5 yd. ≈ _____ in.

5 yd. = _____ in.
Hint: 1 yd. = ? in.

2 mi. ≈ _____ yd.

2 mi. = _____ yd.
Hint: 1 mi. = ? yd.

4. $8\frac{1}{2}$ ft. ≈ _____ in.

$8\frac{1}{2}$ ft. = _____ in.

$6\frac{1}{2}$ yd. ≈ _____ ft.

$6\frac{1}{2}$ yd. = _____ ft.

$2\frac{1}{3}$ yd. ≈ _____ in.

$2\frac{1}{3}$ yd. = _____ in.

$1\frac{3}{10}$ mi. ≈ _____ ft.

$1\frac{3}{10}$ mi. = _____ ft.
Hint: 1 mi. = ? ft.

The English Ruler

A common measuring tool found around many homes is the **English ruler.**
A 6-inch English ruler is pictured below.

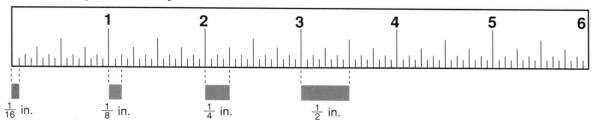

Each inch is divided into $\frac{1}{16}$-, $\frac{1}{8}$-, $\frac{1}{4}$-, and $\frac{1}{2}$-inch fractions. Different fraction units are shown using marks of different heights. For example, $\frac{1}{2}$-inch marks are taller than $\frac{1}{4}$-inch marks.

Reading Rulers

Example: A machinist needs to measure the length of the bolt below.

Line up the bolt.

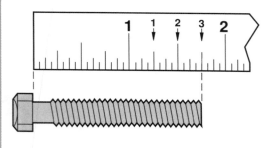

The bolt is longer than 1" but shorter than 2".* Because the end of the bolt is on a $\frac{1}{4}$" mark, count the number of $\frac{1}{4}$" marks between the 1" line and the end of the bolt. The bolt's length is 1" plus three $\frac{1}{4}$" marks, or $1\frac{3}{4}$". Notice that if you count $\frac{1}{8}$" marks, you would write the bolt length as 1" plus six $\frac{1}{8}$" marks: $1\frac{6}{8}$" simplifies to $1\frac{3}{4}$".

* The symbol " stands for *inch* or *inches*.

The bolt length is $1\frac{3}{4}$ **in.**

A. How far from the left end of the ruler is each point below?

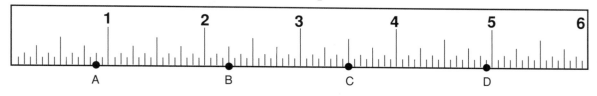

1. Point A =   Point B =   Point C =   Point D =

B. Based on part A, determine each of the following distances.

2. the distance between   the distance between   the distance between
point A and point B   point B and point C   point C and point D

C. Complete the measurement problem using the ruler provided.

3. **Draw** Pam is going to place gold sequins on the ribbon shown below. She wants to place one sequin every $\frac{9}{16}$ inch, starting at $\frac{9}{16}$ in. Mark along the center of the ribbon to show where Pam should place the sequins.

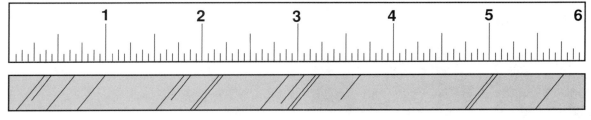

ribbon

Making Connections: Tape Measures

Another common measuring tool found in the home and shop is the **tape measure.** Tape measures are flexible rulers that are used to measure longer distances. Tape measures come in lengths from 3 feet up to about 150 feet. You read a tape measure in the same way that you read a ruler.

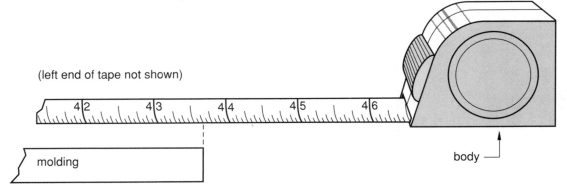

(left end of tape not shown)

molding

body

Measure from the end of the tape toward the body, in the order of increasing numbers. The length of the molding is $43\frac{5}{8}$ in. You can also read this length as 3 ft. $7\frac{5}{8}$ in.

Read the lengths measured with the tape measures below.

1.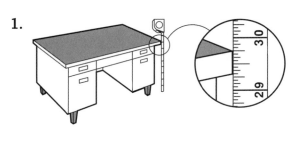

height of the desk, nearest $\frac{1}{4}$ inch

2.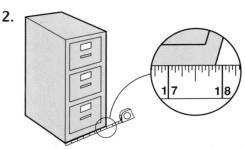

width of the filing cabinet, nearest $\frac{1}{8}$ inch

Metric Units of Length

Besides the English system of measurement, you may also know the **metric system.**
The metric system is based on the **decimal system** and is used in most countries
around the world today.

The standard metric unit of length is the **meter.** The most frequently used metric units
are shown here.

Unit	Comparing Units	Unit	Comparing Units
meter (m*)	1 m = 1,000 mm	centimeter (cm*)	1 cm = 10 mm
	1 m = 100 cm		1 cm = 0.01 m
	1 m = 0.001 km		
yard (to scale)		inch (actual size)	
millimeter (mm*)	1 mm = 0.1 cm	kilometer (km*)	1 km = 1,000 m
	1 mm = 0.001 m		
$\frac{1}{16}$ inch (actual size)		mile (to scale)	

*Note: You do not write a period after a metric unit abbreviation.

Converting to Larger Metric Units

To change to a larger metric length unit, *divide by the number of smaller units in the
larger unit.* The answer can be written as a decimal number of the larger unit or as
separate units.

Example: Rafael is renting a pair of skis that are 209 cm long. How can he write this
length as a decimal number of meters or as meters and centimeters?

Step 1
Set up the problem.

209 cm = _____._____ m
or
209 cm = _____ m _____ cm

Step 2
Estimate first.

209 ÷ 100 ≈
200 ÷ 100 = 2 m

Step 3
Divide 209 by 100.* (100 cm = 1 m)

209 ÷ 100 = **2.09 m** *or* **2 m 9 cm**

* To divide by 100, move the decimal point 2 places to the left.

A. Express each length in both ways indicated. Estimate first.

1. 21 mm ≈ _____ cm   189 cm ≈ _____ m   1,150 m ≈ _____ km

    21 mm = _____ cm _____ mm   189 cm = _____ m _____ cm   1,150 m = _____ km _____ m

          = _____ . _____ cm   = _____ . _____ m   = _____ . _____ km

    (10 mm = 1 cm)   (100 cm = 1 m)   (1,000 m = 1 km)

2. 48 mm ≈ _____ cm   325 cm ≈ _____ m   5,950 m ≈ _____ km

    48 mm = _____ cm _____ mm   325 cm = _____ m _____ cm   5,950 m = _____ km _____ m

          = _____ . _____ cm   = _____ . _____ m   = _____ . _____ km

---

Converting to Smaller Metric Units

To change a larger unit to a smaller unit, *multiply by the number of smaller units* in the larger unit.

Example: Pablo measured his ski pole to be 1.15 m long. How does he write this length as a number of centimeters?

Step 1
Set up the problem.

1.15 m = _____ cm

Step 2
Estimate first.

1.15 × 100 ≈
1 × 100 = 100 cm

Step 3
Multiply 1.15 by 100.*
(1 m = 100 cm)

1.15 × 100 = **115 cm**

---

* To multiply by 100, move the decimal point 2 places to the right.

B. Change each length to the smaller unit indicated. Estimate first.

3. 8 cm ≈ _____ mm   62 cm ≈ _____ mm   11.5 cm ≈ _____ mm   4.75 cm ≈ _____ mm

    8 cm = _____ mm   62 cm = _____ mm   11.5 cm = _____ mm   4.75 cm = _____ mm

4. 3 m ≈ _____ cm   5.25 m ≈ _____ cm   5 km ≈ _____ m   6.1 km ≈ _____ m

    3 m = _____ cm   5.25 m = _____ cm   5 km = _____ m   6.1 km = _____ m

The Metric Ruler

Shown below is a 15-centimeter **metric ruler.** Each centimeter (cm) is divided into 10 millimeters (mm).

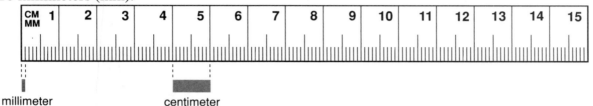

millimeter   centimeter

Using a metric ruler, you usually read length (or distance) as centimeters plus a number of millimeters. You can write each measured length in any of three ways: as millimeters only, as a whole number of centimeters and millimeters, or as a decimal number of centimeters.

Example: Renae measures the brooch shown below. How can she write its length?

The brooch is 2 cm and 6 mm long. Renae can write this length in three ways:

- *millimeters only:* 26 mm

- *whole number of centimeters and millimeters:* 2 cm 6 mm

- *decimal number of centimeters:* 2.6 cm

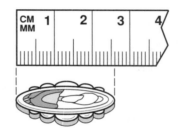

The brooch length is **26 mm** *or* **2 cm 6 mm** *or* **2.6 cm.**

A. Write each length below in the two ways indicated.

1.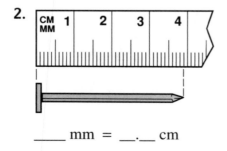

_____ mm = _____ cm _____ mm

2.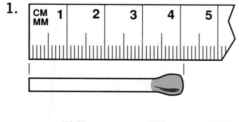

_____ mm = __.__ cm

3.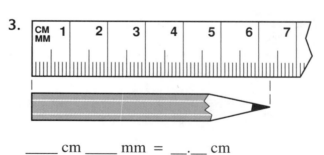

_____ cm _____ mm = __.__ cm

4.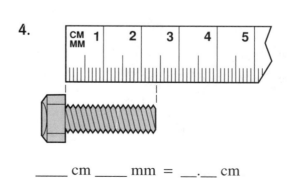

_____ cm _____ mm = __.__ cm

B. Answer the questions about the gold chain pictured below. Express your answers in any correct way.

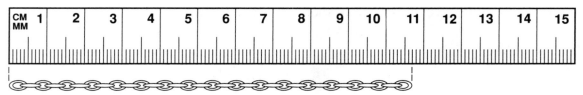

5. What is the length of the gold chain?

6. How much shorter than 15 cm is the chain?

7. If each new link adds 2 mm, what will be the new length of the chain after 6 links are added? Using an arrow, show this new length on the ruler.

8. How many additional links would you need to add to the *original* chain if you want the chain to be exactly 13.5 cm long?

Making Connections: English Decimal Rulers

The metric ruler doesn't use fractions because it is based on the decimal system. Each unit is related to another unit by 10, 100, or 1,000.

To simplify English measurement in machine shops and in many other workplaces, **English decimal rulers** are used. On an English decimal ruler, each inch is divided into 10 parts. (Each part is .1 inch.) An English decimal ruler is shown below.

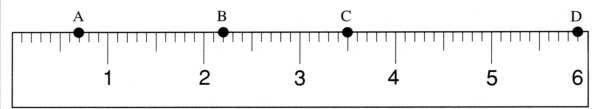

How far from the left end of the ruler is each point above?

Point A =   Point B =   Point C =   Point D =

Adding and Subtracting Lengths

When working with lengths (distances), add or subtract each unit separately. Estimate first. To estimate, round to the nearest whole number of larger units and then add or subtract.

Adding or Subtracting English Length Units

Example: Julio has two lengths of copper tubing. One is 6 ft. 3 in. long and the other is 2 ft. 10 in. long.

What is the combined length of the copper tubing?

Estimate first: 6 ft. + 3 ft. = 9 ft.

$$
\begin{array}{r}
6 \text{ ft.} \quad 3 \text{ in.} \\
+\ 2 \text{ ft. } 10 \text{ in.} \\
\hline
8 \text{ ft. } 13 \text{ in.} = 8 \text{ ft.} + 1 \text{ ft. } 1 \text{ in.} \\
= 9 \text{ ft. } 1 \text{ in.}
\end{array}
$$

The sum is **9 ft. 1 in.**

What is the difference in length of the pieces of copper tubing?

Estimate first: 6 ft. − 3 ft. = 3 ft.

Since 10 in. is larger than 3 in., regroup 6 ft. as 5 ft. 12 in. Add the 12 in. to the 3 in., getting 15 in.

$$
\begin{array}{r}
6 \text{ ft.} \quad 3 \text{ in.} = \quad \overset{5}{\cancel{6}} \text{ ft. } \overset{15}{\cancel{3}} \text{ in.} \\
-\ 2 \text{ ft. } 10 \text{ in.} = -\ 2 \text{ ft. } 10 \text{ in.} \\
\hline
3 \text{ ft.} \quad 5 \text{ in.}
\end{array}
$$

The difference is **3 ft. 5 in.**

Adding or Subtracting Metric Length Units

When working with metric units, you may find it easier to change each length (distance) to a decimal number of the largest unit before you add or subtract.

Example: Stephanie used a metric ruler to measure two tables. The larger table is 73 cm 2 mm wide. The smaller table is 62 cm 9 mm wide. What is the combined width of the tables?

Method 1. Combine separate units, and simplify your answer.

Estimate first: 73 cm + 63 cm = 136 cm

$$
\begin{array}{r}
73 \text{ cm} \quad 2 \text{ mm} \\
+\ 62 \text{ cm} \quad 9 \text{ mm} \\
\hline
135 \text{ cm } 11 \text{ mm} = \textbf{136 cm 1 mm}
\end{array}
$$

Regroup 11 mm as 1 cm 1 mm and combine the 1 cm with the 135 cm, getting 136 cm.

Method 2. First write lengths as decimal numbers. Then add.

$$
\begin{array}{r}
73 \text{ cm } 2 \text{ mm} = \quad 73.2 \text{ cm} \\
+\ 62 \text{ cm } 9 \text{ mm} = +\ 62.9 \text{ cm} \\
\hline
\textbf{136.1 cm}
\end{array}
$$

Regrouping is done as part of the addition of the decimal numbers.

A. Add the following lengths. Simplify answers when possible. Estimate before finding exact answers.

	Estimate	Estimate	Estimate
1.	8 ft. 5 in. *8 ft.*	4' 11"	6 yd. 2 ft.
	+ 3 ft. 9 in. *+ 4 ft.*	+ 2' 8"	+ 4 yd. 1 ft.
	12 ft.		

	Estimate	Estimate	Estimate
2.	9 yd. 31 in.	2 mi. 1,600 yd.	3 mi. 4,000 ft.
	+ 6 yd. 9 in.	+ 1 mi. 350 yd.	+ 2 mi. 3,000 ft.

To add metric lengths, use either method you prefer.

	Estimate	Estimate	Estimate
3.	8 cm 2 mm *8 cm*	12 cm 7 mm	6 m 75 cm
	+ 3 cm 9 mm *+ 4 cm*	+ 7 cm 5 mm	+ 2 m 80 cm
	12 cm		

B. Estimate first. Then subtract the following lengths. Regroup when necessary.

	Estimate	Estimate	Estimate
4.	7 ft. 8 in. *8 ft.*	5' 4"	3 ft. 2 in.
	− 2 ft. 9 in. *− 3 ft.*	− 3' 7"	− 1 ft. 11 in.
	5 ft.		

	Estimate	Estimate	Estimate
5.	3 yd. 1 ft.	8 yd. 10 in.	5 yd.
	− 1 yd. 2 ft.	− 5 yd. 26 in.	− 2 yd. 2 ft.

To subtract metric lengths, use either method you prefer.

	Estimate	Estimate	Estimate
6.	4 m 50 cm *5 m*	8 m 45 cm	12 cm 7 mm
	− 1 m 70 cm *− 2 m*	− 5 m 68 cm	− 3 cm 9 mm
	3 m		

Multiplying and Dividing Lengths

Lengths (distances) can also be multiplied and divided. First estimate an answer by rounding each length (distance) to the nearest whole number of larger units. Then multiply or divide.

- To find an exact answer when multiplying, multiply the number of each unit separately. Simplify each answer when possible.

- To find an exact answer when dividing, divide the number of each unit separately, starting with the larger unit. Regroup as necessary.

Multiplying Lengths

Example: In order to make a long serving table for the school barbecue, Arland plans to place 6 cafeteria tables end-to-end. If each table is 4 ft. 11 in. long, how can Arland determine how long the serving table will be?

Step 1
To find the combined length of the tables, multiply 4 ft. 11 in. by 6.
Estimate first: 5 ft. × 6 = 30 ft.

$$\begin{array}{r} 4 \text{ ft. } 11 \text{ in.} \\ \times \quad\quad 6 \\ \hline 24 \text{ ft. } 66 \text{ in.} \end{array}$$

Step 2
Simplify the number of inches:
66 in. = 5 ft. 6 in.
Now combine 24 ft. and 5 ft. 6 in.

$$\begin{array}{r} 24 \text{ ft.} \\ + \quad 5 \text{ ft. } 6 \text{ in.} \\ \hline 29 \text{ ft. } 6 \text{ in.} \end{array}$$

The smaller tables will combine to form a table **29 ft. 6 in.** long.

Dividing Lengths

Example: Arland now wants to divide the 29 ft. 6 in. serving table into 3 equal sections: salads, main dishes, and desserts. How long should each section be?

To find the length of each section, divide 29 ft. 6 in. by 3.
Estimate first: 30 ÷ 3 = 10 ft.

```
        9 ft.    10 in.
      _____
  3 ) 29 ft.    6 in.
     − 27
     _____
       2 ft. = 24 in.
              _____
               30 in.  ◄──── Divide 30 by 3.
             − 30 in.
             _____
                 0
```

When division of the larger unit results in a remainder, regroup the remainder and add it to the next smaller unit. In this problem, regroup 2 ft. as 24 in. and add it to the 6 in., getting 30 in.

0 shows no remainder of the smaller unit.

Each section of serving table should be **9 ft. 10 in.** long.

A. Estimate each answer. Then multiply the following lengths and simplify answers.

1.   Estimate   Estimate   Estimate

     3 ft. 2 in.   3 ft.   8 ft. 11 in.   7' 5"

     ×   7   × 7   ×   3   ×   4

                    21 ft.

2.   Estimate   Estimate   Estimate

     1 yd. 2 ft.   6 yd. 13 in.   9 yd. 1 ft.

     ×   4   ×   5   ×   5

To multiply metric units, multiply each unit separately or use decimal numbers.

3.   Estimate   Estimate

     8 cm 3 mm *or* 8.3 cm   8 cm   9 m 21 cm *or* 9.21 m

     ×   4   × 4   × 4   ×   3   × 3

                            32 cm

B. Divide these lengths. Estimate before finding exact answers.

4.   Estimate   Estimate   Estimate

     4)5 ft. 8 in. $1\frac{1}{2}$ ft.   3)8 ft. 3 in.   7' 11" ÷ 5

               4)6 ft.

5.   Estimate   Estimate   Estimate

     3)7 yd. 6 in.   4)10 yd. 8 in.   5 yd. 28 in. ÷ 2

To divide metric units, divide each unit separately or use decimal numbers.

6.   Estimate   Estimate

     4)7 cm 6 mm *or* 4)7.6 cm   5)24 m 80 cm *or* 5)24.80 m

Mixed Problem Solving

Solve each of the following problems. Read each one carefully and decide whether to add, subtract, multiply, or divide.

1. Brent places a couch that is 6 ft. 4 in. long next to a matching chair that is 2 ft. 3 in. wide. How much room do the couch and chair take up when placed side by side with 8 in. separating them?

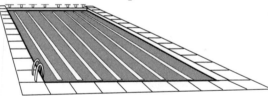

2. The Benson Aquatic team consists of 5 swimmers. Each team member will swim an equal portion of a 2.5-km long-distance race. How many *meters* will each swimmer be required to swim?

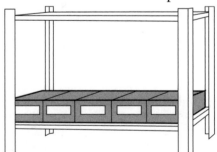

3. A camera comes in a box that measures 14 cm 4 mm wide. What total shelf width will a row of 5 cameras take up?

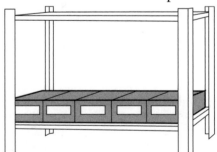

For another look
at measuring units,
turn to page 222.

4. Judy's kitchen window measures 1 m 12 cm wide. If she buys a curtain labeled "1.65 m wide," how many centimeters of extra material should be available for bunching?

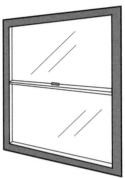

5. The new Comet sedan measures 15 ft. 11 in. long. Karl wants to display 2 of these cars in the showroom. If he lines them up end-to-end with 2 ft. between them, what total distance will the cars take up?

6. **Explain** Esther makes ribbon bows to adorn presents. Each bow requires 1 ft. 3 in. of ribbon. In addition, each time she makes a bow, Esther wastes about 1 in. of ribbon due to cutting the ends at an angle. Explain how Esther can estimate how much ribbon she needs to make 75 bows.

7. Carpet comes in 12-ft.-wide rolls. To carpet a room that is 9 ft. 4 in. wide by 10 ft. long, you buy a piece of carpet that is 12 ft. wide and 10 ft. long. Before putting the carpet in place, what width of carpet should you cut from the edge of the roll?

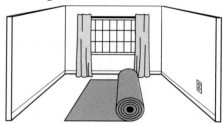

8. To make cabinet shelves, Jason plans to cut a fir board into 3 equal pieces. If the uncut board measures 17 ft. 3 in. long, how long should Jason cut each piece?

9. Wallpaper comes in rolls that are 2 ft. 3 in. wide. To paper a wall that is 14 ft. wide, you would need to place 6 full strips and 1 partial strip side-by-side.

  a. What is the width of 6 full strips?

  b. How wide should you cut the partial strip?

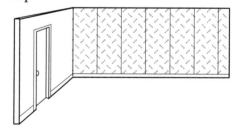

10. Carla cut a hole 2 cm 4 mm wide in a piece of wallboard. She then widened the hole by 1 cm 8 mm. How wide is the hole now?

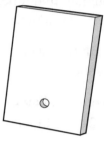

11. A stack of 10 identical boards measures 27 cm 8 mm high. What is the thickness of each board?

12. Estimate As the Warren family drives past a stopped train, they estimate its length is about 0.8 mi. They also count that the train has 106 railroad cars.

  a. Estimate the average length *in yards* of each railroad car.
(*Hint:* 1 mi. = 1,760 yd.)

  b. Do you think the exact answer would be greater than or less than your estimate? Why?

Converting Length

Sometimes you may find it necessary to change from units of the English system to units of the metric system or vice versa. This is called **converting between systems.**

To convert length (distance) measurements, use the following facts and multiply by the appropriate number.

Converting from English to Metric

    1 inch ≈ 2.5 centimeters

    1 foot ≈ 30 centimeters

    1 yard ≈ 91 centimeters = 0.91 meters

    1 mile ≈ 1,600 meters = 1.6 kilometers

Converting from Metric to English

    1 centimeter ≈ 0.4 inch

    1 meter ≈ 39 inches

    1 meter ≈ 3.3 feet = 1.1 yards

    1 kilometer ≈ 0.6 mile

Converting Measurements

Example: Wilhelm is 5 ft. 11 in. tall. His friend Hiroko is 170 cm tall. How much taller in inches is Wilhelm than Hiroko?

Step 1
Write Wilhelm's height in inches.

5 ft. 11 in. = 60 in. + 11 in.
        = 71 in.

Step 2
Convert Hiroko's height to inches. To convert 170 cm to inches, multiply 170 by 0.4.

    170
×   0.4
  68.0 in.

Step 3
Subtract Hiroko's height from Wilhelm's height.

  71 in.
− 68 in.
  3 in.

Wilhelm is **about 3 in.** taller than Hiroko.

A. To the nearest whole number, convert from metric to English.

1. 30 cm ≈ _____ in.   5.2 m ≈ _____ ft. $8\frac{1}{2}$ m ≈ _____ yd.
(*Hint:* 30 × 0.4)

2. 6 m ≈ _____ in.   3 km ≈ _____ mi.   90 km ≈ _____ mi.

B. To the nearest whole number, convert from English to metric.

3. 24 in. ≈ _____ cm   4.5 ft. ≈ _____ cm   3 yd. ≈ _____ cm
(*Hint:* 24 × 2.5)

4. 2 yd. ≈ _____ m $1\frac{1}{2}$ mi. ≈ _____ m   9.4 mi. ≈ _____ km

C. Solve these conversion word problems.

5. The maximum width of paper that Erik can use in his computer printer is $11\frac{1}{4}$ in. Will paper that is 30 cm wide fit in this printer?

6. Referring to the map below, determine the following distances to the nearest mile.
   a. Glendale to Lapine
   b. Lapine to Harrisburg
   c. Glendale to Jefferson

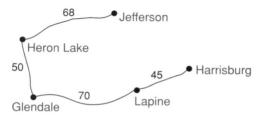

All distances are in kilometers.

7. In many states in the United States, the shortest size trout that can be caught and kept is 6 in. What is the equivalent "legal length" of this fish in Canada, a country that uses the metric system?

8. For many U.S. fans, the most exciting track race is the mile run. In the Olympics, though, only the "metric mile" is run, a distance of 1,500 m. In which of these two races would a runner have the faster finishing time? Why?

9. As shown at right, what is the height in feet and inches of the rim of the basketball net used in the Olympics?

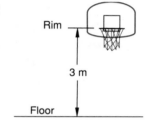

Making Connections: English and Metric Measurements

Below are listed some interesting facts involving distance. Fill in the blank lines below, showing *approximate* equivalent distances between metric and English systems.

		Metric	English
1.	height of Mount Everest (highest mountain in the world)	8,848 m	_____ ft.
2.	length of Switzerland's St. Gotthard Tunnel (second longest car tunnel in the world)	16.9 km	_____ mi.
3.	distance around Earth at the equator	_____ km	25,048 mi.
4.	deepest point in the ocean	10,915 m	_____ ft.
5.	average distance of the Moon from Earth	384,400 km	_____ mi.
6.	average distance of Earth from the Sun	_____ km	92,900,000 mi.

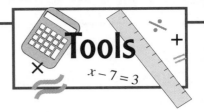

Gridding in Answers

Some tests, including the GED, require you to record the answers to problems on special grids. These questions measure your ability to find a solution without the benefit of selecting from multiple-choice answers.

A sample grid is shown to the right. It has the following features:

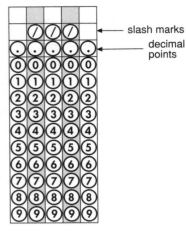

- Five columns of numbers and symbols.
- A row of blank boxes at the top to record your answer.
- A row of slash marks (/) to record fractions.
- A row of decimal points (.) to record decimal numbers.
- Rows of numbers from 0 through 9.

To grid the answer to a measurement problem, read the problem carefully to find out what measurement unit to use. The measurement unit is usually stated in the question at the end of the problem. When you grid your answer, it must match the unit stated in the question or your answer will be incorrect.

Follow these steps to grid in measurement answers:

1. Work the problem using the measurement unit that is easiest for you.

2. Convert your answer, if necessary, to the measurement unit stated in the question.

3. Mixed numbers cannot be entered in the grid. Convert any mixed number answer to an improper fraction or decimal.

Filling in the Grid

Example: Spiro is building a model using plastic blocks that are each 16 millimeters in height. How tall is a stack of 6 blocks in centimeters?

Step 1
Read the problem carefully. The measurement of the block is given in millimeters, but you are asked to find the answer in centimeters.

Change 16 mm to cm. Use the fact: 1 cm = 10 mm.

16 mm ÷ 10 = 1.6 cm

Step 2
Solve the problem.

1.6 cm × 6 blocks = 9.6 cm

You can also solve the problem in millimeters and change the answer to centimeters:
16 mm × 6 = 96 mm
96 mm ÷ 10 = 9.6 cm

Step 3
Write the answer in the top row of boxes. You can start in any column as long as your answer fits. Using the digits in the top row as a guide, fill in the correct circles.

Using Fractions in the Grid

Example: A board is 58 inches long. If a 19-inch piece is cut from one end of the board, what is the remaining length of the board in feet?

Step 1
Solve the problem.
58 in. − 19 in. = 39 in.

Express the answer in feet. Use the fact: 1 ft. = 12 in.

39 in. ÷ 12 in. = 3 ft. 3 in.

3 ft. 3 in. = $3\frac{3}{12}$ = $3\frac{1}{4}$ ft.

Step 2
You cannot enter a mixed number in the grid. Convert the mixed number to an improper fraction.

$$3\frac{1}{4} = \frac{3 \times 4 + 1}{4} = \frac{13}{4}$$

Step 3
Fill in the correct circles on the grid. Use the slash symbol (/) to represent the fraction bar.

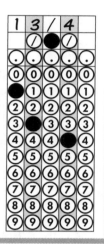

Solve the following problems. Record your answers in the grids.

1.

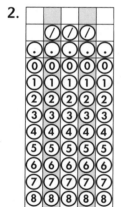

At a swimming competition, each swimming lane is 2.5 meters wide. To the nearest <u>foot</u>, how wide is a swimming lane?

Use the fact:
1 meter ≈ 3.3 feet.

3.

Jim is 6 feet 4 inches tall. His daughter Lisa is 4 feet 10 inches tall. How many <u>feet</u> taller than Lisa is Jim?

2.

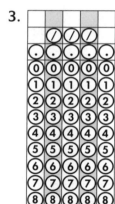

Denise is making awards for a school track-and-field event. Each award uses 9 inches of ribbon. How many <u>yards</u> of ribbon will she need to make 25 awards?

4.

An 8-foot piece of string is cut into 16 equal lengths. How long is each of the smaller pieces of string in <u>inches</u>?

Mixed Review

A. Change each length to the unit(s) indicated.

1. 7 ft. = _____ in. $1\frac{1}{2}$ yd. = _____ in.   18 ft. = _____ yd.   60" = _____ '

2. 5 m = _____ cm   4 km = _____ m   90 mm = _____ cm   8,000 m = _____ km

3. a. 45 in. = ___ ft. ___ in.

    b. 17 ft. = ___ yd. ___ ft.

    c. 138 cm = ___ m ___ cm = ___.___ m

B. Solve the problems. Simplify answers when possible.

4.
    2 ft. 8 in.   6 yd. 1 ft.   1 yd. 2 ft.   4)9' 4"
  + 1 ft. 9 in.   − 1 yd. 2 ft.   ×   3

5.
    6 cm 8 mm   2 km 500 m   3 m 50 cm   2)3 m 20 cm
  + 3 cm 3 mm   − 1 km 750 m   ×   6

C. Write the lengths of the two chains shown below in both English and metric units.

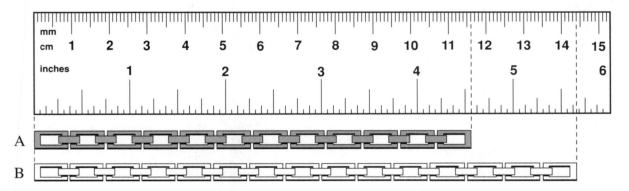

6. the length of chain A

    a. _____ in.   **b.** _____ cm _____ mm

                     or _____ mm

    (nearest $\frac{1}{16}$ inch)

7. the length of chain B

    a. _____ in.   **b.** _____ cm _____ mm

                     or _____._____ cm

    (nearest $\frac{1}{8}$ inch)

D. Gwen put new carpet and padding in her living room. Unfortunately, as shown below, the closet door is now too low and hits the carpet. Answer the following questions to help Gwen decide by how much she should shorten the door.

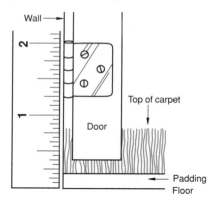

8. To the nearest $\frac{1}{16}$ inch, how thick is the carpet and padding?

9. To the nearest $\frac{1}{16}$ inch, how far is the bottom of the door above the floor?

10. If Gwen wants the bottom of the door to be $\frac{1}{8}$ in. above the top of the carpet, how much should she shorten the bottom of the door?

E. Solve these measurement problems.

11. The garage door on Mari's house is 8 ft. wide. She's thinking about buying a small boat trailer that is 100 in. wide. Will this trailer fit through the garage door opening?

12. Juanita bought a silk tree that stands 5 ft. 11 in. high. If the ceiling in Juanita's apartment is 7 ft. 8 in. high, how far is the top of the tree below the ceiling?

13. Knowing that 1 yd. = 0.9144 m, determine which is longer: a 440-yd. run or a 400-m run.

14. A storage warehouse is divided into 16 separate storage garages. If each garage is 4 yd. 2 ft. wide, how long is the warehouse? (Ignore the width of exterior and interior walls.)

15. **Explain** Sheila wants to figure out the approximate distance around her school. She doesn't have a tape measure, so she measured her stride, which is about 50 cm. How can Sheila estimate the distance around her school in *meters?*

16. **Measure** Determine your height to the nearest centimeter and to the nearest $\frac{1}{4}$ inch.

F. Grid in the answer to each problem.

17.  One board measures 3 feet 9 inches in length. Another board is 33 inches long. Express the combined length of the boards in <u>feet</u>.

18. 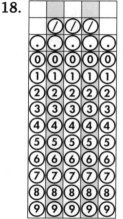 Patrick needs to replace 11 feet of fencing with new fence boards. The fence boards are installed side by side, and each new board is 6 inches wide. How many boards will Patrick need to do the job?

Finding Perimeter

Perimeter is a measure of distance. The distance around a two-dimensional (flat, or **plane**) figure is called its *perimeter*. You can measure the perimeter of objects ranging from a triangle to a house lot. The perimeter of a piece of land is often called its **boundary.**

Plane Figures

Blue Lake

table top

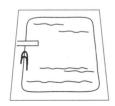

Perimeter is measured in length units such as inches, feet, yards, centimeters, or meters. The symbol for perimeter is P.

The perimeter of a geometric figure is often written as a **formula.** A formula shows how to solve a certain type of problem.

Triangle	**Square**	**Rectangle**
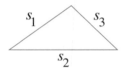		
$P = s_1 + s_2 + s_3$	$P = s + s + s + s = 4s$	$P = l + w + l + w$ $= 2(l + w)$ or $2l + 2w$
sum of sides, where s_1, s_2, and s_3 are the three sides	4 times s, where s stands for *side*	2 times (length + width), where l is the length and w is the width

---

Finding Perimeter

Example: Ellen wants to place a fence around her garden. The garden has the shape of a rectangle and measures 46 ft. long and 32 ft. wide. If she wants to leave a 3-ft. space for a gate, how many feet of fence material should Ellen buy?

Step 1
Write the perimeter formula and substitute 46 for l and 32 for w.

$P = 2(l + w) = 2(46 + 32)$

Step 2
First add 46 and 32. Then multiply the sum by 2.

$P = 2(78) = 156$ ft.
⌐— perimeter

Step 3
Subtract 3 ft. from 156 ft. to leave room for the gate.

$156 - 3 = 153$ ft.
⌐— gate width

Ellen should buy **153 ft.** of fence material.

A. Find the perimeter of each figure.

1. $P =$ _____

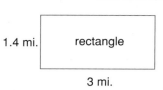

9 cm | square

2. $P =$ _____

1.4 mi. | rectangle

3 mi.

3. $P =$ _____

8 in.

7 in.

12 in.

B. Solve these perimeter problems. Draw a picture if needed.

4. Alan's office is square in shape, 18 ft. on a side. If you allow 3 ft. for a door, how much baseboard is needed to trim this office?

5. Janelle runs laps around a rectangular field that is 250 yd. long and 190 yd. wide.

  a. What distance is a complete lap?

  b. How many laps must Janelle run for a total distance of 3 mi.?

6. Kelley made 3 rectangular tablecloths, each measuring 6 ft. 9 in. long and 4 ft. 8 in. wide. What is the least length of decorative trim that Kelley should buy to place a border along the edge of each tablecloth?

7. You know the perimeter of a square field is 432 yd. 2 ft. What is the length of each side of this field? (*Hint:* To find the side of a square, divide the perimeter by 4.)

Making Connections: Discovering Pi

The perimeter of a circle is related to its **diameter** (*d*)—the distance across a circle through its center. The **circumference** (*C*)—the distance around a circle—is its diameter multiplied by a value that is slightly larger than 3. This value is called π (**pi**—pronounced "pie"). Written as a formula, this relationship is $C = \pi d$.

To draw a circle 1 ft. in diameter, use a thumbtack to hold one end of a string in place. (This is the center.) Then attach a pencil to the string 6 in. (half the diameter, or radius) from the center and draw a circle.

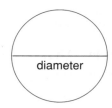

diameter

Now cut a piece of string 12 in. long (the diameter of the circle). Count how many times this string goes around the outside of the circle. Write the number of times the whole length went around. This is the number of feet. Add on any remaining amount as a fraction of a foot. Estimate π from your measurements. Test your value of π on circles of different diameters.

Finding the Area of a Rectangle

Area is a measure of the surface within a two-dimensional figure. The surface may be the inside part of a geometric figure, such as a rectangle, or it may be the surface of a physical object, such as a floor in a house.

Two-Dimensional Figures

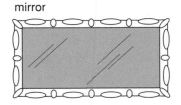
mirror

Illinois

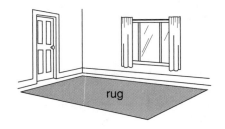
rug

Area is measured in **area units.** Picture an area unit as a **square,** a four-sided figure with four equal sides and four **right angles.** In fact, the word *square* is used to identify an area unit.

Sample Area Unit
1 square foot

1 foot

1 foot

right angle

Common English Area Units

> square inch (sq. in.)
>
> square foot (sq. ft.)
>
> square yard (sq. yd.)
>
> square mile (sq. mi.)

Common Metric Area Units

> square millimeter (mm^2)
>
> square centimeter (cm^2)
>
> square meter (m^2)
>
> square kilometer (km^2)

A **rectangle** is a common shape you'll want to know how to find the area of. A rectangle has two pairs of equal sides and four right angles. Think of the area of a rectangle as the number of square units the rectangle can be divided into.

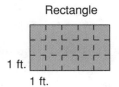

Rectangle

1 ft.

1 ft.

Area = 5 × 3
= 15 square feet

▶ To find the area of a rectangle, multiply length (*l*) by width (*w*). The formula for area is $A = lw$, where *A* stands for area.

Finding Area

Example: Alicia plans to put new carpet in her living room. The room measures 5 yd. long by $4\frac{1}{3}$ yd. wide. How does Alicia find the area of this room?*

Step 1
Write the area formula for a rectangle.

$A = lw$

Step 2
Substitute 6 yd. for *l* and $4\frac{1}{3}$ yd. for *w*.

$A = 6 \times 4\frac{1}{3}$

Step 3
Multiply. Check your answer by estimating: 6 × 4 = 24 sq. yd.

$A = \frac{6}{1} \times \frac{13}{3} = \textbf{26 sq. yd.}$

---

* The area formula works even when the lengths involved are not whole numbers.

A. Find the area of each of the figures. In problems 2 and 3, check your answers by drawing a grid (as in problem 1) and counting the number of area units in the grid.

1. _____

Count the exact number of area units.

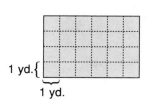

1 yd.{

1 yd.

2. _____

Use the area formula.

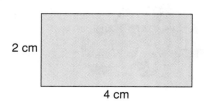

2 cm

4 cm

3. _____

Use the area formula.

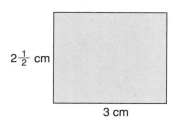

$2\frac{1}{2}$ cm

3 cm

B. Solve the area problems.

4. a. Find the perimeter and area of each figure shown below.

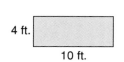

4 ft.

10 ft.

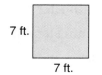

7 ft.

7 ft.

$P =$ _____

$A =$ _____

$P =$ _____

$A =$ _____

b. What conclusion can you draw about the areas of figures with the same perimeter?

5. Draw Think about what's being described and then do the following:

a. Draw a lake, shaped like a square, that has a perimeter of 12 mi. and an area of 9 sq. mi.

b. Draw a lake, shaped like a rectangle, that has a perimeter of about 12 mi. and an area of less than 1 sq. mi.

Making Connections: Unusual Units of Measure

Before standard length and area units were invented, people used parts of the body as measuring units. For fun, determine the following.

1. Find the approximate length and width of your desk in *cubits* (a distance unit equal to the distance from your elbow to the tip of your longest finger).

2. Find the approximate area of your desk in *palms* (the amount of surface your flat hand can cover).

3. Compare your answers with the answers of other students. Why do answers vary from student to student?

Finding Volume

Volume is a measure of the space within a **three-dimensional** figure. The volume of a box is the space within it. The volume of a brick is the space the brick takes up.

Three-Dimensional Figures

 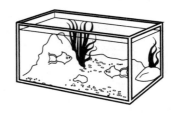 

Volume is measured in **volume units.** Picture a volume unit as a **cube,** a six-sided figure in which all sides are squares and all angles are right angles (as shown at right). Volume units are identified by the word *cubic.*

Sample Volume Unit
1 cubic yard

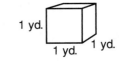

Common English Volume Units	**Common Metric Volume Units**
cubic inch (cu. in.)	cubic millimeter (mm^3)
cubic foot (cu. ft.)	cubic centimeter (cm^3)
cubic yard (cu. yd.)	cubic meter (m^3)
cubic mile (cu. mi.)	cubic kilometer (km^3)

The most common volume you'll ever need to find is that of a **rectangular solid,** the shape of a box. Think of the volume of a box as the number of cubic units the box can hold.

The quickest way to find the volume of a rectangular solid such as a box is to multiply its length (*l*) by its width (*w*) by its height (*h*). The formula for volume is $V = lwh$, where *V* stands for volume.

Rectangular Solid

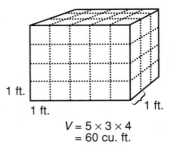

$$V = 5 \times 3 \times 4$$
$$= 60 \text{ cu. ft.}$$

Finding Volume

Example: Reuben measures the inside of his shed to be $5\frac{1}{2}$ yd. long, 4 yd. wide, and 2 yd. high. How does Reuben determine the volume of storage space available inside the shed?

Step 1
Write the volume formula for a rectangular solid. *Hint:* For volume, multiply 3 measures (*l*, *w*, and *h*).

$V = lwh$

Step 2
Substitute $5\frac{1}{2}$ for *l*, 4 for *w*, and 2 for *h*.

$V = 5\frac{1}{2} \times 4 \times 2$

Step 3
Multiply. Check your answer by estimating: $6 \times 4 \times 2 = 48$ cu. yd.

$V = \frac{11}{2} \times \frac{4}{1} \times \frac{2}{1} = 44$ cu. yd.

The volume of storage space available is **44 cu. yd.**

A. Find the volume of each figure.

1. _____
in cubic units shown

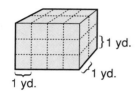

2. _____
Use the volume formula.

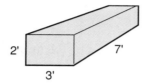

3. _____
Use the volume formula.

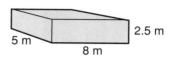

B. Solve the volume problems.

4. Lucinda bought a new freezer that claims to have "more than 21 cubic feet of storage." She measured the inside dimensions of the freezer to be length, 4 ft.; width, 2 ft.; and height, $2\frac{2}{3}$ ft. Does this freezer have the storage space advertised?

5. How many cubic feet of water does an aquarium hold if the aquarium is 30 in. long, 18 in. wide, and 12 in. high?

6. Ephran bought a waterbed mattress that measures 6 ft. long, 5 ft. wide, and 8 in. ($\frac{2}{3}$ ft.) high.

  a. How many cubic feet of water does this mattress hold when full?

  b. Using the fact that water weighs about 62 pounds per cubic foot, find what the water in Ephran's mattress will weigh when the mattress is full.

Making Connections: Decisions with Area and Volume

Aquarium Products Company is trying to decide which of two boxes to use for packaging colored aquarium sand. The two boxes being considered are shown below.

1. Which box holds more sand?

2. Which box takes more cardboard to make?

A.

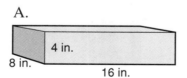

B.

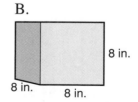

3. **Explain** If you owned Aquarium Products Company, which box would you choose? Give your reasons why.

Using Units of Time

The English and metric systems both use the same units for time.

Clock Time

    1 minute = 60 seconds

    1 hour = 60 minutes

    1 day = 24 hours

Calendar Time

    1 week = 7 days

    1 month = 28–31 days

    1 common year = 365 days

    1 leap year = 366 days

Month Number and Number of Days Each Month

1. January	31	**5.** May	31	**9.** September	30
2. February	28 (29)	**6.** June	30	**10.** October	31
3. March	31	**7.** July	31	**11.** November	30
4. April	30	**8.** August	31	**12.** December	31

A **common year** has 365 days, with the month of February having 28 days. Three out of every four years are common years. Each fourth year is called a **leap year,** a year with 366 days. During a leap year, February has 29 days. The leap years for the 1990s were 1992 and 1996. What year was the first leap year in the 2000s?

Writing Clock Time

You write clock time as the number of hours followed by a colon and the number of minutes.

- The letters A.M. refer to hours between midnight and noon.
- The letters P.M. refer to hours between noon and midnight.

hour — ⌐ 30 minutes after 6 o'clock
6:30 A.M.
└ after midnight and before noon

hour — ⌐ 15 minutes after 5 o'clock
5:15 P.M.
└ after noon and before midnight

Writing Dates

A date (for example, November 15, 2002) is often written as numbers. Job application forms and other documents may ask you to write dates as numbers placed between slashes or placed within boxes.

11/15/02

month/day/year

|1|1|1|5|0|2|

month/day/year

A. Determine each of the following numbers.

1. number of seconds in an hour

2. number of minutes in 2 hours

3. number of hours in a week

4. number of weeks in a common year

B. Determine each earlier or later time.

5. time now: 6:10 A.M.

time in 20 minutes: _____

6. time now: 8:25 P.M.

time in 48 minutes: _____
(*Hint:* In 35 minutes, the time will be 9:00 P.M.)

7. time now: 11:41 A.M.

time 24 minutes ago: _____

8. time now: 12:25 P.M.

time 39 minutes ago: _____
(*Hint:* 25 minutes ago, the time was noon.)

C. Write each date as numbers between slashes or in boxes.

9. September 14, 1957 _____/_____/_____

10. July 4, 1994 _____/_____/_____

11. February 26, 1967 ☐☐ ☐☐ ☐☐
(Write 0 in the first box.)

12. December 9, 1986 ☐☐ ☐☐ ☐☐

Making Connections: Military Time

The military and many other organizations around the world use a **24-hour clock.** On a 24-hour clock, there are no A.M. and P.M. times. For example, 1:00 A.M. is just 1:00 (one hundred hours), while 1:00 P.M. is called 13:00 (twelve hundred + one hundred = thirteen hundred hours). Ten o'clock P.M. becomes 22:00 (twelve hundred + ten hundred = twenty-two hundred hours). Midnight is 0:00 (zero hundred hours) and noon is 12:00 (twelve hundred hours).

Write the following times as 24-hour clock times.

1. 5:00 A.M. _____

2. 8:20 A.M. _____

3. 3:00 P.M. _____

4. 7:00 P.M. _____

5. 8:45 P.M. _____

6. 11:17 P.M. _____

Working with Time Schedules

Keeping track of time helps you decide when to get up, when to leave for work or school, or when to send holiday and birthday cards.

Marking Days on a Calendar

Georgia works part-time and keeps track of workdays and special days on a **calendar.**

On the calendar, write the following information for Georgia.

Workdays: Every Tuesday from 9:00 A.M. to 3:00 P.M.
Every Thursday from 11:00 A.M. to 5:00 P.M.
The first and third Saturdays from 8:00 A.M. to noon.

Birthdays: Aunt Rosie, 11/17; Lou Peterson, 11/24

Special Days: Annual office party, third Friday of the month from 4:00 P.M. to 7:00 P.M.

November

Sunday	Monday	Tuesday	Wednesday	Thursday	Friday	Saturday
	1	2	3	4	5	6
7	8	9	10	11	12	13
14	15	16	17	18	19	20
21	22	23	24	25	26	27
28	29	30				

Answer these questions about the information on the calendar.

1. It takes Georgia 45 minutes to get ready for work and 30 minutes to get to work. What is the latest time she can set her alarm clock for on November 16 and still get to work on time?

2. Georgia earns $7.50 per hour for each hour she works on Tuesdays and Thursdays. She earns $10.50 for each hour she works on Saturdays. How much will Georgia earn during November?

Scheduling Employees

Chuck is scheduling his three employees for work next Sunday. He wants each employee to work a 4-hour shift, and he needs all three employees to be at work from 11:30 A.M. to 2:00 P.M.

- Juanita's ride home arrives at 2:30 P.M.
- Frank can start between 8:30 A.M. and 10:00 A.M.
- Viola wants to start "as late as possible."

3. Fill in the schedule below for Chuck.

Sunday Work Schedule		
Employee	Start Time	Leave Time
Juanita		
Frank		
Viola		

Reading a Bus Schedule

The bus schedule at right lists the times that Sergey's bus leaves the Walnut Street stop. Sergey catches the 7:24 A.M. bus, which he rides to the Central Station stop. Use this schedule to answer the following questions.

4. If Sergey arrives at the bus stop at 7:18 A.M., how long will he have to wait until the bus arrives?

5. How long does it take to go from the Walnut Street stop to Central Station?

6. On Tuesday the bus is running 15 minutes late. What time can Sergey expect to catch his bus?

Bus Schedule

Walnut Street	Franklin Boulevard	Central Station
7:00 AM	7:14	7:31
7:24	7:38	7:55
7:48	8:02	8:19
8:10	8:24	8:41

Filling in a Time Card

Shown on the clocks below are the times Lanny arrived at work (In) and then left work (Out) on Tuesday and Wednesday.

7. Fill In On the time card, record the time that Lanny arrived at work, the time he left work, and the total hours he was there each day on Tuesday and Wednesday.

Time Card			
	In	Out	Total Hours
Tuesday			
Wednesday			

Tuesday

In 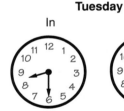 Out

Wednesday

In  Out

Using the Distance Formula

Time is related to distance. You can travel 200 miles in a lot less time if you drive at 50 miles per hour rather than at 20 miles per hour.

► Time, distance, and rate are related by the **distance formula:**

distance (d) = rate (r) × time (t) or $d = rt$

Using the Distance Formula

Example 1: Driving an average of 52 miles per hour, how far can Katie drive in 4 hours?

To find the *distance,* substitute 52 for r and 4 for t in the formula.

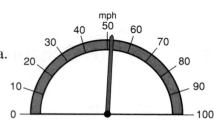

$d = rt = 52 \times 4 = $ **208 miles**

Katie can drive **208 miles** in 4 hours at 52 miles per hour.

Example 2: What average speed does Katie need to drive if she wants to travel 350 miles in 7 hours?

Rewrite the distance formula as a **rate formula.** (The speed is a rate.)

rate $(r) = \frac{\text{distance } (d)}{\text{time } (t)}$ or $r = \frac{d}{t}$ 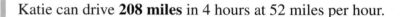 (means $d \div t$)

To find the *rate,* substitute 350 for d and 7 for t in the rate formula.
$r = \frac{d}{t} = \frac{350}{7} = $ **50 miles per hour**

Katie needs to drive **50 miles per hour** to travel 350 miles in 7 hours.

Example 3: How long will it take Katie to drive 360 miles if she drives at an average speed of 45 miles per hour?

Rewrite the distance formula as a **time formula.**

time $(t) = \frac{\text{distance } (d)}{\text{rate } (r)}$ or $t = \frac{d}{r}$ ◄ (means $d \div r$)

To find the *time,* substitute 360 for d and 45 for r in the time formula.
$t = \frac{d}{r} = \frac{360}{45} = $ **8 hours**

It will take Katie **8 hours** to drive 360 miles at 45 miles per hour.

Use the correct form of the distance formula to solve for distance, rate, or time. You may use a calculator.

1. How far can Betsy drive in 5 hours if she averages 55 miles per hour?

2. On the way to Atlanta, Ahmed drove 270 miles in 6 hours. What average speed did Ahmed drive on this part of his trip?

3. Driving at an average speed of 45 miles per hour, how long will it take Nathan to drive from Oak Grove to Skyler Lake?

All distances are in miles.

4. Averaging 60 miles per hour, what distance can Ella drive in 2 hours and 30 minutes? (*Hint:* Write 30 minutes as a fraction of an hour.)

5. During the Formula 1 race, Davy Smith drove 50 laps in a time of 1 hour and 15 minutes. If each lap is 2.5 miles, what was Davy's average speed during this race?

6. A marathon is a little bit over 26 miles in length.

   a. If Santino runs at a 10 minute-per-mile pace, how many miles per hour can he run?

   b. At this pace, how long will it take Santino to complete a marathon?

For another look at using a calculator, turn to page 219.

Making Connections: Speedometers and Odometers

In a car, speed is indicated on a **speedometer.** The speedometer shown at right has both English and metric speed readings. A car's speed is indicated by the position of a needle. Near the bottom of the speedometer is the **odometer,** a device that keeps track of the total mileage the car has traveled.

1. Driving at the speed indicated at right, what new mileage will the odometer show after you drive for 4 hours and 30 minutes?

2. Driving at the speed indicated at right, *about* how long does it take the car to travel a distance of 220 kilometers?

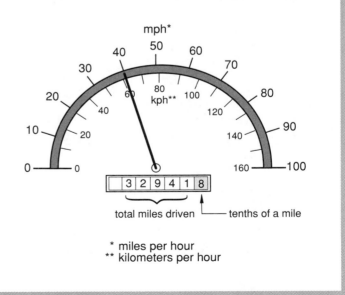

total miles driven — tenths of a mile

* miles per hour
** kilometers per hour

Working with Time Zones

When breakfast is being served at 7:00 A.M. in New York City, what time is it where you live? To find out, you must know which **time zone** you're in. If you're in Miami, the time is also 7:00 A.M. If you live in Seattle, you're probably still sleeping because the time is 4:00 A.M.

The map below shows the six times zones of the United States. Each time zone differs by one hour from the time zone next to it. Because the Sun rises in the east, time zones decrease by one hour as you move from east to west.

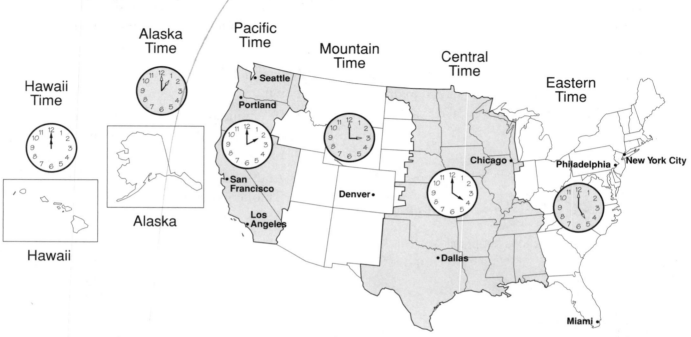

Use the map above to solve these time-related problems.

1. When it is 2:00 P.M. in San Francisco, what time is it in Miami?

2. At 6:00 P.M. Denver time, Kelley received a call from her mother. What time did Kelley's mother in Philadelphia place the call?

3. Tomaz is driving from Portland to San Francisco. If he leaves Portland at 7:00 A.M. and the trip takes 12 hours, what time will it be in San Francisco when Tomaz arrives?

4. When it's lunchtime in Dallas, Texas, which meal are they most likely having in Hawaii (breakfast, lunch, or dinner)?

5. If the sun rises at 6:45 A.M. in New York City, at approximately what time does it rise that day in Seattle, Washington? (2:45 A.M., 6:45 A.M., 10:45 A.M.)

6. At 8:00 A.M., Jeff gets on an airplane in Seattle to begin a nonstop flight to Miami. If the flight lasts 6 hours, what time will it be in Miami when Jeff lands?

7. Suppose you live in Chicago (Central Time) and need to place a conference call to Portland and Philadelphia. If you want to call at 11:30 A.M. Chicago time, what time should you tell the other parties the call will take place (their times)?

Portland: _____   Philadelphia: _____

8. Kali is flying out of New York City at 2:00 P.M. on a nonstop flight to Seattle. If this flight takes 5 hours, what time will it be in Seattle when Kali arrives?

Making Connections: International Date Line

As shown at right, the Earth is divided into 24 time zones. As you move from east to west, subtract one hour from your clock as you cross each new time-zone boundary. Also, regions east of the **international date line** are considered as being one day earlier than regions west of this line. When figuring time differences between two points on opposite sides of the international date line

THE WORLD TIME ZONES

- Figure the difference in clock time as usual.

- Add a day if you cross the line from east to west.

- Subtract a day if you cross the line from west to east.

As you go from San Francisco to Tokyo, you cross 7 time-zone boundaries (7 hours time difference). You also cross the international date line from east to west (add 1 day). When it is 12:00 noon on Monday in San Francisco, it is 5:00 A.M. Tuesday in Tokyo (7 hours earlier, but 1 day later).

Now you try crossing the international date line.

1. When it is 7:00 P.M. on Wednesday in San Francisco, what time and day is it in Tokyo?

2. When it is 12:00 noon on Friday in Tokyo, what time and day is it in San Francisco?

3. When it is 10:00 A.M. on Sunday in Chicago, what time and day is it in Tokyo?

4. When it is 1:00 P.M. on Sunday in Tokyo, what time and day is it in New York City?

Unit 1 Review

A. Change each quantity to the unit(s) indicated.

1. 2 ft. = _____ in. $\frac{2}{3}$ yd. = _____ in.   2.5 hr. = _____ min.   3 weeks = _____ days

2. 4.6 km = _____ m   26 ft. = ___ yd. ___ ft.   175 cm = ___ m ___ cm = ___.___ m

B. Solve each problem. Simplify answers when possible.

3.   5 ft. 9 in.   4 yd. 1 ft.   2 yd. 1 ft.   2$\overline{)3\text{ ft. 8 in.}}$
     + 3 ft. 7 in.   − 2 yd. 2 ft.   ×   8

4.   8 cm 9 mm   3 km 125 m   5 m 125 cm   3$\overline{)4\text{ m 50 cm}}$
     + 4 cm 6 mm   − 1 km 900 m   ×   7

C. Solve the following problems.

5. The largest bedroom in Dee's house is rectangular. It's $4\frac{1}{2}$ yd. long and $3\frac{2}{3}$ yd. wide.

   a. Using the formula $A = lw$, determine the area of this room in square yards.

   b. If Dee pays $9.50 per square yard for carpet, how much will it cost her to carpet this room?

6. a. Use the volume formula $V = lwh$ to find the volume of a spare gas tank measuring $2\frac{1}{2}$ ft. by 9 in. by 2 ft. (*Hint:* Write 9 in. as a fraction of a foot.)

   b. 1 cu. ft. can hold about $7\frac{1}{2}$ gallons of liquid. Find how many gallons of gas the spare tank can hold.

D. Grid in the answer to each problem.

7.  How many miles can you travel in 3.5 hours if you drive at an average speed of 48 miles per hour?

   Use the distance formula: $d = rt$

8. How many hours will it take Mark to bicycle a distance of 30 miles if he rides at an average speed of 12 miles per hour?

   Use the formula: $t = \frac{d}{r}$

48

E. Problem 9 refers to the drawing below.

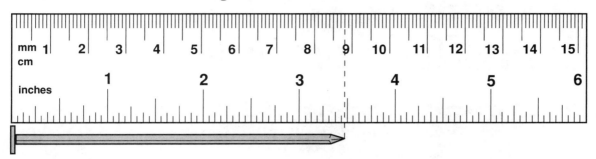

9. What is the length of the nail to the nearest

   a. $\frac{1}{8}$ inch? _____   **b.** $\frac{1}{16}$ inch? _____   **c.** $\frac{1}{10}$ cm? ___ cm ___ mm = ___.___ cm

F. Solve the following time problems as indicated.

10. Write the following dates as numbers.

    November 6, 1956 _____/_____/_____   October 4, 1994 ⬜⬜ ⬜⬜ ⬜⬜

    May 29, 1973   _____/_____/_____   April 1, 1980   ⬜⬜ ⬜⬜ ⬜⬜

Working Together

Do the following activities with a partner or with other students.

1. Discuss how often you use metric lengths (distances) in your life. Make a list of any consumer products that you use or own that have parts measured in metric lengths.

2. Make a list of 15 two-dimensional surfaces in your classroom. Without measuring the surfaces, arrange your list in order of approximate size, writing the largest surface area as number 1 and the smallest as number 15.

3. Make a list of 15 three-dimensional objects in your classroom. Without measuring, arrange this list in order of approximate size, writing the largest volume as number 1 and the smallest as number 15.

4. *Estimate* the length of your classroom. Then, in groups, measure the actual length and compare it to your estimate.

5. *Estimate* how long it would take to walk the length of your classroom. Then time yourself or another member of your group and compare the actual time to your estimate. Choose longer distances and repeat this experiment.

Capacity, Weight, and Temperature

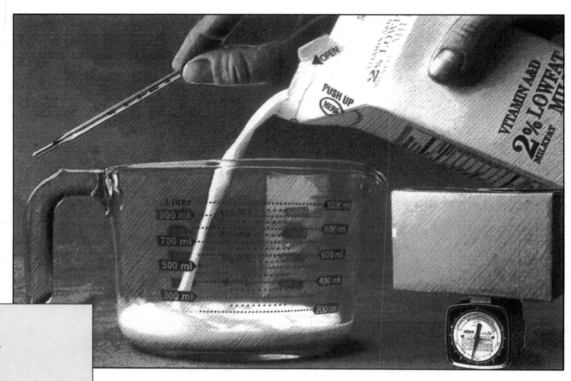

Skills

Defining capacity

Defining weight

Measuring temperature changes

Tools

English measuring spoons and cups

Metric measuring spoons and cups

Weight scales

Problem Solver

Estimating equivalent units

Applications

Using laboratory measuring containers

Relating volume, capacity, and weight

Measuring isn't limited to distance and time. You also measure how much a container holds, how much an object weighs, and how hot or cold an object is.

You think about **capacity** when you

- order a large soda rather than a small one
- fill a car's tank with gasoline

You think about **weight** each time you

- step on a scale
- buy a package of hamburger or chicken

Temperature is important when you

- dress to go outside
- bake

In this unit, you'll use the basic facts of measuring capacity, weight, and temperature in a wide variety of problems.

When Do I Measure These Things?

When do you think about capacity, weight, and temperature? Check off the sentences that apply to you.

☐ I buy milk in half-gallon or gallon containers.

☐ I step on a scale when I want to know how much I weigh.

☐ I prefer to buy a large soft drink rather than a small or medium.

☐ I check the price per pound when buying fruit at the store.

☐ I use a thermometer (part of a thermostat) to check room temperature.

☐ I set an oven temperature before I bake a cake or cookies.

☐ I use a thermometer to check my temperature when I feel ill.

As you begin this unit, think about some instances in your life that involved capacity, weight, or temperature.

1. Describe two times this week when you ordered or bought something that comes in cups, quarts, or gallons.

   a. _____

   b. _____

2. Describe a time when you wanted to know the weight of something (other than yourself). How did you determine this weight?

   _____

   _____

3. Name three things whose weight may be given in grams or kilograms. (*Hint:* Think of items from countries other than the United States.)

   a. _____

   b. _____

   c. _____

Talk About It

Talk with other students about temperature. What do you consider a very hot day or a very cold day? Do you know what your normal body temperature is? Do you know at approximately what temperature a refrigerator keeps food cold? What about a freezer?

Throughout this unit, you may use a calculator wherever that would be useful. Information about using a calculator appears on page 219.

English Units of Capacity

What is **capacity?** See if you can decide what capacity is by reading the brief situations described here.

- Mark picked up a quart of milk on his way home. He bought a quart instead of a gallon because the last gallon he bought spoiled before he drank it all.

- Angela estimated it would take 5 gallons to paint the storefront.

- Eric measured out 8 scoops (4 fluid ounces) of coffee to make a pot of 6 cups of coffee.

What do you think capacity measures? If you think capacity measures liquid or granular amounts, you are correct.

Pictured below are English capacity units you may be familiar with.

1 fluid ounce (fl. oz.)

1 cup (c.) = 8 fl. oz.

1 pint (pt.) = 2 c.
(1 pt. = 16 fl. oz.)

1 quart (qt.) = 2 pt.
(1 qt. = 32 fl. oz.)

1 gallon (gal.) = 4 qt.
(1 gal. = 128 fl. oz.)

A. Answer the following questions.

1. What is the smallest English capacity unit shown above?

2. What is the largest English capacity unit shown above?

3. **Discuss** What English capacity unit do you most often use in your home? Provide examples.

Converting to Larger Units

Sometimes you need to change measuring units. To change from a smaller unit to a larger unit, *divide by the number of smaller units in the larger unit.* Since the units are larger, your answer will show *fewer* units. When estimating, any reasonable estimate is acceptable.

Example: Patti combined ingredients totaling 94 fl. oz. in a large pot. She wants to freeze this soup in quart containers. How many quart containers will she need?

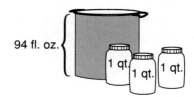

94 fl. oz. { 1 qt. 1 qt. 1 qt.

Step 1
Set up the problem.

94 fl. oz = _____ qt. _____ fl. oz.

Step 2
Estimate first.*

94 ÷ 32 ≈
90 ÷ 30 = 3 qt.

Step 3
Divide 94 by 32. (1 qt. = 32 fl. oz.) In the quotient, write the whole number as quarts and the remainder as fluid ounces.

$$\begin{array}{r} 2\ R30 \\ 32\overline{)\ 94} \\ -\ 64 \\ \hline 30 \end{array} = 2\ qt.\ 30\ fl.\ oz.$$

number of fluid ounces in 1 qt.

The amount **2 qt. 30 fl. oz.** is just 2 fl. oz. less than 3 qt. Patti will need **3 quart containers** to freeze the soup.

Check to see that the answer, **3 quart containers,** is close to (or the same as) the estimate.

---
* ≈ means "is approximately equal to"

B. Change each amount into the larger unit indicated. Estimate first.

4. 15 fl. oz. ≈ ___ c.

15 fl. oz. = ___ c. ___ fl. oz.
Hint: 1 cup = ? fluid ounces

35 fl. oz. ≈ ___ qt.

35 fl. oz. = ___ qt. ___ fl. oz.
Hint: 1 quart = ? fluid ounces

13 qt. ≈ ___ gal.

13 qt. = ___ gal. ___ qt.
Hint: 1 gallon = ? quarts

5. 47 fl. oz. ≈ ___ c.

47 fl. oz. = ___ c. ___ fl. oz.

75 fl. oz. ≈ ___ qt.

75 fl. oz. = ___ qt. ___ fl. oz.

29 qt. ≈ ___ gal.

29 qt. = ___ gal. ___ qt.

Converting to Smaller Units

To change a larger unit to a smaller unit, *multiply by the number of smaller units in the larger unit.* You'll need *more* smaller units for the same amount in larger units. When estimating, any reasonable answer is acceptable.

Example: Mai Li made $4\frac{3}{4}$ gal. of stew to sell at a church fund-raiser. If she sells the stew by the quart, how many quart-size containers will Mai Li need?

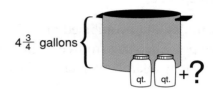

$4\frac{3}{4}$ gallons

Step 1
Set up the problem.
$4\frac{3}{4}$ gal. = _____ qt.

Step 2
Estimate first: $4\frac{3}{4} \approx 5$
$5 \times 4 = 20$ qt.

Step 3
Multiply $4\frac{3}{4}$ by 4.
$4\frac{3}{4} \times 4 = \frac{19}{4} \times \frac{4}{1} = 19$ qt.

Is the answer of **19 qt.** close to the estimate of 20 qt.?

C. Change each amount to the smaller unit indicated. Estimate first.

6. 3 c. $\approx$ ___ fl. oz.

   3 c. $=$ ___ fl. oz.

   Hint: 1 c. = ? fl. oz.

   $4\frac{1}{2}$ qt. $\approx$ _____ fl. oz.

   $4\frac{1}{2}$ qt. $=$ _____ fl. oz.

   Hint: $\frac{1}{2}$ qt. = ? fl. oz.

   $2\frac{3}{4}$ qt. $\approx$ _____ c.

   $2\frac{3}{4}$ qt. $=$ _____ c.

   Hint: 1 qt. = ? c.

   5.25 gal. $\approx$ ___ qt.

   5.25 gal. $=$ ___ qt.

   Hint: 1 gal. = ? qt.

7. $\frac{7}{8}$ c. $\approx$ _____ fl. oz.

   $\frac{7}{8}$ c. $=$ _____ fl. oz.

   $1\frac{1}{4}$ qt. $\approx$ _____ fl. oz.

   $1\frac{1}{4}$ qt. $=$ _____ fl. oz.

   6 qt. $\approx$ ___ fl. oz.

   6 qt. $=$ ___ fl. oz.

   1.9 gal. $\approx$ ___ qt.

   1.9 gal. $=$ ___ qt.

D. Solve the following problems.

8. Georgia has 52 fl. oz. of olive oil to use in making salad dressing for the school picnic. If she pours 1 c. of oil into each serving bottle, how many bottles of dressing can Georgia make?

9. **Estimate** Leon, a mechanic, collects a little more than 3 *qt.* of used motor oil from each oil change. If Leon has 25 *gal.* of used oil to recycle, about how many oil changes does that represent? Do you think your estimate is high or low? Explain.

10. **Discuss** Describe a time when you needed to convert a quantity to smaller units.

English Cups and Spoons

Pictured below are an English **measuring cup, tablespoon,** and **teaspoon.** Each of these tools is used to determine English measuring units in cooking. Note that measuring cups vary in size. The amount they can hold may range from $\frac{1}{4}$ c. to 4 c.

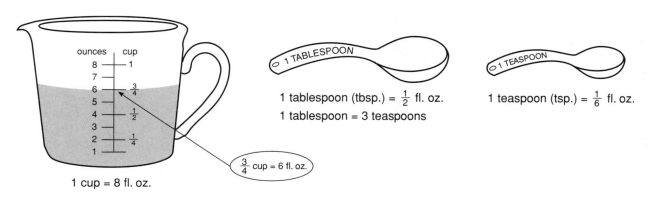

1 tablespoon (tbsp.) = $\frac{1}{2}$ fl. oz.

1 tablespoon = 3 teaspoons

1 teaspoon (tsp.) = $\frac{1}{6}$ fl. oz.

$\frac{3}{4}$ cup = 6 fl. oz.

1 cup = 8 fl. oz.

The cup contains two scales. On the right scale, you read what *fraction* of the cup is filled. On the left scale, you read the *number of fluid ounces.* One cup contains 8 fluid ounces.

A. How much liquid does the cup below contain? Write your answer in the units indicated.

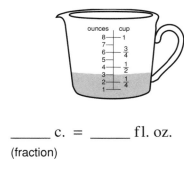

_____ c. = _____ fl. oz.
(fraction)

B. Draw a line to show a liquid level of 5 fl. oz. in the cup. Then fill in the lines below the drawing.

5 fl. oz. = _____ tbsp.

= _____ tsp.

C. Solve each measurement problem below.

1. If you start with $\frac{1}{2}$ c. of melted butter and remove 4 tbsp., how many fluid ounces of butter remain in the cup?

2. Alternative Solution Ellen's salad dressing recipe calls for 4 tbsp. of mustard. Ellen can't find her tablespoon.

  a. What other measuring tool can she use?

  b. Using this other measuring tool, how much mustard should Ellen use?

Metric Units of Capacity

In the United States, the metric system is slowly gaining acceptance. Cars, food items, and other goods carrying metric labels are now almost as common as products carrying English labels.

Because of the ease of using metric measurement, many people now believe that the United States should switch to the metric system. What do you think about this idea?

Sometimes people use metric measurements without realizing it. Can you think of examples in your own life similar to the ones below?

Andy had a prescription filled for his daughter. The recommended dosage of medicine was 1.5 milliliters every 6 hours.

The grocery store advertised 2-liter bottles of cola on sale for $1.29.

$1.29

Pictured below are the two most common metric capacity units.

A **milliliter** is a small unit. It takes almost 30 milliliters to equal 1 fluid ounce.

A **liter** is slightly larger than a quart.

1 liter ≈ 1.06 qt.

about the size of a sugar cube

1 milliliter (ml)

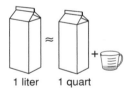

1 liter   1 quart

1 liter
(1 liter = 1,000 ml)

A. Which metric capacity unit would you use to measure each of the following?

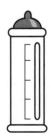

1. _____   2. _____   3. _____   4. _____

Converting Milliliters to Liters

Sometimes it is useful to convert smaller units to larger units. To convert milliliters to liters, *divide the number of milliliters by 1,000.**

Example: Raul has six 375-ml containers of brake fluid. Can he combine this fluid and store it all in one 2-liter container?

Step 1	**Step 2**	**Step 3**
Multiply to determine how many milliliters of brake fluid Raul has in all.	Estimate the number of liters.	Divide 2,250 by 1,000. You can write the quotient (the answer) in either of two ways.

375 × 6 = 2,250 ml	2,250 ÷ 1,000 ≈ 2,000 ÷ 1,000 = 2 liters	2,250 ÷ 1,000 = 2.250 liters (*or* 2.25 liters) = 2 liters 250 ml

*Note: To divide by 1,000, move the decimal point of the number being divided 3 places to the left.

No. Raul has a little more than 2 liters of brake fluid in all.

Check to see that the answer **2.25 liters** is close to the estimate of 2 liters.

B. Change from milliliters to a decimal fraction of a liter. The first one is done for you.

5. 50 ml = 0.05   30 ml = 0.___ liter   700 ml = 0.___ liter
   50 ÷ 1,000 = .050 liter

C. Estimate first. Then change each amount as indicated. Write each answer in two ways.

6. 3,180 ml ≈ ____ liter(s)   1,875 ml ≈ ____ liter(s)   6,250 ml ≈ ____ liter(s)
   3,180 ml = ____.____ liter(s)   1,875 ml = ____.____ liter(s)   6,250 ml = ____.____ liter(s)
        = ____ liter(s) ____ ml   = ____ liter(s) ____ ml   = ____ liter(s) ____ ml

► To convert liters to milliliters, multiply the number of liters by 1,000.

D. Change each number of liters to a number of milliliters.
   The first one is done for you.

7. 0.6 liter = 600 ml   0.9 liter = _____ ml   5 liters = _____ ml
   0.6 × 1,000 = 600. ml

8. 2.3 liters = _____ ml $3\frac{1}{2}$ liters = _____ ml   4.125 liters = _____ ml

Metric Cups and Spoons

Pictured below are a metric measuring cup, tablespoon, and teaspoon. Each of these tools is used to determine metric measuring units in cooking.

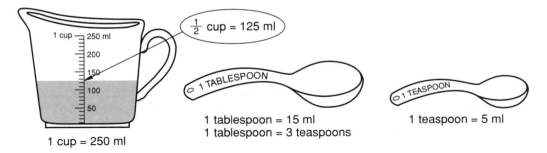

$\frac{1}{2}$ cup = 125 ml

1 cup = 250 ml

1 tablespoon = 15 ml
1 tablespoon = 3 teaspoons

1 teaspoon = 5 ml

A metric cup is equal to 250 ml. On the metric scale, the smallest divisions (not numbered) are 10 ml apart. Numbered divisions are given at 50-ml intervals. (Many kitchen cups show both scales.)

A. How much liquid does the cup below contain? Write your answer in the units indicated.

_____ ml = _____ cup
(fraction)

B. Draw a line to show a liquid level of 225 ml in the cup. Then answer the questions below.

How many more milliliters would you add to get 1 full cup? What combination of teaspoon and/or tablespoon amounts could you use to measure this small amount?

C. Solve each measurement problem below.

1. **Choose** Which metric measuring tool (cup, tablespoon, or teaspoon) would be most useful for measuring the following amounts?

   a. 10 ml of sugar

   b. 700 ml of flour

   c. 30 ml of chili powder

   d. 150 ml of vinegar

   e. 5 ml of salt

2. How many metric teaspoons would it take to fill a metric cup to the 50-ml mark?

3. How many metric tablespoons would it take to fill a metric cup to the 150-ml mark?

Metric Containers

If the United States decides to "go metric," manufacturers will need to design metric containers that hold about the same amount U.S. customers are now used to. For example, people who prefer to buy milk in half-gallon containers will want to buy *about* the same amount of milk in a metric-size container.

On each blank line below, write a *whole number* of metric units so that the metric container holds *about the same* amount as the English container.

1. 4 fl. oz ($\frac{1}{2}$ cup) pudding ≈ _____ ml _____ ml

4. 8 fl. oz (1 cup) yogurt ≈ _____ ml _____ ml

2. 1 pint cream ≈ _____ ml _____ ml

3. $\frac{1}{2}$ gallon milk ≈ _____ liters _____ liters

5. 1 quart orange juice ≈ _____ liter _____ liter

6. 1 gallon milk ≈ _____ liters _____ liters

For another look
at measurement comparisons, turn to page 222.

Making Connections: Shopping for Metric Sizes

Suppose you are shopping in a store that sells products that are packaged in metric containers like those above. What size of each of the following items would you be most likely to buy?

1. milk _____

3. dish soap _____

2. soda pop _____

4. bleach _____

Working with Capacity

Capacity units can be added or subtracted. An estimate will give you an approximate answer. To estimate an answer, round each capacity to the nearest whole number of larger units and then add or subtract.

Adding or Subtracting English Capacity Units

Example: To make her customers' favorite tropical fruit punch, Lena combined 3 qt. 10 fl. oz. of fruit drink with 1 qt. 28 fl. oz. of orange juice.

How much tropical fruit punch did Lena make by combining these two liquids?

Estimate first: 3 qt. + 2 qt. = 5 qt.
To determine the combined amount, add each unit separately.

$$
\begin{array}{r}
3 \text{ qt. } 10 \text{ fl. oz.} \\
+ \ 1 \text{ qt. } 28 \text{ fl. oz.} \\
\hline
4 \text{ qt. } 38 \text{ fl. oz.}
\end{array}
$$

4 qt. 38 fl. oz. =
4 qt. + 1 qt. 6 fl. oz. = **5 qt. 6 fl. oz.**

The answer is close to the estimate.

How much more fruit drink did Lena use than orange juice?

Estimate first: 3 qt. − 2 qt. = 1 qt.
To determine the difference in amounts, subtract each unit separately.
Since 28 fl. oz. is larger than 10 fl. oz., regroup the 3 qt. (32 + 10 = 42)

$$
\begin{array}{rr}
3 \text{ qt. } 10 \text{ fl. oz.} = & 2 \text{ qt. } 42 \text{ fl. oz.} \\
- \ 1 \text{ qt. } 28 \text{ fl. oz.} & - \ 1 \text{ qt. } 28 \text{ fl. oz.} \\
\hline
& \textbf{1 qt. 14 fl. oz.}
\end{array}
$$

The answer is close to the estimate.

For another look at measurement units, turn to page 222.

A. Add the following capacities. Simplify answers when possible. Estimate before finding exact answers. Refer to page 222 if you need to review English capacity units.

	Estimate		Estimate		Estimate
1. 2 c. 7 fl. oz.	3 c.	3 qt. 27 fl. oz.		9 gal. 3 qt.	
+ 1 c. 2 fl. oz.	+ 1 c.	+ 1 qt. 12 fl. oz.		+ 5 gal. 2 qt.	

B. Estimate first. Then subtract, regrouping when necessary.

	Estimate		Estimate		Estimate
2. 2 c. 7 fl. oz.		6 qt. 2 c.		7 gal. 1 qt.	
− 1 c. 1 fl. oz.		− 2 qt. 3 c.		− 3 gal. 3 qt.	

Adding or Subtracting Metric Capacity Units

To simplify working with metric capacity units, change each capacity to a decimal number of liters before adding or subtracting. *Write milliliters as the first three numbers to the right of the decimal point.*

Example: Tomaz, a photographic technician, has two bottles of fluid developer. One contains 3 liters 250 ml, and the second contains 1 liter 825 ml.

How much developer does Tomaz have in all?

Add to determine the total amount.
Estimate first: 3 liters + 2 liters = 5 liters

3 liters 250 ml	=	3.250 liters
+ 1 liter 825 ml	=	+ 1.825 liters
		5.075 liters
		or **5 liters 75 ml**

The answer is close to the estimate.

How much more developer is in one bottle than the other?

Subtract to determine the difference.
Estimate first: 3 liters − 2 liters = 1 liter

3 liters 250 ml	=	3.250 liters
− 1 liter 825 ml	=	− 1.825 liters
		1.425 liters
		or **1 liter 425 ml**

The answer is close to the estimate.

C. Write each capacity below as a decimal number of liters.

3. 2 liters 400 ml =   4 liters 125 ml =   1 liter 750 ml =   5 liters 125 ml =

D. Write each capacity below as a number of liters and milliliters.

4. 3.250 liters =   1.850 liters =   2.875 liters =   4.525 liters =

E. Add or subtract as indicated. Write each answer as decimal liters *and* as liters and milliliters. The first one is an example.

	Estimate		Estimate		Estimate
5.	7.125 liters		5.350 liters		4.750 liters
	+ 3.790 liters		+ 2.675 liters		+ 2.250 liters
	10.915 liters				
	= 10 liters 915 ml				

	Estimate		Estimate		Estimate
6.	4.250 liters		7.075 liters		8.125 liters
	− 2.600 liters		− 5.275 liters		− 3.700 liters

On the Job

Laboratory technicians use metric containers unlike those found in grocery stores. Shown below are four common types of glassware used to measure capacity in metric units in a lab setting.

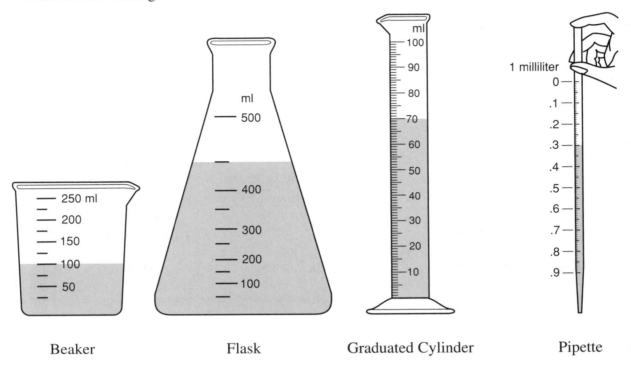

| Beaker | Flask | Graduated Cylinder | Pipette |

A. Answer the following questions.

1. What is the capacity of the *beaker?* (How much liquid will it hold when filled to the top labeled line?)

2. How many milliliters are in the *beaker* now?

3. What is the capacity of the *flask?*

4. Leroy, a lab technician, wants to lower the liquid level in the *flask* to 200 ml. How much liquid should Leroy remove from the flask?

5. On the *graduated cylinder,* how much difference in capacity is represented by the distance between each pair of shortest lines?

6. How much liquid would need to be added to raise the liquid in the *graduated cylinder* to the top labeled line?

7. What is the capacity of the *pipette?*

8. Georgia first filled the *pipette* with 1 ml of liquid (represented by the 0 mark on the scale). How much liquid did she then take out? (*Hint:* Notice that the labeled lines are 0.1 ml apart.)

People in many professions and jobs work mainly with metric measurement. Becoming familiar with metric units is an important job skill.

B. Problems 9 and 10 contain the same information, but one should be solved in English units and one in metric units.

9. The side of A1 Garage needs painting. The side measures about 58 ft. long and 10 ft. high. How much paint will be needed to paint this side? (*Note:* 1 gal. will cover about 325 sq. ft.)

   Estimate: _____ gal.
   whole number

   Exact to nearest $\frac{1}{4}$ gallon: _____

10. The side of A1 Garage needs painting. The side measures about 21 m long and 3 m high. How much paint will be needed to paint this side? (*Note:* 1 liter will cover about 8 m^2.)

   Estimate: _____ liters
   whole number

   Exact to nearest 0.1 liter: _____

Making Connections: The United States and the Metric System

Students often ask, "Why should the United States use the metric system?" One answer is that the metric system simplifies measurement calculations. To see this for yourself, work the problems below.

1. **a.** Colby, a machinist, needs to divide a 4 ft. 8 $\frac{1}{2}$ in. aluminum bar into 3 equal pieces. Assuming no waste, how long should each piece be?

   b. Colby also wants to divide a second aluminum bar, measuring 1.56 m, into 3 equal pieces. Assuming no waste, how long should each piece be?

2. **a.** You've been asked to place a label on the outside of a 2.6-gal. container to show its capacity in fluid ounces. What number should you write?

   b. You've been asked to place a label on the outside of a 9.7-liter container to show its capacity in milliliters. What number should you write?

3. Choose the two problems that were easier for you.

   1. a.   1. b.   2. a.   2. b.

4. **Explain** Why did you find these two problems easier to work?

Mixed Review

A. Change each capacity to the unit indicated.

1. 3 c. = _____ fl. oz. $6\frac{1}{4}$ qt. = _____ fl. oz.   5 gal. = _____ qt.   24 fl. oz. = _____ c.

2. 16 c. = _____ qt.   12 qt. = _____ gal.   4 liters = _____ ml   2.9 liters = _____ ml

3. 9 c. = _____ qt. _____ c.   17 qt. = _____ gal. _____ qt.   14 fl. oz. = _____ c. _____ fl. oz.

4. a. 700 ml = 0._____ liter

    b. 4.750 liters = _____ liter(s) _____ ml

    c. 5,400 ml = _____ liter(s) _____ ml = _____._____ liter(s)

B. Solve the problems. Simplify answers when possible.

5.
```
   2 c. 4 fl. oz.        4 qt. 20 fl. oz.        3 gal. 2 qt.          5.650 liters
 + 1 c. 5 fl. oz.      + 3 qt. 18 fl. oz.      + 1 gal. 3 qt.        + 2.875 liters
```

6.
```
   3 c. 5 fl. oz.        5 qt. 10 fl. oz.        6 gal. 1 qt.          4.500 liters
 - 1 c. 7 fl. oz.      - 2 qt. 16 fl. oz.      - 4 gal. 3 qt.        - 2.750 liters
```

C. Problems 7 and 8 are based on the measuring cup.

7. What *approximate* amount of vinegar is shown in the cup:

    a. as a fraction of a cup?   _____ c.

    b. in fluid ounces?   _____ fl. oz.

    c. in milliliters?   _____ ml

8. Using a dotted line, indicate how much vinegar would be in the cup if 6 more tbsp. of vinegar were added. (1 tbsp. = $\frac{1}{2}$ fl. oz.)

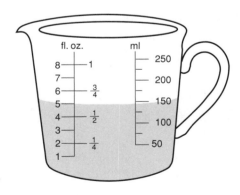

The measuring cup contains both English and metric scales.

D. The two containers below are partially filled with liquid. Determine how much liquid is in each container and write your answers on the lines as indicated.

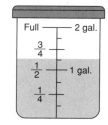

9. ___ gal. ___ qt. or _____ gal.
                   mixed number

10. ___ liter(s) ___ ml or _____ liter(s)
                      decimal number

E. Solve these measurement problems.

11. According to the instructions, Lanny should put "no more than 1 quart" of oil in the new lawnmower engine. If Lanny has only a 1-liter container of oil, what would you advise Lanny to do?

12. A recipe for a lemon cheesecake calls for 4 fl. oz. of evaporated milk. What is the *approximate* equivalent amount of milk in metric units?

F. Grid in the answer to each problem.

13.

Josh has 75 fluid ounces of paint thinner in a metal can. How many 1-cup containers can he completely fill from the contents of the can?

14.

Shelley has four liters of soda pop. After pouring eight full glasses, how many liters of soda does she have left if each glass holds 350 milliliters?

G. Which capacity unit would you use to measure the amount of liquid in each container below? Give both English (gal., qt., or fl. oz.) and metric (liters or ml) capacity units.

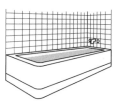

15. _____ _____
English   metric

16. _____ _____
English   metric

17. _____ _____
English   metric

18. _____ _____
English   metric

English Units of Weight

Weight is a measure of how heavy an object is. From your own experience you already have good intuition about weight. As an example, choose the heaviest of the three objects below.

You are correct if you chose the brick in the center.

In the English system, weight is most often measured in the three basic units listed below.

1 ounce (oz.)　　　　　　1 pound (lb.) = 16 oz.　　　　1 ton (tn.) = 2,000 lb.

▶ Be sure not to be confused by the use of the word *ounce* in both capacity *and* weight measurement. An *ounce* is a measure of weight, while a *fluid ounce* is a measure of capacity.

A. Fill in the blank lines with the correct answers.

1. *Fluid ounce* is a measure of _____, while *ounce* is a measure of _____.

2. There are _____ ounces in a pound and _____ pounds in a ton.

B. Which English weight unit would you most likely use to measure each of the following?

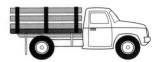

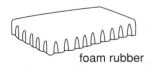

foam rubber

3. _____　　4. _____　　5. _____　　6. _____

Converting to Larger Units

To change from a smaller to a larger unit, *divide by the number of smaller units in the larger unit.* Since the units are larger, your answer will show *fewer* units.

Example: Glenn shredded a total of 324 oz. of mozzarella cheese this morning.

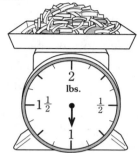

    a. How would he record this amount in pounds and ounces?

    b. How many 1-lb. packages can Glenn get from this amount?

Step 1
Set up the problem.

324 oz. = ___ lb. ___ oz.

Step 2
Estimate first.

324 ÷ 16 ≈*
320 ÷ 16 = 20 lb.

Step 3
Divide 324 by 16. (1 lb. = 16 oz.) In the quotient, write the whole number (20) as pounds and the remainder (4) as ounces.

$$
\begin{array}{r}
20 \text{ R4} = 20 \text{ lb. } 4 \text{ oz.} \\
16 \overline{)\ 324} \\
-32 \\ \hline
04 \\
-\ 0 \\ \hline
4
\end{array}
$$

number of ounces in 1 lb.

Answers: **a.** 324 oz. = 324 ÷ 16 = **20 lb. 4 oz.**

        b. Glenn can get **20 1-lb. packages.** (You do not use the remainder to answer this question.)

---

* Remember: ≈ means "is approximately equal to."

Notice that the estimate is the same as the exact answer.

C. Change each weight to the larger unit indicated. Estimate first.

7. 31 oz. ≈ ___ lb.

31 oz. = ___ lb. ___ oz.
Hint: 1 lb. = ? oz.

17 oz. ≈ ___ lb.

17 oz. = ___ lb. ___ oz.

167 oz. ≈ ___ lb.

167 oz. = ___ lb. ___ oz.

8. 4,125 lb. ≈ ___ tn.

4,125 lb. = ___ tn. ___ lb.
Hint: 1 tn. = ? lb.

9,800 lb. ≈ ___ tn.

9,800 lb. = ___ tn. ___ lb.

3,075 lb. ≈ ___ tn.

3,075 lb. = ___ tn. ___ lb.

Converting to Smaller Units

To change a larger unit to a smaller unit, *multiply by the number of smaller units in the larger unit.* Since the units are smaller, your answer will show *more* units.

Example: Joel wants to determine how many 4-oz. patties he can make out of 11 lb. of hamburger. (To find how many he can make, write 11 lb. as ounces only, and then divide the number of ounces by 4.)

Step 1
Set up the problem.

9 lb. = _____ oz.

Step 2
Estimate first.

16 oz. × 11 ≈
20 × 10 = 200 oz.
200 ÷ 4 = 50 patties

Step 3
Multiply 11 by 16.

11 × 16 = 176 oz.

Step 4
Divide 176 oz. by 4 oz.

$$\begin{array}{r} 44 \\ 4\overline{)176} \\ -16 \\ \hline 16 \\ -16 \\ \hline 0 \end{array}$$

Joel can make **44 patties** out of 11 lb. of hamburger. This is close to the estimate of 50 patties.

D. **Change each weight to the smaller unit indicated. Estimate first.**

9. 5 lb. ≈ ___ oz.

5 lb. = ___ oz.
Hint: 1 lb. = ? oz.

$1\frac{1}{8}$ lb. ≈ _____ oz.

$1\frac{1}{8}$ lb. = _____ oz.

9.4 lb. ≈ ___ oz.

9.4 lb. = ___ oz.

10. 3.2 tn. ≈ ___ lb.

3.2 tn. = ___ lb.
Hint: 1 tn. = ? lb.

$\frac{9}{10}$ tn. ≈ _____ lb.

$\frac{9}{10}$ tn. = _____ lb.

1.9 tn. ≈ ___ lb.

1.9 tn. = ___ lb.

E. **Solve each measurement problem.**

11. Tonya wants to divide $4\frac{1}{2}$ lb. of mixed nuts into treat bags. How many treat bags can Tonya make if each bag holds 3 oz. of nuts?

12. **Estimate** To help stop a river from flooding nearby farmland, residents piled sandbags along the riverbank. *About* how many 38-lb. sandbags can they make out of the 8 tn. of available sand? Do you think your estimate is high or low? Explain.

English Weight Scale

To measure weight of a few ounces or pounds, you can use a **pound scale** such as the one shown below. Each numbered division represents 1 pound, while the smaller divisions represent fractions of a pound. You read each of the 16 smallest divisions as 1 ounce.

You read a weight on this scale as pounds and ounces or as a mixed number of pounds.

Examples: On the pound scale shown below

Point A is at 2 lb. 8 oz. $= 2\frac{1}{2}$ lb.

Point D is at 4 lb. 12 oz. $= 4\frac{3}{4}$ lb.

Point G is at 1 lb. 3 oz.

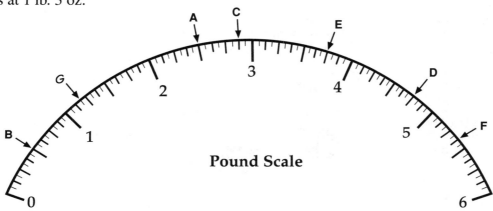

Pound Scale

A. Using the pound scale shown above, write the weight represented by each point as pounds and ounces *and* as a mixed number of pounds. Points A and D are done as examples.

1. Point A = __2__ lb. __8__ oz.　　　Point B = ____ oz.　　　Point C = ____ lb. ____ oz.

   = __$2\frac{1}{2}$__ lb.　　　　　　　= ____ lb.　　　　　　　= ____ lb.

2. Point D = __4__ lb. __12__ oz.　　　Point E = ____ lb. ____ oz.　　　Point F = ____ lb. ____ oz.

   = __$4\frac{3}{4}$__ lb.　　　　　　　= ____ lb.　　　　　　　= ____ lb.

B. Using letters and arrows, indicate the following weights on the pound scale above. Point G is done as an example.

3. Point G = 1 lb. 3 oz.　　　Point H = 13 oz.　　　Point I = 2 lb. 2 oz.

4. Point J = $3\frac{1}{2}$ lb.　　　Point K = $4\frac{1}{4}$ lb.　　　Point L = $5\frac{3}{4}$ lb.

Metric Units of Weight

Metric weight units, as well as metric capacity units, often appear on many U.S.-made food products such as the examples shown at right. U.S. food producers place metric equivalent amounts in parentheses to help U.S. customers get used to metric units.

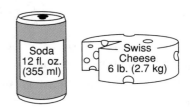

The most commonly used metric weight units are pictured below.

 about the weight of a grain of sand

 about the weight of a raisin

> ► Even though a gram is equal to 1,000 milligrams, it is still a small weight unit. In fact, it takes 28 grams to equal 1 ounce, and 454 grams to equal 1 pound.

1 milligram (mg)*

1 gram (g) = 1,000 mg

---

*A **milligram** is a very small weight unit. The English system doesn't have a similar small unit. That is why tiny amounts, such as ingredients in vitamin pills, are given in milligrams.

about the weight of a quart (or liter) of milk (≈ 2.2 lb.)

about the weight of a small car (≈ 2,200 lb.)

1 kilogram (kg) = 1,000 g

1 metric ton (t) = 1,000 kg

A. Answer the following questions.

1. What is the metric weight unit most like the English ton?

2. What is the metric weight unit most like the English pound?

3. How many grams equal 1 kilogram?

B. Which metric weight unit would you most likely use to measure each of the following?

Stew

4. _____

5. _____

6. _____

7. _____

70

Converting to Larger Units

To change from one metric unit to the next larger unit, *divide by the number of smaller units in the larger unit.* Since the units are larger, your answer will show *fewer* units.

Example: A shipping box contains 48 cans of imported sardines. If each can weighs 275 g, the total weight of 48 cans is 13,200 g (275 × 48). How do you express this weight as a decimal number of kilograms?

Step 1	**Step 2**	**Step 3**
Set up the problem.	Estimate first.	Divide 13,200 by 1,000.*
13,200 g = __.__ g	13,200 ≈ 13,000 13,000 ÷ 1,000 = 13 kg	13,200 ÷ 1,000 = 13.200 kg = 13.2 kg *or* = 13 kg 200 g

Note: To divide by 1,000, move the decimal point of the number being divided 3 places to the left.

Your answer, **13.2 kg,** is close the estimate of 13 kg.

C. **Change from grams to a decimal fraction of a kilogram. The first one is done for you.**

8. 6 g = 0.*006* kg   20 g = 0.____ kg   750 g = 0.____ kg

   6 ÷ 1,000 = 0.006

D. **Express each weight to the next higher unit as shown. Estimate first.**

9. 2,900 mg ≈ ____ g   4,100 g ≈ ____ kg   8,750 kg ≈ ____ t

   2,900 mg = ____.____ g   4,100 g = ____.____ kg   8,750 kg = ____.____ t

   = ____ g ____ mg   = ____ kg ____ g   = ____ t ____ kg

   Hint: 1 g = 1,000 mg   *Hint:* 1 kg = 1,000 g   *Hint:* 1 t = 1,000 kg

10. 3,100 mg ≈ ____ g   5,800 g ≈ ____ kg   2,250 kg ≈ ____ t

   3,100 mg = ____.____ g   5,800 g = ____.____ kg   2,250 kg = ____.____ t

   = ____ g ____ mg   = ____ kg ____ g   = ____ t ____ kg

Converting to Smaller Units

To change from one metric unit *of weight* to the next smaller unit, *multiply by the number of smaller units in the larger unit.* Since the units are smaller, your answer will show *more* units.

Example: The weight of a French-made truck is listed as 2.1 t. How do you express this weight in kilograms?

Step 1
Set up the problem.

2.1 t = _____ kg

Step 2
Estimate first.

$2.1 \approx 2$
$2 \times 1,000 = 2,000$ kg

Step 3
Multiply 2.1 by 1,000.*

$2.1 \times 1,000 = $ **2,100 kg**

*Note: To multiply by 1,000, move the decimal point of the number being multiplied 3 places to the right.

E. Change each weight to the smaller unit indicated.

11. 0.6 t = _600_ kg   0.3 t = _____ kg   5.2 t = _____ kg
$.6 \times 1,000 = 600$

12. 0.5 kg = _____ g   0.9 kg = _____ g   3.4 kg = _____ g

13. 0.9 g = _____ mg   0.15 g = _____ mg   6.7 g = _____ mg

F. Solve each problem below.

14. A truck is carrying 14 new Japanese sports cars. Each car weighs 1,425 kg.

   a. What is the total weight of these cars in kilograms?

   b. Express this total weight as a decimal number of metric tons.

15. Compare The Johnson Company ordered 8.5 t of gravel to be delivered to their construction site. The truck brought 9,000 kg. Compare the amount delivered to the amount ordered. Express any difference in kilograms.

16. Investigate What metric unit is used most often to measure daily vitamin requirements?

Metric Weight Scale

To measure weights of a few kilograms, use a **kilogram scale** like the one shown below. Each numbered division represents 1 kilogram, while each smaller division represents 0.1 kilogram (100 grams). Stores that use metric measurement weigh food on kilogram scales.

You read a weight on this scale as a decimal number of kilograms or as a number of kilograms and grams.

Examples: On the kilogram scale shown below

Point A is at 0.8 kg = 800 g

Point D is at 4.9 kg = 4 kg 900 g

Point G is at 1.5 kg

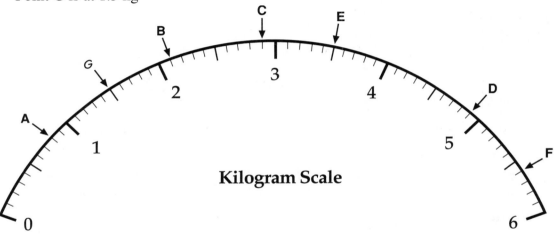

Kilogram Scale

A. Using the kilogram scale shown above, write the weight represented by each point as indicated. Points A and D are done as examples.

1. Point A = __0__.__8__ kg   Point B = ____.____ kg   Point C = ____.____ kg
    = __0__ kg __800__ g   = ____ kg ____ g   = ____ kg ____ g

2. Point D = __4__.__9__ kg   Point E = ____.____ kg   Point F = ____.____ kg
    = __4__ kg __900__ g   = ____ kg ____ g   = ____ kg ____ g

B. Using letters and arrows, indicate the following weights on the kilogram scale above. Point G is done as an example.

3. Point G = 1.5 kg   Point H = 2.25 kg   Point I = 3.9 kg

4. Point J = 1 kg 300 g   Point K = 2 kg 700 g   Point L = 3 kg 100 g

Working with Weight

You can also add or subtract weight units. To estimate, round each weight to the nearest whole number of larger units as your first step.

Adding or Subtracting English Units

Example: While shopping at Family Market, Lucinda bought 5 lb. 12 oz. of cabbage and 3 lb. 15 oz. of carrots.

What total weight of vegetables did Lucinda buy?

Step 1. Estimate first.
    6 lb. + 4 lb. = 10 lb.

Step 2. Determine the combined weight.
    Add each unit separately.

    5 lb. 12 oz.
 + 3 lb. 15 oz.
    8 lb. 27 oz. = 8 lb. + 1 lb. 11 oz.
                = **9 lb. 11 oz.**

Your answer is close to your estimate.

How much more cabbage did Lucinda buy than carrots?

Step 1. Estimate first.
    6 lb. − 4 lb. = 2 lb.

Step 2. Determine the difference in weight.
    Subtract each unit.
Since 15 oz. is larger than 12 oz., regroup the 5 lb.
  5 lb. 12 oz. =   4 lb. 28 oz. (16 + 12 = 28)
− 3 lb. 15 oz.   − 3 lb. 15 oz.
                 1 lb. 13 oz.

Your answer is close to your estimate.

For another look at measurement units, turn to page 222.

A. Add the following weights. Simplify answers when possible. Estimate as your first step.

	Estimate		Estimate		Estimate
1. 15 oz.		13 lb. 1 oz.	13 lb.	2 lb. 12 oz.	
+ 3 oz.		+ 7 lb. 12 oz.	+ 8 lb.	+ 1 lb. 15 oz.	

	Estimate		Estimate		Estimate
2. 2 tn. 1,500 lb.		3 tn. 1,650 lb.		8 tn. 740 lb.	
+ 900 lb.		+ 1 tn. 800 lb.		+ 6 tn. 1,650 lb.	

B. Estimate an answer first. Then subtract. Regroup if needed.

	Estimate		Estimate		Estimate
3. 5 lb. 12 oz.		7 lb. 6 oz.		12 lb. 1 oz.	
− 3 lb. 7 oz.		− 4 lb. 10 oz.		− 9 lb. 3 oz.	

	Estimate		Estimate		Estimate
4. 1 tn. 500 lb. – 900 lb.		5 tn. 750 lb. – 3 tn. 1,000 lb.		12 tn. 1,000 lb. – 8 tn. 1,200 lb.	

Adding or Subtracting Metric Weight Units

To simplify working with metric weight units, change each weight to a decimal before adding or subtracting.

Example: Alvin, a chemist's assistant, needs to determine the weight difference of two rock samples. The larger rock weighs 2 kg 925 g, and the smaller rock weighs 1 kg 850 g. What is the difference in weight?

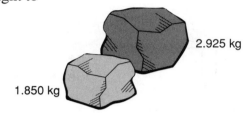
2.925 kg

1.850 kg

Step 1	**Step 2**	**Step 3**
Change each weight to its decimal equivalent.	Estimate first.	Subtract 1.850 kg from 2.925 kg.
2 kg 925 g = 2.925 kg 1 kg 850 g = 1.850 kg	2.925 ≈ 3; 1.850 ≈ 2 3 – 2 = 1 kg	2.925 kg – 1.850 kg 1.075 kg *or* 1 kg 75 g

Your answer of **1.075 kg** is close to your estimate of 1 kg.

C. Write each weight below in decimal form.

5. 2 kg 300 g =   5 kg 250 g =   1 t 500 kg =   3 g 680 mg =

D. Write each weight below in the units indicated.

6. 4.275 kg = ___ kg _____ g   6.5 g = ___ g _____ mg   2.65 t = ___ t _____ kg

E. Add or subtract as indicated. Estimate as your first step.

	Estimate		Estimate		Estimate
7. 5.3 mg + 3.9 mg		6.4 kg + 1.9 kg		1.75 t + 1.65 t	

	Estimate		Estimate		Estimate
8. 6.25 g – 2.7 g		9.35 kg – 2.5 kg		3.28 t – 1.725 t	

Volume, Capacity, and Weight

In the metric system, volume, capacity, and weight are all simply related:

- 1 milliliter is the same volume as 1 cubic centimeter.

- 1 gram is the weight of 1 milliliter (or 1 cubic centimeter) of water.

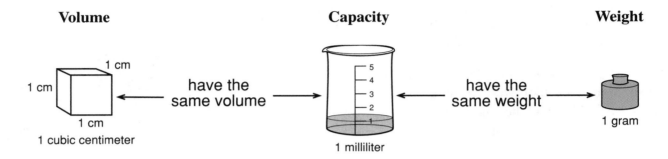

You can use these facts to quickly determine the weight of 1 liter of water. Since 1 liter of water is 1,000 milliliters, 1 liter of water weighs 1,000 grams or 1 kilogram (about 2.2 pounds).

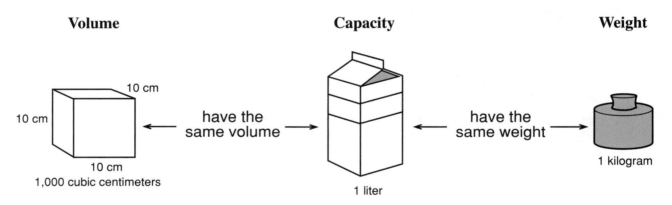

A. Determine the weight of each of the following.

1. 2 liters of water   _____ kg
(about $\frac{1}{2}$ gal.)

2. 4 liters of water   _____ kg
(about 1 gal.)

3. 8 liters of water   _____ kg
(about 2 gal.)

4. a metric cup of water   _____ g
(250 ml)

5. a metric tablespoon of water   _____ g
(15 ml)

6. a metric teaspoon of water   _____ g
(5 ml)

B. What is the *approximate* weight (in metric units) of liquid in each container below? Each of these liquids is made up mainly of water.

1 liter

milk

4 liters
Orange Juice

7. _____

8. _____

9. _____

C. Remembering that 1 liter ≈ 1 qt. and that 1 kg ≈ 2.2 lb., *estimate* the weight in pounds of each of the following.

MILK
1 quart

Apple Juice
1 gallon

8 fl. oz. soda pop

10. _____

11. _____

12. _____

D. Determine the volume of water in each container below. Then write the weight of this water in the units given.

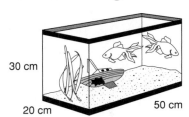

30 cm

20 cm   50 cm

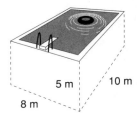

5 m   10 m

8 m

13. Volume = _____ cm³ (cubic centimeters)

Weight = _____ g

= _____ kg

≈ _____ lb.

14. Volume = _____ m³ (cubic meters)

Weight = _____ t*

_____
*1 m³ of water weighs 1 t.

Measuring Temperature

Temperature is a measure of how much heat energy an object contains. To measure temperature we use a **thermometer.** The most common thermometer used in homes is the weather thermometer.

The Weather Thermometer

The weather thermometer shown here has two scales, the **Fahrenheit** scale (°F) and the metric **Celsius** scale (°C). The ° symbol means "degree(s)." Notice that each scale has both positive and negative numbers.

- Positive readings represent temperatures above 0.
- Negative readings represent temperatures below 0.

The temperature is indicated by the top of the liquid in the center tube. The temperature indicated at right is 68°F, which is equal to 20°C.

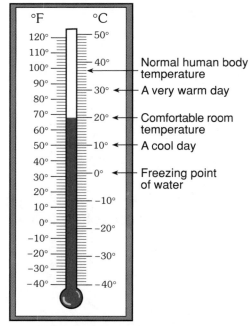

Weather Thermometer

A. Solve.

1. Use the thermometer above to identify the following temperatures.
   a. very warm day: _____ °F or _____ °C
   b. freezing point of water: _____ °F or _____ °C

2. What word best describes a day that has the following temperature?
   a. 10°C:
   b. 42°C:

B. Write the temperature in both °F and °C indicated by each thermometer below.

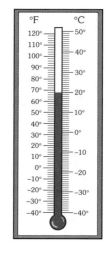

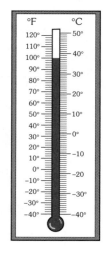

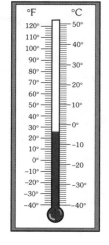

3. _____ °F ≈ _____ °C   4. _____ °F ≈ _____ °C   5. _____ °F ≈ _____ °C

The Clinical Thermometer

A second type of thermometer found in many homes is the **clinical thermometer,** used to measure human body temperature. The temperature range of a clinical thermometer is narrow, limited to about 92°F to 110°F, or about 33°C to 44°C. Fahrenheit and Celsius clinical thermometers are shown below.

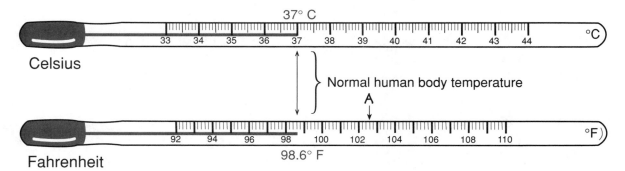

Human beings are *warm-blooded,* which means that their internal body temperature remains almost constant. As shown above, normal human body temperature is about 98.6°F or 37°C. Most people have a temperature of between 97°F and 99°F.

- When people are ill, their body temperature usually rises above normal.
- When people are exposed to cold for a long time or are very tired, their body temperature often falls below normal.

C. On the thermometers above, label the following points with a letter and a small arrow. Point A is done as an example.

On the Fahrenheit thermometer

- **A.** an elevated temperature of 102.6°F
- **B.** 3.5°F below normal
- **C.** a high fever of 3.7°F above 98.6°F
- **D.** a chill of 95.9°F

On the Celsius thermometer

- **E.** a low temperature of 35.2°C
- **F.** 1.6°C below 37°C
- **G.** a fever of 1.3°C above 98.6°F
- **H.** a high temperature of 38.9°C

D. What is the temperature reading on each thermometer below?

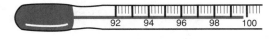

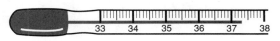

6. _____ °F

7. _____ °C

Gridding in Measurement Answers

As you know, decimals and fractions are two ways of expressing part of a whole. Many measurement answers include a decimal or a fraction. For example, the measurement 2 feet 6 inches can be written as $2\frac{1}{2}$ or 2.5 feet.

When you answer grid-in questions on a test, you can choose whether to use fractions or decimals. The scoring machine will score both as correct. Use these tips to fit fraction and decimal answers in the five-column grid:

- You cannot enter mixed numbers. Convert any mixed number to an improper fraction or decimal before you enter it.

- The decimal point (.) or slash symbol (/) must be in a column by itself. You have room in the grid for four numbers and one symbol.

- You don't have to write a fraction in lowest terms to receive credit for your answer, but you may have to write it in lowest terms so that it will fit within the five-column grid.

- You don't have to enter the leading zero in a decimal. (0.75 = .75)

- If your answer has many decimal digits, read the problem carefully for instructions about rounding to a certain place.

Filling in the Grid

Example: Monica ordered six craft kits. If each kit weighs 1 lb. 4 oz., what is the total weight of her order in pounds?

Step 1
Solve the problem.

$$\begin{array}{r} 1 \text{ lb. 4 oz.} \\ \times \quad\quad 6 \\ \hline 6 \text{ lb. 24 oz.} \end{array}$$

24 oz. = 1 lb. 8 oz.
6 lb. 24 oz. = 7 lb. 8 oz.

The total weight is 7 lb. 8 oz.

Step 2
Express the answer in pounds.
7 lb. 8 oz. = $7\frac{8}{16}$ = $7\frac{1}{2}$ lb.

Change to an improper fraction:
$7\frac{1}{2} = \frac{15}{2}$

Since $\frac{1}{2}$ = .5, you can also express the answer as a decimal: $7\frac{1}{2}$ = 7.5

Step 3
Fill in the grid. Both of these answers would be scored as correct.

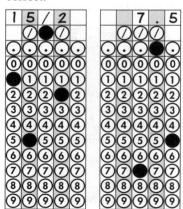

80

Solve the following problems. Record your answers in the grids.

1.

A prescription tablet contains 250 milligrams of medication. How many <u>grams</u> of medication are in 50 of the same tablets?

4.

A spoon weighs 50 grams. How many <u>kilograms</u> does the spoon weigh?

2.

The gas tank of a garden tiller can be filled $6\frac{2}{3}$ times from a 5-gallon container of gasoline. How many <u>gallons</u> of gasoline can the garden tiller hold?

5.

A food pantry has a 6-pound box of white rice. Hilda uses 1 lb. 12 oz. to prepare a meal. How many <u>pounds</u> of white rice are left in the box?

3.

The product Water Shock is added to the water of a home spa once a week. If a 32-ounce bottle of Water Shock lasts 8 weeks, how many <u>cups</u> of the product are added to the water at one time?

6.

Sally has two bottles of pet shampoo. One bottle holds 475 milliliters. The other holds 1.25 liters. How many <u>liters</u> of pet shampoo does Sally have in all?

Unit 2 Review

A. Change each capacity or weight to the units indicated.

1. 2 c. = _____ fl. oz.   2 lb. = _____ oz.   8 qt. = _____ gal.   3 tn. = _____ lb.

2. 3 liters = _____ ml   4 kg = _____ g   2.9 liters = _____ ml   3.5 g = _____ mg

3. 17 qt. = _____ gal. _____ qt.   24 oz. = _____ lb. _____ oz.   2,800 lb. = _____ tn. _____ lb.

4. 4,750 ml = _____ liter(s) _____ ml   5,400 mg = _____ . _____ g   3,500 g = _____ kg _____ g

B. Solve each problem as indicated. Simplify answers when possible.

5.
    3 lb. 9 oz.
  + 1 lb. 7 oz.

    2 tn. 1,500 lb.
  + 1 tn. 1,600 lb.

    12.750 kg
  + 9.500 kg

    7 g 800 mg
  + 2 g 900 mg

6.
    3 lb. 6 oz.
  − 1 lb. 10 oz.

    8 tn. 1,200 lb.
  − 6 tn. 1,000 lb.

    4.150 g
  − 2.500 g

    6 kg 250 g
  − 3 kg 750 g

C. Grid in the answer to each problem.

7.  Leonard has 3 qt. 20 fl. oz. of liquid soap. How many soap dispensers can he completely fill if each dispenser holds 12 fl. oz.? (*Hint:* Change 3 qt. 20 fl. oz. to fluid ounces.)

8. 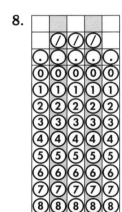 At 6 P.M., Liu's temperature was 97.4°F. Two hours later, her temperature was 102.1°F. How many degrees did Liu's temperature rise?

D. Many food products list both English and metric units. In each list below, match the equivalent metric unit with the English unit. Remember 1 qt. ≈ 1 liter and 1 kg ≈ 2.2 lb.

Capacity

_____ **9.** 1 quart   **a.** 0.48 liter

_____ **10.** 1 gallon   **b.** 3.8 liters

_____ **11.** 16 fluid ounces   **c.** 0.95 liter

Weight

_____ **12.** 32 oz.   **a.** 142 g

_____ **13.** 5 oz.   **b.** 3.41 kg

_____ **14.** 7.5 lb.   **c.** 0.91 kg

E. Which weight unit would you use to measure the weight of each object below?
Give both English (oz., lb., tn.) and metric (mg, g, kg, t) weight units.

15. _____ _____
    English metric

16. _____ _____
    English metric

17. _____ _____
    English metric

18. _____ _____
    English metric

F. What reading is shown on each measuring tool below?

 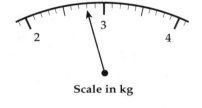 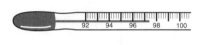

Scale in kg

19. _____

20. _____

21. _____

Working Together

Do the following activities with a partner or with other students.

1. Make a list of 10 consumer products in a local market whose containers are labeled with one or more metric capacity units.

2. *Estimate* the weight of both the heaviest and the lightest book in your class. Weigh each book and see how close your estimates are.

3. Write down a list of five food items whose weight (or list of ingredients) is given in milligrams (mg).

4. Write the names of five things that you consider very large, yet surprisingly light. Then write the names of five things that you consider small, yet surprisingly heavy.

5. Measure your own body temperature. Most likely, you'll find that your temperature will usually be between 97°F and 99°F.

Organizing and Summarizing Data

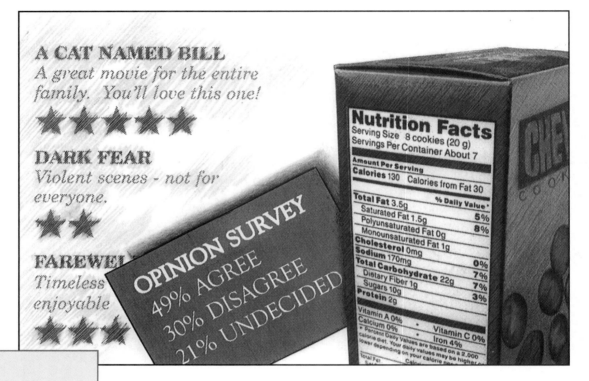

Skills

Summarizing data

Reading a table

Understanding typical value

Displaying data on a line plot

Sorting data

Tools

Tally sheet

Problem Solvers

Comparing sets of data

Completing a table

Applications

Choosing a typical value

Sorting data in a table

Working with spreadsheets

Data is a group of numbers that gives us information about some subject. Data can be personal, such as numbers that give your height, weight, and age. Or data can be general, such as a nutrition label on a vitamin bottle.

You may not think about it, but you use data in everyday activities such as:

- counting the change in your pocket
- totaling monthly bills
- looking at sale items in a catalog
- comparing the costs of cereals
- reading a restaurant menu

In this chapter you'll organize data by putting it into lists and tables. You'll also learn how to summarize data by finding and using three types of "typical values." You'll compare different groups of data by using percents. And you'll learn how to organize data visually by drawing a line plot.

When Is Data Important to Me?

When have you used data or participated in data collection? Check the sentences that apply to you.

☐ I have used a menu in a restaurant.

☐ I have answered a telephone survey.

☐ I have been weighed in a doctor's office or medical clinic.

☐ I have been counted in a census poll.

☐ I have filled out a consumer product questionnaire.

☐ I have voted in an election.

☐ I have heard political polls predict winners on the news.

As you begin this unit, describe situations that involve data in your life.

1. Describe two times when you compared the prices of two or more food items before you decided which to buy.

   a. _____

   _____

   b. _____

   _____

2. Describe a time when you wrote down a list of numbers, such as telephone numbers or street addresses. Why did you write the numbers, and how did you use the list?

   _____

   _____

3. Describe a list or table of data that you commonly use, such as a bus or train schedule. Tell how the data is organized.

   _____

   _____

   _____

Throughout this unit, you may use a calculator wherever that would be useful. Information about using a calculator appears on page 219.

Talk About It

Talk with other students about average values. For example, the typical price you pay for a large pizza may be $15.00. The typical wait for a bus may be 10 or 15 minutes. Name three more situations where typical values are all you need to know. Can you think of situations where a typical value is not enough?

How Is Data Used?

Data is all around us. Whether we realize it or not, data influences our lives, much of it gathered and used by people we'll never meet.

You collect and use data to make informed decisions.

- You read the nutritional information on a cereal box.

- You check a bus schedule to find bus stop locations, arrival and departure times, and ticket rates.

- You study the voting record of a politician running for reelection.

Groups and individuals collect data to find the public's opinions.

- A food company tests different recipes for low-fat cookies to see which one people prefer.

- Before taking a position on the cost of health care, a politician polls voters to find out how people in the district feel about the issue.

Groups and individuals provide data as helpful information.

- The League of Women Voters provides information about political candidates and their stands on various issues.

- *Consumer Reports* provides data about the quality, features, customer satisfaction, and performance of different products.

Groups and individuals use data to support their point of view or interests.

- Opponents of a school tax hike point out that teachers' salaries in their district are the highest in the county.

- In its advertising, a company claims that 4 out of 5 consumers prefer its product to the competition's product.

Nutrition Facts		
Serving Size 1 Box (32g)		
Amount Per Serving		
Calories 100 Calories from Fat 5		
		% Daily Value*
Total Fat 0.5g		1%
Saturated Fat 0g		0%
Cholesterol 0mg		0%
Sodium 170mg		7%
Total Carbohydrate 25g		8%
Fiber 4g		17%
Sugars 10g		
Protein 2g		
Vitamin A	6% • Vitamin C	0%
Calcium	0% • Iron	20%
Vitamin D	6% • Thiamin	10%
Riboflavin	10% • Niacin	10%
Vitamin B_1	10% • Folate	10%
Vitamin B_{12}	10% • Phosphor.	10%
Magnesium	10% • Zinc	10%
Copper	8%	
*Percent Daily Values (DV) are based on a 2,000 calorie diet.		

A. How is the following data most likely used: information for your own use, finding public opinion, providing helpful information, or supporting someone's interests or point of view? Any reasonable answer is acceptable.

1. A school board candidate telephones 400 local residents to get their thoughts on the question of school crowding.

2. The city newspaper publishes a copy of this year's city budget.

3. Johnny's Burgers displays a chart showing how its hamburger is lower in fat than the hamburgers of its competitors.

4. You read an automotive magazine that compares the gas mileage of seven new cars it tested.

B. What type of data (information) would be most useful to you in each of the following situations? Any reasonable answer is acceptable.

5. You are in charge of scheduling the staff at a new restaurant.

   _____

6. You are part of a neighborhood committee that wants to estimate how much interest there is in building a park on a nearby empty lot.

   _____

7. You want to know which kind of car averages the fewest repairs during its first five years.

   _____

Making Connections: Designing a Questionnaire

Often the most effective way to gather data is to use a questionnaire—a list of questions. The answers to these questions provide needed information. If you've ever taken part in a phone survey or poll, you've listened to the caller read questions from a questionnaire.

Writing a good questionnaire is challenging. For example, suppose you want to survey 200 people about opening a small restaurant in their neighborhood.

On the form below, write five questions you'd like to know the answers to before deciding to open the restaurant. Any reasonable questions are acceptable.

Restaurant Questionnaire

1. _____

2. _____

3. _____

4. _____

5. _____

Writing a Data Summary

Once you've collected data, you may want to organize it for easy reference. A good way to do this is to list the data in categories on a **data summary.** Here's an example.

Writing a Data Summary

Example: As an assignment, Erin surveyed shoppers entering Valley Foods, a local supermarket. The questionnaire she designed is shown below. Beneath the questionnaire is a summary of the answers she received. Notice that Erin grouped the answers to each question into categories.

Supermarket Questionnaire

1. About how often do you shop at Valley Foods each month?
2. Approximately how far do you live from Valley Foods?
3. What is your average grocery bill each time you shop at Valley Foods?
4. How do you usually get to Valley Foods? (walk, bus, car, other)
5. Why do you shop at Valley Foods? Choose only one: food prices, food selection, customer service, store location.

Supermarket Data Summary
(number of people whose answers fall in each category)

1. Number of monthly shopping trips to Valley Foods:
   - **a.** 1–2 _4_
   - **b.** 3–4 _8_
   - **c.** 5 or more _38_

2. Average distance from home to Valley Foods:
   - **a.** less than 1 mile _27_
   - **b.** 1–2 miles _17_
   - **c.** more than 2 miles _6_

3. Average grocery bill each visit:
   - **a.** less than $20 _9_
   - **b.** $20–$50 _33_
   - **c.** more than $50 _8_

4. Method of transportation:
   - **a.** walk _12_
   - **b.** bus _14_
   - **c.** car _20_
   - **d.** other _4_

5. Reason for shopping at Valley Foods:
   - **a.** food prices _21_
   - **b.** food selection _9_
   - **c.** customer service _3_
   - **d.** store location _17_

A. Problems 1 and 2 refer to the supermarket data summary on page 88.

1. How many people answered Erin's survey? (Assume each person who answered gave a single answer to each question.)

2. **Discuss** What was the main reason given for why people shop at Valley Foods? What is the main reason you shop at your favorite grocery store?

B. Melissa surveyed 14 students and asked each of them three questions. Below each question she wrote their names and answers. Summarize her findings on the television data summary by counting the answers in each category.

On the average, how many times each month do you watch a television . . .

movie?	news show?	sporting event?
Marlo 5	Marlo 3	Marlo 1
Stacey 12	Stacey 12	Stacey 5
Romero 2 ✔	Romero 20	Romero 0
Valerie 3 ✔	Valerie 11	Valerie 3
Phan 1 ✔	Phan 14	Phan 4
Odessa 7	Odessa 18	Odessa 2
Rayella 10	Rayella 3	Rayella 8
Manuel 4 ✔	Manuel 6	Manuel 12
Fremont 8	Fremont 4	Fremont 15
Rajesh 16	Rajesh 14	Rajesh 0
Raymond 0 ✔	Raymond 9	Raymond 7
Trevan 14	Trevan 8	Trevan 1
Rhonda 6	Rhonda 7	Rhonda 6
Stephen 11	Stephen 16	Stephen 9

Television Data Summary
(number of people in each category)

1. Number of TV movies watched each month

   a. 0 to 4 __5__

   b. 5 to 8 ____

   c. 9 to 12 ____

   d. more than 12 ____

2. Number of TV news shows watched each month

   a. 0 to 4 ____

   b. 5 to 8 ____

   c. 9 to 12 ____

   d. more than 12 ____

3. Number of TV sporting events watched each month

   a. 0 to 4 ____

   b. 5 to 8 ____

   c. 9 to 12 ____

   d. more than 12 ____

x − 7 = 3

Using a Tally Sheet

Data is often collected by recording responses on a **tally sheet.** A tally sheet is simply a record of slashes (called **tally marks**) that are used to keep track of the number of responses. Tally marks allow you to quickly count by groups of 5.

Examples:

|||| stands for 4 responses
(4)

卌 stands for 5 responses
(4 + 1)

卌 卌 || stands for 12 responses
(5 + 5 + 2)

Using a Tally Sheet

Example: Amelia was hired to take a poll of registered voters on how they planned to vote in the upcoming election. Amelia must record how each male or female voter plans to vote. The choices are Darrel Jenkins and Beverly Myers.

Amelia surveyed potential voters and tallied the responses on the tally sheet below.

Male Voters			Female Voters		
Darrel Jenkins	**Beverly Myers**	**Undecided**	**Darrel Jenkins**	**Beverly Myers**	**Undecided**
卌 卌 卌 卌 卌 卌 卌 卌 卌 卌 卌 卌 卌 卌 卌 卌 卌 卌 ||	卌 卌 卌 卌 卌 卌 卌 卌 卌		卌 卌 卌 卌 卌 卌 卌 卌 卌 卌 卌 |||	卌 卌 卌 卌 卌 卌 卌 卌 卌 卌 |||	卌 卌 卌 卌 卌 卌 卌 卌 卌 卌 卌 卌 卌 卌 卌 卌 卌 卌 卌 |||	卌 卌 卌 卌 卌 |||

The data can now be summarized by adding up the tally marks in each category (counting by fives) and writing the total in the voting summary below.

A. **Add the tally marks in each category and write each total on the voting summary. (Count each tally group by fives.)**

Voting Summary

Male Responses	Female Responses
a. For Darrel Jenkins _____	**a.** For Darrel Jenkins _____
b. For Beverly Myers _____	**b.** For Beverly Myers _____
c. Undecided _____	**c.** Undecided _____

B. As part of a bus company survey, Harrison polled downtown shoppers during lunch hour to find how these shoppers get downtown. Harrison tallied his results on the tally sheet below. Write each category total on the summary at right.

Transportation Tally Sheet			
Bus	Car	Carpool	Other
卌 卌 卌	卌 卌 卌	卌 卌 卌	卌 卌 卌
卌 卌 卌	卌 卌 卌	卌 卌 卌	|||
卌 卌 卌	卌 卌 卌	||	
卌 卌 |||	||||		

Transportation Data Summary
Method of Transportation Used
a. bus ▢
b. car ▢
c. carpool ▢
d. other ▢

Making Connections: Working with Data

Survey 20 classmates or friends to determine their favorite leisure-time activities. Use the leisure-time survey (**1**) below, and record answers on the tally sheet (**2**). Then summarize the data on the survey summary (**3**).

1.

Leisure–Time Survey
Place a check by each activity you usually do for five or more hours each week. You may check more than one activity.
___ Read   ___ Exercise
___ Watch TV   ___ Attend Class
___ Visit Friends   ___ Do a Hobby

2.

Tally Sheet		
Read	Watch TV	Visit Friends
Exercise	Attend Class	Do a Hobby

3.

Survey Summary
Number of people who do each activity for five or more hours each week.*
1. Read ___   4. Exercise ___
2. Watch TV ___   5. Attend Class ___
3. Visit Friends ___   6. Do a Hobby ___
* Why is the sum of all responses most likely to be larger than 20?

Displaying Data on a Line Plot

One way to display data is to draw a **line plot.** A line plot is made up of three parts:

- a **horizontal line,** drawn from left to right
- labels of **ranges of values** written under the line
- *X*s drawn above the line to represent **specific values**

Constructing a Line Plot

Example: Marsha, a real estate agent, wants to display a listing of house prices by drawing a line plot. The prices of the 18 houses for sale in Edgewood Estates are given below.

Address	Price	Address	Price	Address	Price
1254 Hayes	$89,500	2031 Allen	$76,800	423 4th Ave.	$76,500
858 Shelton	$87,300	8769 Hope	$93,750	198 Queens	$93,500
345 Garfield	$78,900	124 Placer	$84,500	768 McCoy	$98,900
2300 7th Ave.	$103,000	89 Laser	$82,400	890 Franks	$106,100
875 Smythe	$82,700	1287 Bly	$96,600	345 Elmwood	$87,900
932 Harris	$88,700	827 Robin	$81,400	698 Sparks	$84,800

Marsha plotted this data on the line plot shown below.

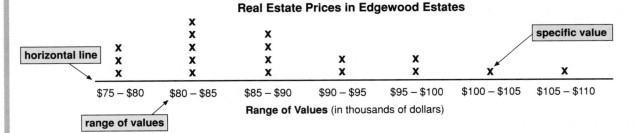

Looking at the line plot, you can summarize this data much more quickly than by looking at the list.

- Most houses are selling for between $75,000 and $90,000.
- More lower-priced houses are available than higher-priced houses.
- The largest category is houses priced between $80,000 and $85,000.
- Lowest house prices are between $75,000 and $80,000.
- The highest-priced house costs between $105,000 and $110,000.

A. Plot the following data on the line plot below. Represent each value by an *X* above the correct range. The first one is done.

Ages of Students Enrolled in Evening Art Class

✓Jillian	26	Samuel	58	Mollie	26	Jason	47
Sharon	20	Hillman	32	Francis	21	Lucinda	33
McKay	33	Darby	46	Young-Jun	35	Brayden	52
Caitlyn	67	Eleanor	31	Andrew	38	Talia	28
Kipp	37	Lauren	26	Vinu	72	Shayda	70
Colin	41	Carrie	56	Saul	27	Ashley	30
Nada	34	Maria	52	Itzel	29	Sheena	44

```
  X
 _____
20–30      31–40      41–50      51–60      61–70      71–80
```
Student Age Ranges

B. Draw a line plot to display the following data. First write these hourly wage categories on the blanks provided: **$5–$7, $7–$9, $9–$11, $11–$13, $13–$15.** Then plot the *X*s.

Hourly Wages of Echo Electronics Production Workers

Shannon	$7.75	Wilson	$8.94	Kermit	$10.82	Ilya	$9.32
Danielle	$8.39	Christine	$10.24	Dennis	$7.31	Ephran	$6.80
Charles	$10.83	Shirley	$14.80	Benita	$6.58	Margaret	$11.89
Michael	$7.80	Kim	$9.40	Schuyler	$12.25	Cynthia	$12.18
Ruben	$8.92	Claude	$7.14	Wilfried	$11.60	Edgar	$9.86
Russell	$10.08	Debra	$13.96	Marilyn	$9.02	Sheena	$5.40

```
 _____
$5–$7      _____     _____     _____     _____
```
Hourly Wage Ranges

Comparing Sets of Data

You may need to compare two or more sets (groups) of data. When the number of people polled is different (or the size of each group of data is different), *you must use percents to summarize and compare data.*

Comparing Data by Comparing Percents

Example: At Johnson Timber Products, 120 of its 200 employees voted to switch to four 10-hour days. At Lane Lumber Company, 100 of its 150 employees voted in favor of the same change. At which company is the proposed change more popular?

At Johnson, the fraction of employees voting *yes* is $\frac{120}{200}$, while at Lane the fraction voting *yes* is $\frac{100}{150}$.

Since the total number of employees differs between companies, you must do more than compare the numbers 120 and 100. To make a fair comparison, *find the percent*[*] *of yes votes* cast at each company.

Johnson Timber Products

$$\% \text{ voting } yes = \frac{\overset{\text{voting } yes}{120}}{\underset{\text{total workers}}{\underset{2}{200}}} \times \frac{\overset{1}{100\%}}{1} = \frac{120}{2}\%$$
$$= 60\%$$

Lane Lumber Company

$$\% \text{ voting } yes = \frac{\overset{\text{voting } yes}{100}}{\underset{\text{total workers}}{\underset{3}{150}}} \times \frac{\overset{2}{100\%}}{1} = \frac{200}{3}\%$$
$$= 66\frac{2}{3}\%$$

Comparing the two percents, you can see that **the proposed change is actually more popular at Lane than at Johnson.**

---

* To change the fraction voting yes to the percent voting yes, multiply the fraction by 100% (= $\frac{100\%}{1}$).

A. Problems 1 and 2 are based on the following data summary. You may use a calculator to help you find the solutions.

Name of Company	Women Managers	Total Managers
Thompson Elec.	4	16
Davis Hardware	3	10
ABC Computers	10	50

1. Which listed company has the *highest*

   a. *number* of women managers? _____

   b. *percent* of women managers? _____

2. Which listed company has the *lowest*

   a. *number* of women managers? _____

   b. *percent* of women managers? _____

B. Problems 3 and 4 are based on the following two tally sheets.

Highland City School Budget Voting Survey		
Voting Yes	Voting No	Undecided
ЖHT ЖHT ЖHT ЖHT ЖHT ЖHT ЖHT ЖHT ЖHT ЖHT	ЖHT ЖHT ЖHT ЖHT ЖHT ЖHT ЖHT I	ЖHT ЖHT ЖHT II

Oak Grove School Budget Voting Survey		
Voting Yes	Voting No	Undecided
ЖHT ЖHT ЖHT ЖHT ЖHT ЖHT ЖHT ЖHT ЖHT ЖHT ЖHT ЖHT I	ЖHT ЖHT ЖHT ЖHT ЖHT ЖHT ЖHT ЖHT ЖHT III	ЖHT ЖHT ЖHT ЖHT ЖHT ЖHT ЖHT IIII

3. What is the total *number* of people surveyed in each of the two surveys above?

   a. Highland City total = _____

   b. Oak Grove total = _____

4. **Estimate** In each survey, *approximately* what *percent* of the people polled said they planned to vote yes on the school budget? Which of the two estimates is easier to make?

   a. Highland City: _____

   b. Oak Grove: _____

C. Problems 5 and 6 are based on the following two line plots. These line plots show the educational level of students in two adult education classes at Mt. Wilson Community College.

Mr. Johnson's Adult High School Class

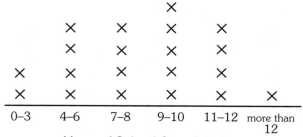

Mrs. Wyman's Workplace Skills Class

5. What *percent* of students in each class has completed *9 or more years* of school?

   a. Mr. Johnson's class: _____

   b. Mrs. Wyman's class: _____

6. Which class has the highest *percent* of students in the

   a. "4–6 years" category? _____

   b. "9–10 years" category? _____

Sorting a List of Data

At times you may want to organize and display data so certain values can be found quickly. One way to do this is to arrange the data in a certain order. This is known as **sorting** data. There are three commonly used ways to sort data:

- **Alphabetic sorting** lists data in alphabetical order. For example, a telephone book arranges names in alphabetical order.

- **Numeric sorting** lists data in numerical order. For example, a rental agency may list apartments by the amount of rent being charged, listing apartments from least to most expensive.

- **Date sorting** lists data in order of date. An electronics company may arrange invoices (purchase records) in order of the date that purchases were made.

There is no one correct way to sort data. How data is sorted depends both on the type of data being collected and for what purpose the data will be used.

Sorting a List of Data

During the Fourth of July sale, the employees at Bradford's Home Store recorded their individual total sales on the list below on the left. The sales manager sorted this information into two lists, the first *sorted by sales amount* and the second *sorted by last name*. The two lists that the manager wrote are shown below on the right.

Fourth of July Sale

Total Sales (original list)		Sorted by Sales Amount		Sorted by Last Name*	
Colleen McCoy	$875	$1,289	Hank White	Hulett, Travis	$824
Hank White	$1,289	$1,048	Greg Keim	Keim, Greg	$1,048
Orly Valdez	$640	$875	Colleen McCoy	McCoy, Colleen	$875
Travis Hulett	$824	$824	Travis Hulett	Musser, Dianne	$472
Dianne Musser	$472	$720	Marianne White	Valdez, Orly	$640
Greg Keim	$1,048	$640	Orly Valdez	White, Hank	$1,289
Marianne White	$720	$472	Dianne Musser	White, Marianne	$720

---

* When sorting by last name, write the last name first. When there are two or more identical last names, further sort these entries by first names—as shown in this example by the two last names of White.

A. Selma, a receptionist in a doctor's office, needs to sort the information on five patients given below. Sort this information for her. The sorting has been started for you.

Name	Date of Birth	Sorted by Date of Birth	Sorted by Last Name
Shelley Lewis	3/9/87	10/6/84 - Peg Swanson	Bissell, Jade - 4/6/90
Joey Petersen	2/17/91		
Peg Swanson	10/6/84		
Jade Bissell	4/6/90		
Erik Hoefler	9/14/85		

B. Imagine you're the bookkeeper for Jones Electronics. Arrange the invoice information below into two sorted lists as indicated.

Name	Amount Owed	Sorted by Amount Owed	Sorted by Last Name
Tom Larsen	$240		
Edith Green	$78		
Israel Putnam	$185		
Kitty Powers	$129		
Twyla Green	$243		

Making Connections: Collecting and Sorting Data

List the names of five classmates (or friends or relatives). Ask each to estimate what yearly salary would make them feel rich. Write three lists below. The first list is your original list of data in the order you collect it. In the next two lists, sort your data as indicated.

Original List	Sorted by Salary Amount	Sorted by Last Name
1. _____	_____	_____
2. _____	_____	_____
3. _____	_____	_____
4. _____	_____	_____
5. _____	_____	_____

Mixed Review

A. Use the information given to complete each summary.

1. As shown on the table, Shauna surveyed eight of her friends and asked each of them three questions. Below each question she wrote their names and answers.

   On the average, how many hours each weekend do you . . .

do household chores?		spend time with friends?		spend time with family members?	
Dorris	6	Dorris	4	Dorris	6
Vikram	1	Vikram	6	Vikram	7
Jenalee	2	Jenalee	12	Jenalee	8
Margaret	7	Margaret	4	Margaret	1
Heidi	4	Heidi	4	Heidi	2
Taylor	3	Taylor	5	Taylor	4
Melissa	4	Melissa	10	Melissa	3
Ruth	5	Ruth	3	Ruth	2

   Summarize Shauna's results on the Survey Summary below.

Survey Summary
(number of people in each category)

Hours spent on household chores	Hours spent with friends	Hours spent with family members
a. 0 to 2 _____	**a.** 0 to 2 _____	**a.** 0 to 2 _____
b. 3 to 4 _____	**b.** 3 to 4 _____	**b.** 3 to 4 _____
c. 5 to 6 _____	**c.** 5 to 6 _____	**c.** 5 to 6 _____
d. more than 6 _____	**d.** more than 6 _____	**d.** more than 6 _____

2. Frank is conducting a telephone survey. He asks people, "From which media source do you get most of your news: newspaper, newsmagazine, radio, or television?" Frank tallied his results as shown below.

   Write each category total on the Tally Summary.

News Information Tally Sheet			
Newspaper	Newsmagazine	Radio	Television
ЖЖ ЖЖ ЖЖ ЖЖ ЖЖ ЖЖ ЖЖ ЖЖ ЖЖ ||	ЖЖ ЖЖ ЖЖ ЖЖ |||	ЖЖ ЖЖ ЖЖ ||||	ЖЖ ЖЖ ЖЖ ЖЖ ЖЖ ЖЖ ЖЖ ЖЖ ЖЖ ЖЖ ЖЖ ЖЖ ЖЖ |||

Tally Summary	
Source	Number
Newspaper	_____
Newsmagazine	_____
Radio	_____
Television	_____

B. Use the information given to create a line plot.

3. The manager of Hillcrest Realty wants a visual display of rental values. Complete the line plot below. Write an *X* above the correct range for each value.

Monthly Rental Rates of Hillcrest Realty Properties

139 Rainbow Lane	$650	135 Harbour Blvd.	$690	462 Ridgeway	$640
895 Crest View	$275	122 Elmwood Pl.	$280	883 Mazor	$780
423 North 5th	$425	932 Roosevelt	$350	622 Fox Lane	$525
160 Jenson Place	$580	83 Harrison	$788	830 Robin Hood	$390
181 Wizard Street	$500	37 Ford Lane	$820	123 Firwood	$515

$200–$300 $301–$400 $401–$500 $501–$600 $601–$700 $701–$800   more than $800

Monthly Rental Rates

C. Problems 4 and 5 are based on the following data summary.

Name of School	Total Female Employees	Total Male Employees
Harden High School	40	22
Taft Middle School	24	16
Harrison Elementary	12	10

4. Which school has the *highest*

   a. *number* of male employees? _____

   b. *percent* of male employees? _____

5. Which school has the *lowest*

   a. *number* of male employees? _____

   b. *percent* of male employees? _____

D. Sort the following data into two sorted lists as indicated.

6. AIM Hardware's warehouse tracks its inventory by computer. They can access information by name or code.

Code Number and Item	Sorted by Name	Sorted by Code Number
a. #137 screwdriver	a.	a.
b. #87 wrench	b.	b.
c. #94 hammer	c.	c.
d. #124 drill	d.	d.
e. #153 chisel	e.	e.

Finding the Mean

When choosing a restaurant for lunch, knowing that lunch at LaMond's costs about $30 may quickly convince you that Burger Village will do just fine. After all, lunch at Burger Village is about $5.

We think of $30 and $5 as **typical values,** numbers that represent the prices at each restaurant. Typical prices are often called *average* prices. There are three common typical values: **mean, median,** and **mode.**

Mean

When most people use the word *average,* they are talking about the mean. For data that does not contain extreme (unusually large or small) values, the mean is what you want to know when you ask, "About how much . . . ?"

Finding the Mean

Example: At Joey's Take Out, hamburgers sell for $1.80, $2.25, $2.95, and $3.60. What is the *mean* (average) price of hamburgers at Joey's?

To find the *mean,* follow these steps.

Step 1
Add the numbers in the set.

$1.80
2.25
2.95
+ 3.60
$10.60

Step 2
Divide the sum by the number of numbers in the set.

$2.65 ← *mean* (average)
4)$10.60
numbers in the set ─ sum

Estimate
To estimate, round each amount to the nearest $1 before adding.

$2
2
3
+ 4
$11
$11 ÷ 4 ≈ $3

The average price of a hamburger at Joey's is **$2.65,** which is close to the estimate of $3.

Note: The mean is usually *not equal* to any number in the set. However, the mean *must fall within* the range of numbers being averaged.

A. Find the mean in each of the following groups of data. You may use a calculator.

For another look at using a calculator, turn to page 219.

1. Weekly grocery bills: $84, $98, $72, $60

2. Prices of microwave ovens: $240, $198, $264, $249, $220

3. Lumber lengths: 5 ft. 5 in., 5 ft. 10 in., 6 ft. 3 in.

Sometimes the mean *does not* give you a good idea of most of the values in a set of data. This happens *when one or more of the values is extreme*—much greater or less than the others. Look at the example.

Knowing When a Mean Is Misleading

Example: Five different rings are on sale. The sale prices are $27, $26, $33, $31, and $108. What is the mean price of these rings?

Notice that *common sense* tells you that you can buy a ring for about $30, *if* you don't consider the $108 ring. Now compute the mean and see how it compares with $30.

Step 1
Add the numbers in the set.

$108
  33
  31
  27
+ 26
$225

Step 2
Divide the sum by the number of numbers in the set.

$45 ◄——— mean
5)$225 ◄——— sum of numbers
└——— numbers in the set

The mean, **$45,** is much higher than the commonsense value $30. Note how the **nontypical value** $108 gives a mean that is misleading—*if we want the mean to represent the typical price.*

B. For each group of data below, do the following:

a. **Quickly estimate a commonsense average for the data amounts that have similar values. When doing this, ignore the nontypical data value.**

b. **Find the mean of the whole set of data. You may use a calculator.**

c. **Subtract to find the difference between the mean and your commonsense average value.**

	Commonsense Average	Mean	Difference Between
4. Watch prices: $56, $128, $54, and $62	_____	_____	_____
5. Weights: 13.4 kg, 14.2 kg, 3.2 kg, and 12.8 kg	_____	_____	_____
6. House prices: $126,000; $74,000; $86,000; $85,000; and $84,000	_____	_____	_____

Finding the Median and the Mode

The **median** is the *middle value* of a set of data. To avoid a misleading typical value, the median is often used when some values in a set of data are extreme. To find the median, numerically sort the data, writing the values in order from *smallest to largest*.

- For an odd number of data values, the median is the middle number.
- For an even number of data values, the median is the mean of the two middle numbers.

Finding the Median

Example 1: What is the median of the following test scores?

Jay 62   Armano 73   Lillian 67
Lauren 78   Henrietta 45

Since there are an odd number (5) of test scores, the median is the middle value.

Step 1

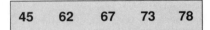

Step 2

Numerically sort the data. The median (middle value) is **67.**

Example 2: Determine the median of the following grocery bills.

Louise $25   Todd $30   Eiko $28
Stacey $36   Bea $97   Dustin $27

Since there is an even number (6) of bills, the median is the average (mean) of the two middle values.

Step 1
Numerically sort the data.

Step 2
Find the mean of the two middle values.

$\frac{\$28 + \$30}{2} = \$29$. The median is **$29.**

A. Find the median in each of the following sets of data.

1. Package weights: 8 lb. 15 oz., 5 lb. 2 oz., 3 lb. 9 oz., 7 lb. 14 oz., and 3 lb. 11 oz.

2. Student heights: 4 ft. 11 in., 4 ft. 9 in., 5 ft. 2 in., 5 ft. 1 in., 4 ft. 6 in., and 5 ft. 4 in.

3. Distances from school: 0.8 mile, 1.4 miles, 2.3 miles, 0.6 mile, and 1.6 miles

4. Movie theater prices: $6.50, $5.75, $6.00, $5.50, $6.00, and $6.75

Mode

The **mode** of a set of data is the value that occurs *most frequently. When each value occurs only once, a set of data has no mode.* The mode is used when one value frequently appears in a set of data while extreme values or the middle values may be misleading.

Finding the Mode

Example: Find the mode in the following salaries:

$28,000	$19,000	$17,000
$21,000	$28,000	$45,000
$14,000	$19,000	$28,000

Numerically sort the data, and count how many times each value appears.

$14,000	$17,000	$19,000 $19,000	$21,000	$28,000 $28,000 $28,000	$45,000
1 time	1 time	2 times	1 time	3 times	1 time

The mode, **$28,000,** appears 3 times in the data. No other value appears this often.

B. Determine the mode in each of the following sets of data.

5. Number of students in classes: 23, 24, 26, 24, 28, 23, 25, 23, 27 and 25

6. Apartment rental prices: $375, $350, $485, $350, $375, $425, and $375

C. Determine both the median and mode in each of the following sets of data.

7. Car mileage ratings: 26 MPG, 24 MPG, 25 MPG, 24 MPG, and 28 MPG

median: _____

mode: _____

8. Fourth grade student ages:
10 years 3 months, 9 years 8 months, 9 years 11 months, and 10 years 4 months

median: _____

mode: _____

Choosing a Typical Value

How do you decide which typical value to use? The answer depends on your needs and on the data you have. In many real-life situations, a commonsense answer is enough. Many work or test situations require a more specific answer such as *mean, median,* or *mode.*

Generally speaking, these rules are followed:

- Use the *mean* as the typical value unless using median or mode is more appropriate. (See example on page 100.)
- Use the *median* as the typical value when some values in a set of data are extreme. (See examples on page 102.)
- Use the *mode* when one value frequently occurs in a set of data. (See example on page 103.)

The following problems will give you additional practice deciding which type of typical value to use.

A. For each situation, choose the most appropriate typical value.

1. You need to find your *average* monthly mileage for insurance rates.

   (1) mean
   (2) median
   (3) mode
   (4) commonsense answer

2. Find the age that divides a swimming class in half.

   (1) mean
   (2) median
   (3) mode
   (4) commonsense answer

3. You quickly look at a menu to see about how much a large pizza costs.

   (1) mean
   (2) median
   (3) mode
   (4) commonsense answer

4. The manager asks you to find which type of pizza sells the most.

   (1) mean
   (2) median
   (3) mode
   (4) commonsense answer

B. In each set of data below, find the median value *and then* determine the actual mean. Choose the answer that you think gives the best typical value.

5. An ad in the newspaper lists the following budget used car prices: $2,600; $2,500; $2,700; $3,200; and $14,800.

   a. _____   b. _____
      median   mean

6. The health clinic record lists the following number of flu shots given during the last 8 days: 1, 3, 38, 43, 40, 39, 36, and 40.

   a. _____   b. _____
      median   mean

C. Beth works at Li-Kim's restaurant. Li-Kim asked Beth to record information between 12:30 and 2:00 P.M. on Saturday on the number of drinks that are ordered at each price. Problems 7–9 refer to Beth's tally.

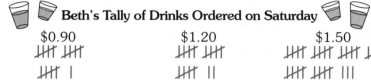

Beth's Tally of Drinks Ordered on Saturday

$0.60	$0.90	$1.20	$1.50	$2.00
ЖЖ ЖЖ |||	ЖЖ ЖЖ ЖЖ		ЖЖ ЖЖ ЖЖ ||	ЖЖ ЖЖ ЖЖ ЖЖ ЖЖ ЖЖ |||	ЖЖ ЖЖ ЖЖ |||

7. a. List the total sold at each price.

at $.60: _____

at $.90: _____

at $1.20: _____

at $1.50: _____

at $2.00: _____

b. Which price drink had the median *number of sales?*

c. Which price drink brought in the most money?

8. At Li-Kim's restaurant, what is the

a. *mean* price of drinks?

b. *median* price of drinks?

9. Describe Which term would you use to describe the price drink that was ordered most often? Choose one: *sales mean, sales median,* or *sales mode.* To which drink would you give this description?

D. In each set of data below, find the mean, median, and mode (if there is a mode). Choose the value that represents the most typical value in each set.

10. Enrollment in Local Elementary Schools

Hoover Elementary	420
Wilson Elementary	390
Harding Elementary	400
St. Jude's Elementary	140
Jefferson Elementary	395

Mean: _____

Median: _____

Mode: _____
(choose one)

11. Average Yearly Income of Local Employment

Electricians	$38,000
Factory Managers	$42,000
Automotive Workers	$34,000
Public School Teachers	$36,000
Restaurant Workers	$12,000
Telemarketers	$12,000

Mean: _____

Median: _____

Mode: _____
(choose one)

Reading a Table

A **table** is often used to organize and display data, especially related data that is classified in different categories. A table may contain both words and numbers written in labeled rows and columns.

A **row** is read from left to right (or from right to left).

| $4.25 | $5.72 | $2.46 | $8.25 |

Read across. ⟶

A **column** is read from top to bottom (or bottom to top).

| $5.34 |
| $6.75 |
| $9.26 |
| $3.40 |

Read down. ↓

Look at the nutrition table below. The table contains a **title,** row and column **headings** (labels), and data.

Row Headings   Title ⟶

Nutritional Information for Selected Vegetables
(for a 100–gram serving)

Column Headings

	Water (percent)	Calories (food energy)	Protein (grams)	Fat (grams)	Carbohydrates (grams)	Calcium (milligrams)
Broccoli	91	25	3	1	5	87
Lima Beans	71	112	8	1	20	46
Mushrooms	93	16	2	Trace	2	6
Onions	89	36	2	Trace	9	27
Potatoes	75	90	3	Trace	21	9

Finding Information on a Table

To find information on a table, read *across* a row and *down* a column. Read the value at the point where the selected row and column meet.

Example 1: How many grams of carbohydrates are contained in 100 g of onions?

Find the row labeled Onions, and scan from left to right. Stop below the Carbohydrates column. The value at this intersection is 9.

There are **9 g** of carbohydrates in 100 g of onions.

Example 2: Which listed vegetable is highest in calories?

Scan down the column labeled Calories. Pick the largest value (112). Read directly left and identify the row label: Lima Beans.

Of the listed vegetables, **lima beans** are highest in calories.

A. Problems 1–6 refer to the table on page 106.

1. How many calories does a 100-g serving of potatoes contain?

2. Which listed vegetable contains the smallest amount of calcium?

3. How many more grams of carbohydrates are contained in a 100-g serving of lima beans than in a 100-g serving of broccoli?

4. How many calories are contained in a *200-g* serving of potatoes?

5. To the nearest ounce, what weight of water is contained in 2 lb. of onions?

6. Of the 5 listed vegetables, what is the
   a. *median* percent of water?
   b. *mean* percent of water (to the nearest percent)?

B. Problems 7–12 refer to the table below.

Summary of Saturday Price Reductions at Spire Records

Item	Original Price	Discount Rate	Sale Price	Sales Tax (5%)	Total Price
Radio Walker	$24.00	25%	$18.00	$.90	$18.90
Videotape	$22.00	10%	$19.80	$.99	$20.79
Compact Disc	$16.00	15%	$13.60	$.68	$14.28
CD Cleaner	$10.00	20%	$8.00	$.40	$8.40
Cassette	$8.00	10%	$7.20	$.36	$7.56

7. What *dollar amount* of sales tax is being charged on a CD cleaner?

8. Which listed item is being discounted at the greatest rate?

9. Including sales tax, what will a customer actually pay for a Radio Walker?

10. Not counting the sales tax, what *dollar amount* of savings is being offered on a compact disc?

11. Not counting the sales tax, on which listed item is the *dollar amount* of savings the largest?

12. **Explain** What steps would you take to determine which of the five discount rates is
    a. closest in value to the *average* (mean) discount rate?
    b. the discount rate *mode?*

13. **Investigate** Does your state have a sales tax? If so, what is the sales tax rate (percent)? Does your city or county have a sales tax that is different from surrounding areas?

Sorting Data in a Table

There are many ways to sort data when entering the data in a table.

- On page 106, the nutritional information is entered in *alphabetical order* by the names of the vegetables.

- On page 107, the pricing information is entered in *numerical order,* listing the item with the largest original price first and the smallest original price last.

There are times when you need to sort data in a table differently from the way it's presented. The exercise below is an example.

Rewrite the information in the table below as described in Problems 1 and 2.

Name	Net Sales	Commission Rate	Weekly Salary	Gross Pay
Crawford, Elaine	$1,776	7.5%	$340.00	$473.20
Kitazawa, Kazuyo	$2,250	6.0%	$325.00	$460.00
Pritchett, Stephanie	$1,500	9.0%	$410.00	$545.00
Zarate, Ephran	$1,625	7.5%	$340.00	$461.88

1. Complete the table below, sorting the given information by *gross pay,* largest amount first.

Organize by gross pay.

Name	Net Sales	Commission Rate	Weekly Salary	Gross Pay

2. Complete the table below, sorting the given information by *net sales,* smallest amount first.

Organize by net sales.

Name	Net Sales	Commission Rate	Weekly Salary	Gross Pay

Completing a Table

 A. Imagine you work in the payroll department for Smith Furniture. Your task is to take the following information and put it in table form as a permanent record. You are to sort this data alphabetically by name. The data for Michael Blanda has been calculated and entered into the table for you. You may use a calculator where needed.

Michael Blanda
40 regular hours at $7.00 per hour
8 overtime hours at $10.50 per hour

Jennie Thompson
40 regular hours at $8.00 per hour
12 overtime hours at $12.00 per hour

Lewis Slovak
40 regular hours at $6.00 per hour
6 overtime hours at $9.00 per hour

Miranda Clausen
40 regular hours at $10.00 per hour
5 overtime hours at $15.00 per hour

Smith Furniture Pay Record for the Week of January 11

Name	Regular hours (a)	Regular pay rate (b)	Regular pay (c = a × b)	Overtime hours (d)	Overtime pay rate (e)	Overtime pay (f = d × e)	Total pay (g = c + f)
Blanda, Michael	40	$7.00	$280.00	8	$10.50	$84.00	$364.00

B. Problems 1–6 are based on the table you completed above.

1. What amount of *regular pay* did Lewis Slovak earn during the week of January 11?

2. Which of the four employees earned the greatest amount of *overtime pay* during the week of January 11?

3. During the week of January 11, how much more *overtime pay* did Michael Blanda earn than Miranda Clausen?

4. What total amount of *regular pay* did the four employees earn during the week of January 11?

5. At Smith Furniture, what is the *median* overtime hourly pay rate?

6. **Explain** Looking at the given data, explain the relationship between regular pay and overtime pay at Smith Furniture.

Computer Spreadsheets

To complete the table on page 109, you needed to do quite a few calculations. These calculations were not difficult—especially if you used a calculator—but they did take time.

Your job would be much easier if you used a computer **spreadsheet program.** A spreadsheet program uses a special table called a **computer spreadsheet** that automatically does calculations for you.

What does a computer spreadsheet look like?

A computer spreadsheet looks like the table below. On a spreadsheet, column headings are letters, and row headings are numbers. You type data inside rectangular boxes called **cells.** Each cell is identified by its column letter and row number.

column

Computer Spreadsheet

	A	B	C	D	E
1					
2					
3					
4					

row→

Cell A1   Cell C3   Cell E2

What can you write in each cell of a spreadsheet? In a spreadsheet cell you can enter data in any of the following ways:

- *Text:* The term *text* is just another way of saying *words.* For example, row and column headings are text.

- *Numbers:* Numbers and monetary amounts are the most common forms of data on a spreadsheet.

- *Formulas:* A formula tells the computer to enter the result of a calculation in a cell.

Below are examples of spreadsheet formulas involving numbers:

Addition	Subtraction	Multiplication	Division
=138+97	=89-45	=17*8	=45/9

Note: The symbol = is written as the first symbol in some formulas.
The symbol * is used to show multiplication.
The symbol / is used to show division. (It means "divided by.")

Here are formulas that involve cell names.

Operation	Cell Formula	Meaning
Addition	=A2+A4	In this cell, the sum is found by adding the number in cell A2 to the number in cell A4.
Subtraction	=B3-B5	In this cell, the difference is found by subtracting the number in cell B5 from the number in cell B3.
Multiplication	=C4*C6	In this cell, the product is found by multiplying the number in cell C4 by the number in cell C6.
Division	=D5/D6	In this cell, the quotient is found by dividing the number in cell D5 by the number in cell D6.

Look at the partially completed computer spreadsheet, and then follow instructions 1–4.

	A	B	C	D	E	F
1	Item	Quantity	Item Cost	Subtotal	Sales Tax	Total Cost
2	Blender		$29.95	=B2*C2	=0.05*D2	=D2+E2
3	Toaster		$19.49			
4	Waffle Iron		$39.79			

If the number of blenders purchased is entered in cell B2, the spreadsheet will automatically show the correct **subtotal** (cell D2), the correct **sales tax** (cell E2), and the correct **total cost** (cell F2).

1. Complete row 3 of the spreadsheet by writing the correct formulas in cells D3, E3, and F3. (*Hint:* Base your formulas on D2, E2, and F2.)

2. Complete row 4 by writing the correct formulas in D4, E4, and F4.

3. Determine the *sales tax rate* on this spreadsheet. (*Hint:* See cell E2.)

4. Determine the dollar amounts that will appear in each cell if the following quantity numbers are typed in: 3 blenders; 5 toasters; and 4 waffle irons. (*Hint:* Use a calculator and the formulas in the spreadsheet above.) Write your answers on the spreadsheet below.

	A	B	C	D	E	F
1	Item	Quantity	Item Cost	Subtotal	Sales Tax	Total Cost
2	Blender	3	$29.95			
3	Toaster	5	$19.49			
4	Waffle Iron	4	$39.79			

Gridding in Mean, Median, and Mode

Answers to data analysis problems can be in the form of whole numbers, decimals, or fractions. Make sure you understand the rules for entering each type of answer in a test grid.

Review these rules for using the grid:

- Remember that you cannot enter a mixed number in the grid. Change mixed numbers to improper fractions or decimals.

- You can begin your answer in any column as long as the entire answer fits within the five columns. Leave unused columns blank.

- A decimal point (.) or a slash mark (/) must occupy its own column. Never grid in both a number and a symbol in the same column.

- Write the answer in the top row as a guide. Then fill in the correct circle in each column. The machine will score only the filled-in circles.

- If you are having trouble fitting a decimal in the grid, read the problem carefully to see whether you should round to a certain place value. Drop any unnecessary zeros.

Filling in the Grid

Example: Linear Industries has eight offices. The number of employees at the offices is 12, 48, 17, 24, 34, 15, 17, and 28. What is the median number of employees at a Linear Industries office?

Step 1
Read the problem carefully. You are asked to find the median.

Numerically sort the data.

12 15 17 **17 24** 28 34 48

Since there is an even number of values, use the two middle values 17 and 24.

Step 2
Find the mean of the two middle values.

$$\frac{17 + 24}{2} = \frac{41}{2} = 20\frac{1}{2} = 20.5$$

Whenever you can, use the decimal equivalent of a fraction so that you can skip the step of changing the mixed number to an improper fraction.

Step 3
Write the answer in the top row of boxes. Then fill in the correct circles on the grid. Use the digits in the top row as a guide.

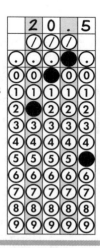

These grids are unacceptable. Don't make these common mistakes.

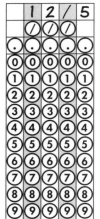 The grid circles are blank. The machine will read only the grid columns, not the answer written in the top row.

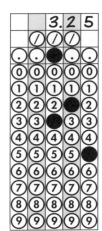 More than one circle in a column has been filled in. The decimal point or slash mark must be in a column by itself.

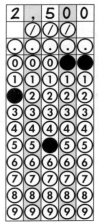 There is a blank column within the answer. Don't use commas to separate place value columns.

Solve the following problems. Record your answers in the grids.

1. 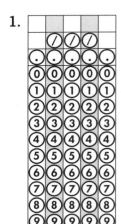 During a 6-day period in March, a city recorded the following amounts of rainfall: 0.2 in., 1.5 in., 3.6 in., 1.8 in., 0.8 in., and 0.5 in. What was the average daily rainfall in inches?

3. 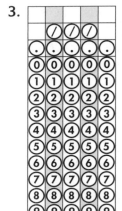 During a 4-day golf tournament, a golfer shot scores of 74, 69, 71, and 72. What was the golfer's average score for the tournament?

2.  Five farms in Utah are 80, 97, 135, 64, and 128 acres in size. What is the median size in acres of the five farms?

4.  On Friday, a shoe store had 12 pair of men's running shoes on sale in these sizes: 9, 9 $\frac{1}{2}$, 9 $\frac{1}{2}$, 10, 10, 10 $\frac{1}{2}$, 10 $\frac{1}{2}$, 11, 11, 11, 11 $\frac{1}{2}$, and 12. What was the mode of the shoe sizes on sale?

Unit 3 Review

A. Find the *mean*, *median*, and *mode* for each set of data below.

1. Sizes of houses for sale in Sunset Estates (total square feet):

1,600	Mean: _____
1,850	
2,150	Median: _____
2,400	
2,400	Mode: _____
2,800	

2. Milk price per gallon in selected local stores:

$2.18	Mean: _____
$2.29	
$2.29	Median: _____
$2.34	
$2.40	Mode: _____

B. In each set of data below, choose a *commonsense* typical value and then compute the actual *mean*. Choose the answer that you think gives the best typical value.

3. Ages of students signed up for a swimming class: 5, 6, 5, 4, 5, and 11

   a. _____   b. _____
      commonsense   mean

4. Race times in a 100-m dash: 12.6 seconds, 12.9 seconds, 12.8 seconds, and 14.9 seconds

   a. _____   b. _____
      commonsense   mean

C. Problems 5 and 6 refer to the table below.

Day-care Data for Alpha Products, Inc.

Department	Number of Employees Who Use Company's Day-care Facilities	Number of Employees Who Use Other Day-care Facilities	Total Number of Employees in Department
Production	110	32	440
Administration	6	8	30
Accounting	6	4	12
Packaging & Shipping	8	2	24
Marketing & Sales	7	2	10

5. Which *department* has the highest

   a. *number* of employees who use the company day-care facilities?

   b. *percent* of employees who use the company day-care facilities?

6. a. What is the *mean* number of employees per department who use the company day-care facilities?

   b. Why is the *mean* you computed in **a** misleading?

114

D. Use the information below to complete the June Earnings Report for Adair Furniture. Then solve and grid in answers to questions 7 and 8.

June Earnings Summary
Name: Ernst Netz
Monthly salary: $1,080
Sales commission: 10%
June sales: $4,650

June Earnings Summary
Name: Judi Garcia
Monthly salary: $1,200
Sales commission: 8%
June sales: $3,280

June Earnings Summary
Name: Kathy Lehrer
Monthly salary: $1,240
Sales commission: 9%
June sales: $6,500

June Earnings Report for Adair Furniture

Name	Total Sales (a)	Commission Rate (b)	Commission (c = a × b)	Salary (d)	Total Earnings (e = c + d)

7.

At Adair Furniture, what is the median of total earnings for the employees listed? Round to the nearest dollar if necessary.

8.

For the three employees shown, what is the average monthly salary to the nearest dollar? Grid in your answer as a whole number.

Working Together

Do the following activities with a partner or a small group.

1. Look in the classified ads of a local newspaper. In groups, make lists of rental costs for different-size apartments: one bedroom (or studio), two bedrooms, and three bedrooms. List at least five rental costs for each apartment size. Cross out any amount that you consider extreme (unreasonable for most people). Find the mean and median rental costs for each apartment size. Compare and discuss your answers.

2. Survey 10 students in your class and have each *rate his or her interest* in writing, math, science, social studies, and literature. Have them rate each subject on a scale from 1 to 10, with 10 as the highest. Write the results in a table. Find the mean and median rating for each subject.

Unit 4

Displaying Data on a Graph

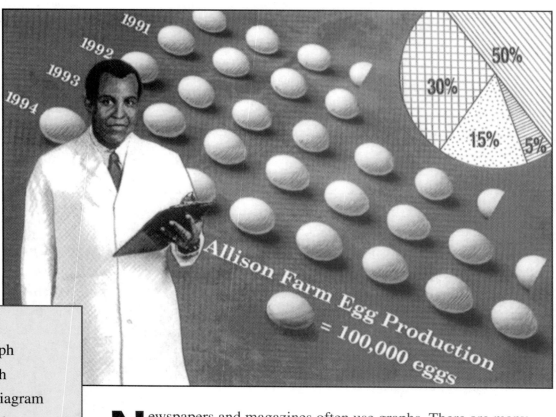

Allison Farm Egg Production = 100,000 eggs

Skills

Reading a pictograph

Reading a bar graph

Reading a scatter diagram

Reading a line graph

Reading a circle graph

Tools

Estimating skills

Problem Solvers

Using two data sources

Changing data to different forms

Applications

Displaying business data

Graphing research data

Drawing growth curves

Graphing family expenses

Newspapers and magazines often use graphs. There are many types of graphs; some use bars or lines, while others use pictures. Presenting data in graph form makes it easier for you to get a quick overview of the main points. Many people also find looking at a graph more interesting than looking at a list or table.

In this unit, you'll study the five types of graphs most commonly used to display data:

- pictographs
- bar graphs
- scatter diagrams
- line graphs
- circle graphs

Besides practicing reading graphs, you'll *construct* similar graphs to display data given in practical applications. And you'll learn how to use data from more than one source.

Why Are Graphs Important?

How often do you see information displayed graphically? Check the statements that apply to you.

☐ I often see graphs in a magazine I like to read.

☐ I see graphs occasionally in newspapers.

☐ I see graphs used in television commercials.

☐ I know that politicians use graphs to try to persuade voters.

☐ Graphs always catch my attention.

☐ I'm more likely to read an article in a newspaper or magazine if the article contains a well-designed graph.

As you begin this unit, describe what you think about graphs and how graphs may already be part of your life.

1. List different features of graphs that you like. For example, do you like colorful graphs, graphs that use pictures, etc.?

   _____

   _____

2. What information would you like to see shown on a graph? For example, would you like to see information about diet, cars, taxes, etc.?

   _____

   _____

3. Magazine articles often contain both photographs and graphs. Can you think of one advantage that each type of display has?

   a. _____

   _____

   b. _____

   _____

Talk About It

Look through a newspaper or magazine and see how many tables and graphs you can find. See if you can name each type of graph.

Do you think that graphs are easy to read? Can you think of any better ways to show data than in graphs? Compare your ideas with others in the class.

Throughout this unit, you may use a calculator wherever that would be useful. Information about using a calculator appears on page 219.

Graphing and Estimating

You may already know that there are many types of graphs and many ways to display data. Do you know, though, that unlike a list or table, a graph *does not* display exact figures very well?

- When you read values on a graph, you almost always *estimate*. Graphed data is often difficult to read exactly.

- When you draw a graph, your first step is usually to *round data* to values that are easy to display. Graphing exact values is often not possible, nor necessary.

Estimating is your most important graph tool. While graphs make data enjoyable to view, estimating enables you to summarize main points and compare values easily. On these two pages you'll practice estimation skills that are useful when working with graphs.

A. Match each number on the left with the *estimation phrase* that best describes it.

_____ **1.** 504,237

_____ **2.** 249,693

_____ **3.** 124,840

_____ **4.** 253,655

_____ **5.** 126,871

_____ **6.** 401,842

a. *slightly more than* two hundred fifty thousand

b. *almost* one hundred twenty-five thousand

c. *a little over* one hundred twenty-five thousand

d. *about* five hundred thousand

e. *approximately* four hundred thousand

f. *a little less than* two hundred fifty thousand

B. Write a number ending in 0 that could be described by each phrase below. Any reasonable answer is acceptable.

7. *close to* $421.99

8. *a little more than* 38

9. *a tad less than* 812

10. *approximately* $349.25

11. *slightly more than* 187

12. *about* $3,579.99

C. If the symbol ✂ stands for the sale of 10 pairs of scissors, draw symbols to represent the following sales totals. Problem 13 is done as an example. (You can draw a half symbol to stand for 5.)

13. 30 scissors

✂ ✂ ✂

(10 + 10 + 10)

14. 20 scissors

15. 45 scissors

For another look at estimation, turn to page 223.

For problems 16–18, *estimate* using only whole symbols and half symbols.

 still stands for 10 pairs of scissors.

16. 18 scissors   **17.** 26 scissors   **18.** 29 scissors

D. Choose the number that is the *best estimate* of the length of each bar below. Only inch marks are labeled on the line ruler. Which length was easier for you to estimate?

19.

```
0            1"            2"
├─────────────┼─────────────┤
■■■■■■■■■■■■■■■■■■■■■■■■
```

(1) $\frac{3}{4}$ in.   (3) $1\frac{1}{8}$ in.

(2) 1 in.   (4) $1\frac{1}{2}$ in.

20.

```
0            1"            2"            3"
├─────────────┼─────────────┼─────────────┤
■■■■■■■■■■■■■■■■■■■■■■■■■■■■■■■■■■■■■■■
```

(1) $1\frac{3}{4}$ in.   (4) $2\frac{3}{4}$ in.

(2) 2 in.   (5) 3 in.

(3) $2\frac{1}{2}$ in.

E. On each number line below, place a dot at the point described. Which problem was the hardest to estimate? Explain why it was the hardest.

21. at the value 1.5

```
0            1            2
←───────────┼────────────┼───────→
```

22. at the value 2.83

```
2            3            4
←───────────┼────────────┼───────→
```

23. two-thirds of the way between 0 and 10

```
0                                    10
←────────────────────────────────────→
```

24. one-fourth of the way between 5 and 30

```
5                                    30
←────────────────────────────────────→
```

F. Shade the part of each circle described below. Which problem was easiest for you to estimate? Explain why it was easiest.

25. one-half of the circle   **26.** three-fifths of the circle   **27.** 29% of the circle

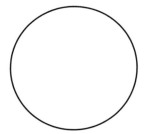   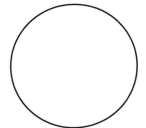   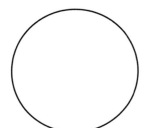

Reading a Pictograph

In a **pictograph,** data is represented by **symbols,** or small pictures. The value of each symbol is given in a **key** on the graph. Half a symbol stands for half of the symbol's value.

A pictograph may be drawn with symbols running **vertically** (up and down) or **horizontally** (left to right). Pictographs are especially useful for quick comparisons of data. Because of rounding, data on a pictograph is not very precise, and small differences in values are not shown.

On the pictograph below, each year's total car production is rounded to the nearest 500,000 (half million) cars.

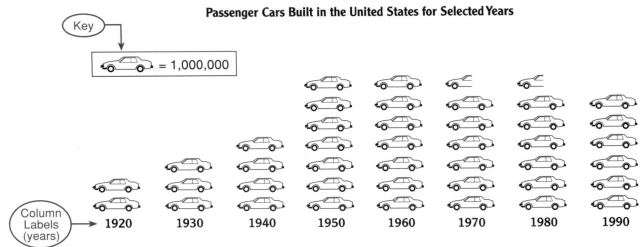

Source: Statistical Abstract of the United States

Finding Information on a Pictograph

To find the total value of a column (or row) of symbols, multiply the number of symbols in the column (or row) by the value of a single symbol.

Example: What was the *approximate* number of cars built in the United States in the year 1970?

Step 1
Count the number of symbols in the column labeled 1970: $6\frac{1}{2}$ (or 6.5)

Step 2
Multiply $6\frac{1}{2}$ (or 6.5) by 1,000,000.
$6\frac{1}{2} \times 1,000,000 = 6,500,000$

About **6,500,000 cars** were built in the United States in 1970.

A. Problems 1–4 refer to the pictograph on page 120.

1. What number does the symbol 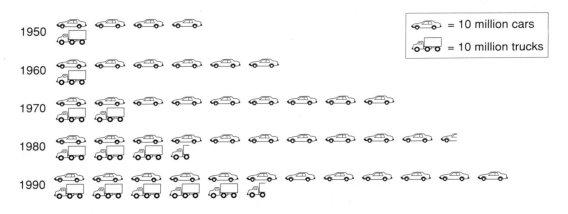 stand for?

2. *Approximately* how many passenger cars were built in the United States in 1920?

3. *About* how many more cars were built in the United States in 1980 than in 1920?

4. *Estimate* the average number of cars built in the United States each month during 1990.

B. Problems 5–8 refer to the *double pictograph* below.

Notice that for each year there are two symbols: one representing cars and one representing trucks. A double pictograph is useful for making side-by-side comparisons of two sets of data.

Example: In 1980, there were about 105 million cars ($10\frac{1}{2}$ car symbols) and 35 million trucks ($3\frac{1}{2}$ truck symbols) on American highways.

Cars and Trucks on American Highways

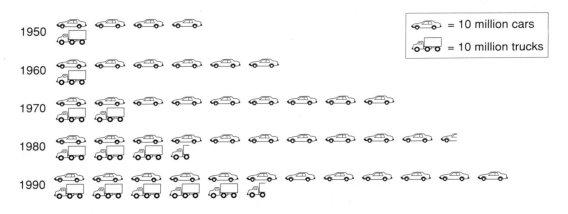

Source: Statistical Abstract of the United States

5. To what number is each total rounded? (*Hint:* What is the lowest value shown by a partial symbol?)

  (1) 50,000

  (2) 500,000

  (3) 5,000,000

6. *About* how many times greater was the number of cars on American highways in 1990 than in 1950?

  (1) 3 times   **(2)** 4 times   **(3)** 5 times

7. By about what *amount* did the number of trucks increase between 1980 and 1990?

  (1) 5 million

  (2) 10 million

  (3) 20 million

8. **Discuss** Using the pictograph above, can you estimate to the nearest 1 million how many cars were on American highways in 1990? Why or why not?

Displaying Business Data

The list below contains yearly sales totals in eight states for Evergreen Computer Company. Assume you've been asked to prepare a pictograph of this information for publication in your local newspaper.

Evergreen Computer Co.
First year sales of Evergreen computers have been much higher than company officials had anticipated.

State	Sales Total
California	🖥🖥🖥🖥🖥🖥🖵

State	Sales Total	State	Sales Total
California	$643,000	New Jersey	$437,000
Delaware	$202,000	New York	$812,000
Illinois	$464,000	Pennsylvania	$604,000
Michigan	$353,000	Texas	$532,000

A. Round each state total to the nearest $50,000. The total for California has been rounded as an example.

State	Rounded Total	State	Rounded Total
California	$650,000*	New Jersey	
Delaware		New York	
Illinois		Pennsylvania	
Michigan		Texas	

* $643,000 is closer to $650,000 than to $600,000.

B. Using the rounded totals from part A, complete the pictograph below to show approximate sales totals for Evergreen Computer Co. California is done as an example.

State	Sales Total
California	🖥 🖥 🖥 🖥 🖥 🖥 🖵
Delaware	
Illinois	
Michigan	
New Jersey	
New York	
Pennsylvania	
Texas	

🖥 = $100,000
🖵 = $50,000

For another look at estimation, turn to page 223.

C. Answer the following questions.

1. How many more symbols did you use for Pennsylvania than for Illinois? What does this mean in terms of sales?

2. Comparing symbols, determine which state had the
   a. least amount of sales
   b. greatest amount of sales

3. a. According to your graph, was a greater sales total achieved in Illinois or New Jersey?
   b. According to the original list of sales totals, was a greater sales total achieved in Illinois or New Jersey?
   c. Are your answers in **a** and **b** the same? If not, explain why they aren't.

4. List two advantages a pictograph has compared to a list or table.
   a.

   b.

5. List two advantages a list or table has compared to a pictograph.
   a.

   b.

Making Connections: Finding and Graphing Data

Using the newest dictionary or almanac you have available, look up the population of each of the six listed states. Then draw a pictograph below to represent this data. Choose a symbol and draw it in the key, writing its value after the = sign. Round the data and choose a symbol value so that no row has more than 15 symbols. Write the name of your dictionary or almanac and the year it was published after the word *Source* below the graph.

Population of Selected States

=

California
Florida
Illinois
New York
Pennsylvania
Texas

Source:

Reading a Bar Graph

In a **bar graph,** data is represented by the height (or length) of **data bars.** The bars may be drawn vertically (up and down) or horizontally (across). Like pictographs, bar graphs display data for easy comparison. Bar graphs often have the advantage of being easier to read when you want to determine numerical values quickly.

The bar graph below has a **title** (United States Population) and labels on both **axes**—lines that show the numerical values being compared. The **vertical axis** shows population in millions and the **horizontal axis** shows years. Data is represented by the height of the vertical bars.

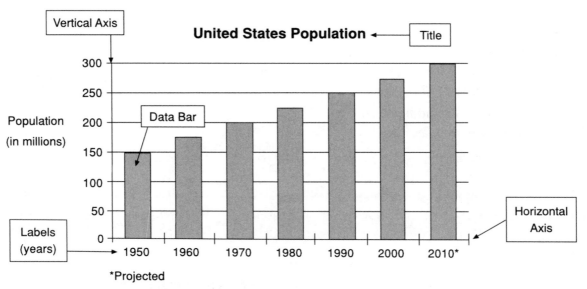

*Projected

Source: Statistical Abstract of the United States

Finding Information on a Bar Graph

To find a value represented by a bar, read the value on the axis directly across from the end of the bar.

Example 1: What was the *approximate* population of the United States in 1970?

Follow the line from the top of the bar labeled 1970. You see that for 1970 the population was **about 200 million.**

Example 2: In which year is the population of the United States projected to be *about* 300 million?

Find 300 million on the vertical axis. Follow across to the right and you see that the bar across from 300 is labeled **2010.**

A. Problems 1–4 refer to the bar graph on page 124.

1. What was the *approximate* population of the United States in 1990?

2. By *about* how much did the U.S. population increase between 1950 and 1990?

3. *Estimate* how much the U.S. population is projected to increase between 1990 and 2010.

4. How accurately do you think *you* can read data on this bar graph? (nearest 1 million, 5 million, or 10 million)

Some bar graphs use double bars to compare even more information. On the graph below, notice that two values (urban *and* rural) are given for each year. *Urban* refers to people living in city areas, while *rural* refers to people living outside of cities.

Example: In 1910 *approximately* 45% of Americans lived in cities, while 55% lived outside of cities.

Percent of the United States Population Living in Urban or Rural Communities

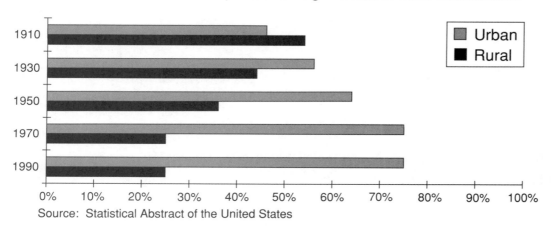

Source: Statistical Abstract of the United States

B. Problems 5–9 refer to the *double bar graph* above.

5. In 1930, *approximately* what percent of Americans did not live in cities?

6. Between which years did little if any change take place in the percent of Americans living in either urban or rural communities?

7. Between which two listed years did the percent of urban population most likely become equal to the percent of rural population?

8. In 1990, *approximately* how many people out of each 1,000 Americans lived in cities?

   (1) 100   **(2)** 250   **(3)** 500   **(4)** 750

9. **Write** What do you think explains the trend shown on the graph? For example, what happened in the United States that led to more people moving to cities? What are the advantages and disadvantages of this population shift?

Graphing Research Data

Imagine you're working with a research group that is investigating the contents of a local landfill. Your group wants to find out the relative amounts of different waste products that local residents throw away.

The group's results, expressed as percents of the total, are summarized in the list below.

Paper: 23.7%	Food: 10.3%	Metal: 6.7%	Plastic: 13.4%
Yard waste: 17.1%	Glass: 8.7%	Wood: 14.8%	Other: 5.3%

A. Round each total to the nearest percent.
The total for Paper is done for you.

Paper: **24%***	Food:	Metal:	Plastic:
Yard waste:	Glass:	Wood:	Other:

*Think: 23.7% is closer to 24% than to 23%.

B. Using the rounded percents from part A, complete the bar graph below to show the components of the waste in the landfill. The bar for Paper is drawn as an example.

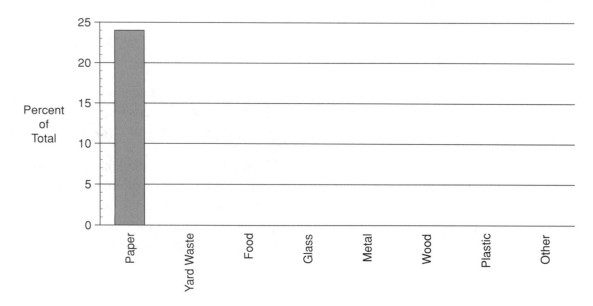

126

C. Using your graphed data, answer the following questions.

1. Which three waste products are represented by the highest bars?

2. Which bar is closest to half the height of the bar representing *paper?*

3. If half the *paper* and *glass* represented on the graph could be recycled, *about* what percent of the waste represented could be recycled?

4. Suppose you want to redraw the bar graph so that the bars are in order of size, *decreasing* as you move from left to right. In what new order should the waste products be listed?

1st: _____   5th: _____

2nd: _____   6th: _____

3rd: _____   7th: _____

4th: _____   8th: _____

Making Connections: Taking a Poll and Graphing

Poll about 20 friends or coworkers about which of the following each would most prefer to eat for breakfast. Tally your results.

Eggs: Pancakes: Toast and coffee:

Cereal: Fruit and juice: Diet drink:

Total your tally count for each of the six choices.

Eggs: _____   Pancakes: _____   Toast and coffee: _____

Cereal: _____   Fruit and juice: _____   Diet drink: _____

Draw a bar graph of your tally data. Draw the data bars vertically (up and down).

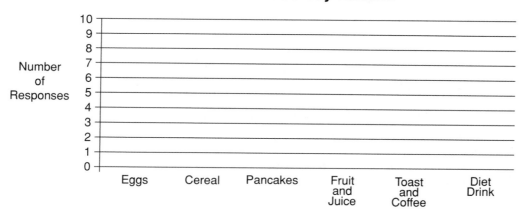

Breakfast Survey Results

Scatter Diagrams

A **scatter diagram** (also known as a *scattergram*) is a graph that shows the relationship between two different groups of data. For example, suppose you want to know whether families with high incomes tend to have more (or fewer) children than families with low incomes. Two groups of data are needed: family income and number of children per family.

Name	Income	Children
Rainey	$12,000	4
Calhoun	$24,000	1
Pomper	$16,000	0
Flowers	$27,000	3
Hunley	$38,000	0
Loring	$13,000	1
Delmont	$42,000	5
Arken	$19,000	2
Ramos	$32,000	4

Suppose you poll 20 families to find the total income *and* number of children in each family. The poll results for 9 of the families are shown in the table at right.

All 20 results are represented on the scatter diagram below.

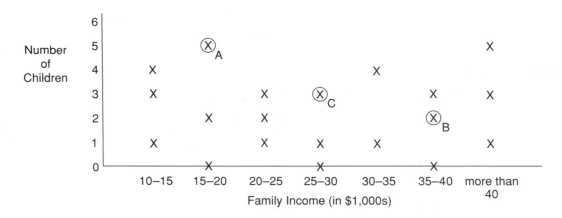

Each *X* on the scatter diagram represents a polled family. The position of the *X* from left to right along the horizontal axis represents family income. The distance of the *X* above the axis represents number of children.

Example 1: The *X* that is circled and labeled *A* represents a family that earns between $15,000 and $20,000 and has 5 children.

Example 2: The *X* that is circled and labeled *B* represents a family that earns between $35,000 and $40,000 and has 2 children.

A. Problems 1–3 are based on the scatter diagram on page 128.

1. Fill in the blanks below:
The circled *X* labeled *C* represents a family that earns between _____ and _____ and has _____ children.

2. Circle the *X* that represents a family that earns between $20,000 and $25,000 and has 3 children. Label this *X* with a *D*.

3. Write Do the results of this poll indicate that there is a relationship between family income and family size? Why or why not?

Bea Allison gave 10 employees a computer literacy test. She asked each employee to write the number of hours he or she had studied the reference material for this test. After the test was over, Bea filled in the table shown at right.

Employee Name	Hours of Study	Test Score (0 to 100 Points)
Blakely	24	82
Liu	7	47
Davis	16	53
Williams	27	95
Ramos	19	91
Porter	9	60
Wright	23	87
Jennings	4	46
McGinty	12	63
Keil	18	71

B. Complete the scatter diagram below to show the data on the table above. The first entry is graphed as an example.

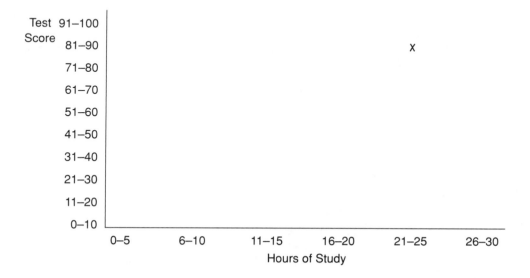

4. Discuss Does the pattern on the scatter diagram tend to show a relationship between employees' *test scores* and *hours of study*?

Mixed Review

A. Problems 1–3 are based on the pictograph.

1. What does the symbol ⌣ stand for?

2. About how many more eggs did Allison Farms produce in 1994 than in 1990?

3. Suppose Allison Farms produces 960,000 eggs in 1995. How many symbols should be drawn to show the 1995 total on this pictograph?

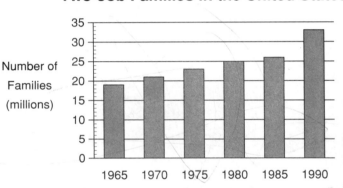

Allison Farms Egg Production

⌣ = 100,000 eggs

B. Problems 4–7 are based on the bar graph.

4. What was the *approximate* number of two-job families in the United States in 1990?

5. In which listed year was the number of two-job families in the United States most nearly equal to 25 million?

6. In which five-year period did the United States experience the greatest increase in the number of two-job families?

7. Since 1965, has the United States had an increase in the number of two-job families? Support your answer.

Two-Job Families in the United States

Number of Families (millions)

1965 1970 1975 1980 1985 1990

Source: Statistical Abstract of the United States

C. Problems 8–10 are based on the scatter diagram.

8. How many applicants took part in the job search shown on the scatter diagram?

9. How many applicants sent out 21 or more resumes?

10. How many applicants received 3 or more job interviews?

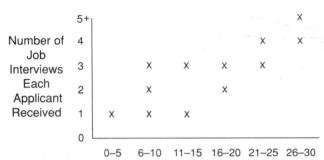

Number of Job Interviews Each Applicant Received

Number of Resumes Each Applicant Sent Out
(Each *x* represents one applicant.)

130

D. Using the information given in the list below, complete the pictograph.
   Be sure to include a key to tell what your chosen symbol represents.

Estimated Number
of Pets
in Harney County

Dogs	24,600
Cats	14,800
Rodents	4,100
Birds	9,900
Fish	5,300
Others	1,900

Estimated Pet Population of Harney County

=

Dogs
Cats
Rodents
Birds
Fish
Others

E. Using the information provided below, complete the bar graph.

Products advertised most in recent issues
of four major newspapers:

Products	Percent of Total
Cars	28%
Food	15%
Furniture	9%
Medicine	22%
Movies	14%
Other	12%

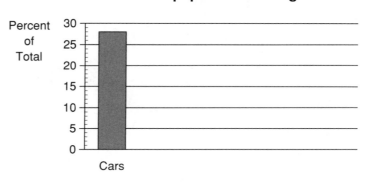

F. Complete the scatter diagram to represent the following information.

Name	Years of Education	Yearly Income
Smith	8	$19,300
White	11	$26,950
Jenkins	6	$14,900
Lewis	14	$32,700
Reina	9	$24,500
Adams	4	$16,750
Franklin	12	$23,400
Clarion	7	$13,800
Zarate	12	$32,900
Van Zeel	16	$38,200

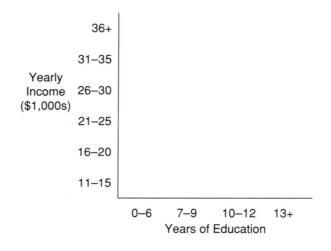

Write Describe the relationship shown on the scatter diagram between years of
education and yearly income.

Reading a Line Graph

A **line graph** displays data as points along a line, drawn from left to right across the graph. The value of each **data point** is found using a value from each axis. In a line graph, each axis contains a scale of numerical values. Line graphs are especially useful when showing how a quantity changes over time.

Look at the line graph below.

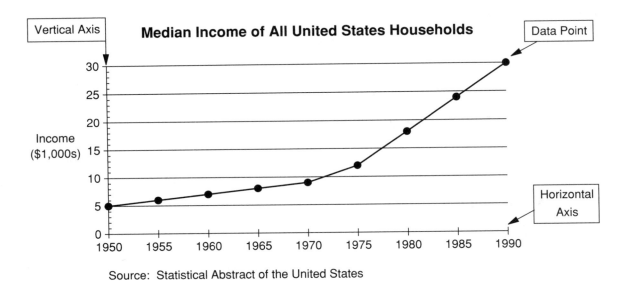

Source: Statistical Abstract of the United States

Finding Information on a Line Graph

One way to find information on a line graph is to select a value on the horizontal axis. Read the point on the line lying directly above the selected value. Then, from that point on the line, read directly across to the value on the vertical axis.

Example: What was the median income of all households in the United States in 1980?

Step 1
Find the year 1980 on the horizontal axis.

Step 2
Find the point on the line directly above 1980.

Step 3
Read the income value on the vertical axis, directly left of the point on the line

In 1980 the median U.S. household income was **about $18,000** (between $15,000 and $20,000).

A. Problems 1–4 refer to the line graph on page 132.

1. On this line graph you can read data points to the nearest

   (1) $100   **(2)** $1,000   **(3)** $5,000

2. *About* how much did the median household income increase between 1960 and 1990?

3. In what listed year was the median household income *closest* to $24,000?

4. About how much larger was the median household income in 1990 than in 1950?

   (1) 2 times   **(2)** 4 times   **(3)** 6 times

B. Problems 5–9 refer to the *double line graph* below. A double line graph contains two lines, each representing one set of data.

Example: In the United States in 1970, the median income of full-time working men was about $9,000 while the median income of full-time working women was about $5,500.

Median Income of Full-time Workers (United States)

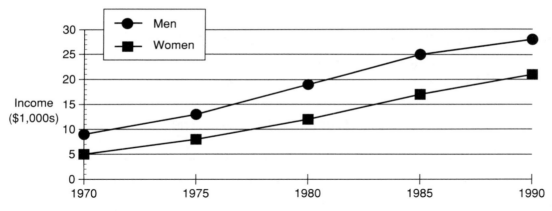

Source: Statistical Abstract of the United States

5. In 1975, *about how much higher* was the median income of men than that of women?

6. In what listed year was women's median income first greater than $10,000?

7. By *about* how much did the median income of men increase between 1970 and 1990?

8. By *about* how much did the median income of women increase between 1970 and 1990?

9. **Write** Between 1970 and 1990, women's median income as a *percent* of men's median income increased from about 59% to about 68%. Why do you think this increase occurred?

Drawing a Growth Curve

Cecilia Barnes has kept a record of her son's height on his first seven birthdays. This information is shown on the table below.

Height Record of Jeremy Barnes

Birthday	Birth	1st	2nd	3rd	4th	5th	6th	7th
Height	$19\frac{1}{4}$ in.	$31\frac{7}{8}$ in.	$36\frac{3}{4}$ in.	$40\frac{1}{4}$ in.	$43\frac{1}{8}$ in.	$45\frac{7}{8}$ in.	$47\frac{5}{8}$ in.	$49\frac{3}{8}$ in.

A. Round each height to the nearest inch. Jeremy's birth height has been rounded as an example.

Birthday	Birth	1st	2nd	3rd	4th	5th	6th	7th
Rounded Height	19 in.*							

*$19\frac{1}{4}$ in. is closer to 19 in. than to 20 in.

B. Using the rounded heights from part A, complete the line graph below to show Jeremy's changes in height. Connect the plotted points with straight line segments. Jeremy's birth height is graphed as an example.

Height Record of Jeremy Barnes

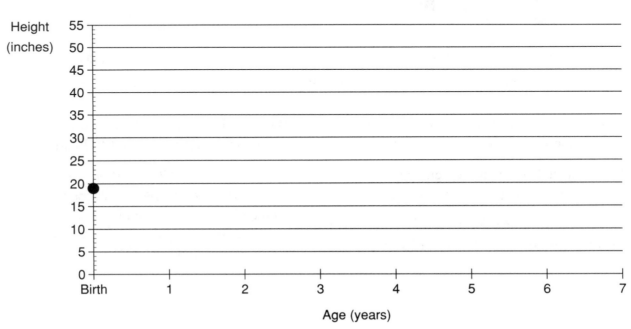

134

C. **Using your graphed data, answer the following questions.**

1. *About* how much has Jeremy grown between the day he was born and his seventh birthday?

2. During which year did Jeremy grow the most? (*Hint:* Look for the line segment that is closest to vertical.)

3. Between which two birthdays did Jeremy grow the least? (*Hint:* Look for the line segment that is closest to horizontal.)

4. Between his fifth and seventh birthdays, what was Jeremy's *average* yearly growth rate?

5. Between which two birthdays did Jeremy first reach a height above 4 ft.?

6. List one advantage that your line graph has compared to the table showing Jeremy's changes in height.

Making Connections: Measurements and Graphing

Suppose you are an assistant at a forestry research center. You've been asked to construct a line graph to show the growth of a branch of a maple tree. Assume you record the growth on the marked line below.

Use a ruler and measure the length of the branch indicated by each mark. Graph your results on the line graph below. Round each measurement to the nearest $\frac{1}{4}$ inch before graphing. The starting value 0 is on the graph.

Growth History Maple Tree Branch

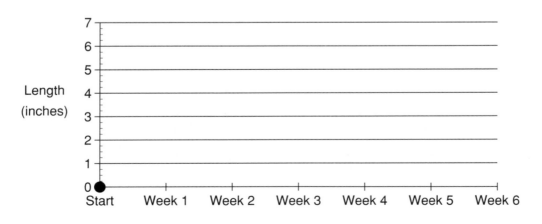

Using Two Data Sources

Sometimes information from more than one source of data is needed to answer a question. Look at the following table and bar graph.

Employee	Monthly Salary	Commission Rate (% of sales)
Banks	$1,250	7%
Clarke	$1,500	8%
Morley	$1,100	6%
Strauss	$1,500	9%

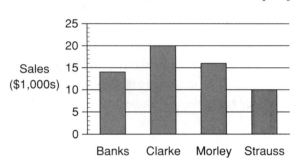

June Sales Totals for Lane Employees

Suppose you want to know how much monthly salary *and* commission on sales Gina Banks earns in June.

- The table tells you Gina's monthly salary ($1,250) and her sales commission *rate* (7%). Unfortunately, it does not tell you the *dollar amount* of her June commission.

- The bar graph tells you only Gina's sales total for June ($14,000). It also does not tell you the *dollar amount* of Gina's June commission.

To determine how much total income Gina Banks earned in June, you need information from both the table and the bar graph.

Gina Banks's June earnings = monthly salary + June commission
$$= \$1,250 + 7\% \text{ of } \$14,000$$
$$= \$1,250 + (0.07 \times \$14,000)$$
$$= \$1,250 + \$980$$
$$= \mathbf{\$2,230}$$

A. To solve problems 1–4, first choose the data source(s) you need to use: table, bar graph, or both. Then solve the problem.

1. What was Emilie Clarke's *sales total* for the month of June?

   (1) table   **(2)** bar graph   **(3)** both

2. What was Art Morley's *total income* for the month of June?

   (1) table   **(2)** bar graph   **(3)** both

3. Which employee had the highest *sales total* for the month of June?

   (1) table   **(2)** bar graph   **(3)** both

4. If Kevin Strauss had a total income of $1,975 during June, how much *commission* did he earn that month?

   (1) table   **(2)** bar graph   **(3)** both

B. Look at the two data sources below and then solve problems 5–9. As a first step in each problem, choose the data source(s) you need to use: pictograph, line graph, or both.

Average Monthly Housing Cost
(Stryker County, family of four)

Average Monthly Income
(Stryker County, family of four)

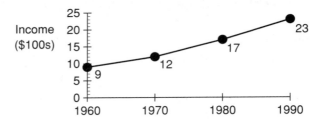

5. By *about* how much did the average monthly income of a family of four increase between 1960 and 1990 in Stryker County?

   (1) pictograph   **(2)** line graph   **(3)** both

6. The Jensen family of four had a monthly family income of $2,000 in 1980. What *percent* of their income went for their average-cost housing?

   (1) pictograph   **(2)** line graph   **(3)** both

7. In 1990 the Wyatt family of four had an income that was $200 per month less than average. What *percent* of their income went for their average-cost housing?

   (1) pictograph   **(2)** line graph   **(3)** both

8. For a family of four in Stryker County, which 1990 amount is most nearly $2\frac{1}{2}$ times the 1960 amount: average monthly housing cost or average monthly income?

   (1) pictograph   **(2)** line graph   **(3)** both

9. Discuss In Stryker County, average housing costs rose much more quickly between 1960 and 1990 than average income. What are some of the consequences to residents in areas where this type of rapid housing cost increase takes place?

Reading a Circle Graph

A **circle graph** displays data as sections of a circle. Circle graphs are especially useful to show how a whole amount, such as a budget, is made up of several parts.

- A whole circle represents the whole amount.

- Each **segment** (part) of the circle represents part of the whole.

- The sum of all segments is equal to the whole.

Here are the most common ways to display data on a circle graph:

- **percents,** where the whole equals 100%

- **fractions,** where the whole equals 1

- **cents per dollar,** where the whole equals $1

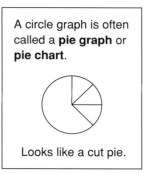

A circle graph is often called a **pie graph** or **pie chart**.

Looks like a cut pie.

Example:

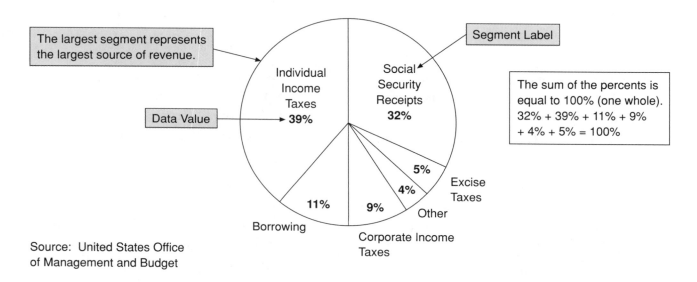

Estimated Revenue Sources in 1995
(United States Budget of $1.5 trillion)

The largest segment represents the largest source of revenue.

Data Value

Segment Label

The sum of the percents is equal to 100% (one whole). 32% + 39% + 11% + 9% + 4% + 5% = 100%

Individual Income Taxes **39%**

Social Security Receipts **32%**

5%

Excise Taxes

4%

11%

9%

Other

Borrowing

Corporate Income Taxes

Source: United States Office of Management and Budget

Finding Information on a Circle Graph

To find information on a circle graph, read and compare data values that appear on circle segments.

Example 1: What is the largest source of revenue in the 1995 U.S. budget?

Answer: individual income taxes (39% is the largest value shown.)

Example 2: What total percent of revenue comes from excise taxes *and* borrowing?

Answer: 16% (5% + 11%)

A. Problems 1–3 refer to the circle graph on page 138.

1. Not including Other, what is the smallest source of revenue in the 1995 U.S. budget?

2. What two sources of revenue together account for almost $\frac{3}{4}$ of the revenue sources in the 1995 budget?

3. Which phrase best describes the relationship of revenue collected from Social Security receipts to revenue collected from borrowing?

   (1) about 2 times as much

   (2) about 3 times as much

   (3) about 4 times as much

B. Problems 4–9 refer to the circle graph below.

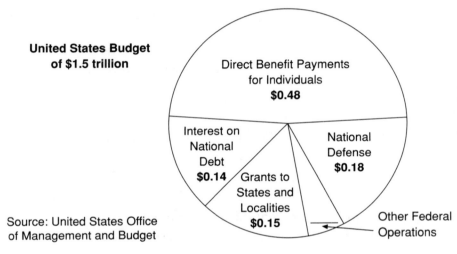

Approximate Expenditures in 1995
(Cents per budget dollar)

United States Budget of $1.5 trillion

Direct Benefit Payments for Individuals **$0.48**

Interest on National Debt **$0.14**

Grants to States and Localities **$0.15**

National Defense **$0.18**

Other Federal Operations

Note that the sum of the segments should be equal to $1.00. Use this fact to solve problem 8.

Source: United States Office of Management and Budget

4. Out of each budget dollar, how much did the United States spend on national defense during 1995?

5. Out of each budget dollar, how much *more* did the United States spend on direct benefit payments to individuals than on grants to states and localities?

6. Which expenditure cost *about half* of each budget dollar?

7. Out of each $100 that the United States spent during 1995, how much went to pay interest on the national debt?

8. How many cents per dollar is the segment Other Federal Operations worth?

9. **Explain** Which type of typical value for the entire graph (mean, median, or mode) best represents the three listed expenditures that are almost equal in value? Give a reason for your answer.

Graphing Family Expenses

The Sanderson family's monthly take-home pay totals *about* $2,000. To help keep track of their spending habits, the Sandersons estimated the amount they spend in each of five categories. They included a sixth category, Miscellaneous, for expenses such as entertainment.

Your task is to determine the *percent of total income* the Sandersons spend in each category and then put your results on a circle graph.

A. The amount the Sandersons spend in each category is given below. To the *nearest percent*, determine what *percent* of total income each amount represents. The percent spent on rent and utilities (see Apartment) is done as an example.

1. Apartment: $800
$$\frac{\$800}{\$2,000} \times \frac{100\%}{1} = 40\%$$

2. Food: $500

3. Transportation: $100

4. Clothing: $200

5. Medical Care: $125

6. Miscellaneous: $275

B. Complete the circle graph below of the Sanderson family's expenses. In (or next to) each segment, write a label to identify the expense category, and write the correct percent within the segment. The category Apartment is done as an example.

▶ **Remember:** When drawing a circle graph, represent the largest amount with the largest segment. The smallest amount will go in the smallest segment.

Sanderson Family Expenses

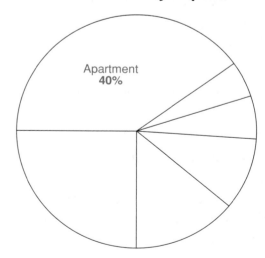

Try this: Add the percents you wrote on the circle graph. Does the sum equal 100%?

If it doesn't, check your calculations in part A.

C. Problems 7–10 refer to your graphed data on page 140.

7. If $\frac{1}{4}$ of the expenses listed as Apartment go to pay utilities, what *percent* of their total take-home pay do the Sandersons spend on utilities?

8. For each dollar of take-home pay, how many cents do the Sandersons spend in each category?
   a. Apartment:
   b. Food:
   c. Transportation:
   d. Clothing:
   e. Medical care:
   f. Miscellaneous:

9. Which phrase best describes the percent of their take-home pay the Sandersons spend on food compared to the percent they spend on medical care?
   (1) 2 times as much
   (2) 3 times as much
   (3) 4 times as much

10. **Explain** List one or two ways in which a circle graph differs from other graphs in this unit. For example, for what type of data is a circle graph most useful?

Making Connections: Choosing an Appropriate Graph

In this unit, you've studied five types of graphs: pictographs, bar graphs, scatter diagrams, line graphs, and circle graphs. Each type of graph has its own features that make it especially useful for certain types of data.

For each description of data below, tell which type of graph you think would be best suited to show the data. Give a reason for your answer.

1. Data that shows the change over time of the U.S. unemployment rate.

2. Data from a survey of 200 families that shows the relationship (if any) between a family's income and the size of a family's house.

3. Data that compares the population of six western states. The purpose of the graph is to show a side-by-side comparison of approximate values.

4. Data that shows a state's budget. The purpose of the graph is to show how many cents of each budget dollar are spent in each expense category.

5. Data that compares the amount of oil produced by the top five oil-producing countries in the world. The purpose of the graph is more to attract the reader's attention than to show precise figures.

Data in Different Forms

On these two pages, you'll learn about changing data from one form to another. For example, at right is a bar graph that shows the *number* of employees in each department of Shield Manufacturing Company.

Suppose we want to use this information to produce a circle graph that shows the *percent* of employees in each department. How do we do this?

Step 1. Find the total number of employees by adding the number of employees in each department:
$94 + 24 + 20 + 18 + 44 = \textbf{200.}$

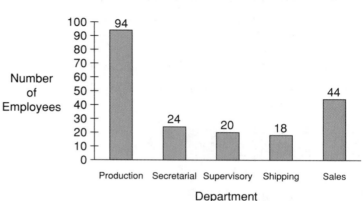

Employees of Shield Manufacturing

Step 2. Determine what percent of 200 each department represents.

Calculations

Production
$\frac{94}{200} \times 100\% = \textbf{47\%}$

Secretarial
$\frac{24}{200} \times 100\% = \textbf{12\%}$

Supervisory
$\frac{20}{200} \times 100\% = \textbf{10\%}$

Shipping
$\frac{18}{200} \times 100\% = \textbf{9\%}$

Sales
$\frac{44}{200} \times 100\% = \textbf{22\%}$

Step 3. Draw a circle graph to represent this percent breakdown.

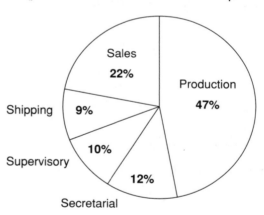

Employees of Shield Manufacturing
(*percent* of 200 total in each department)

A. Problems 1–3 are based on the two graphs above.

1. From which graph can you most easily see which department accounts for *about half* of all employees?

2. From which graph can you most easily find the difference in number of employees in sales and shipping?

3. **Write** From your answers to problems 1 and 2, list one advantage of each type of graph.

B. The bar graph below shows the enrollment totals for each of four middle schools.

4. How many students are enrolled in all four schools combined?

5. What percent of the total is enrolled in each middle school?
   a. Thomas: **b.** Tioga: **c.** Highland: **d.** Worth:

6. Complete the circle graph to show the *percent* of students enrolled in each school. Be sure to include a school name next to each percent.

Middle School Enrollment Total
(*number* of students in each school)

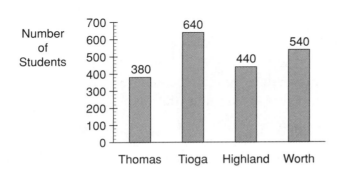

Middle School Enrollment
(*percent* of students in each school)

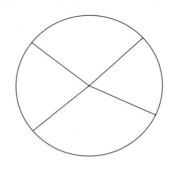

C. The circle graph below shows the percent of students in each grade. The four schools discussed in part B are referred to here.

7. For the middle schools combined, determine the total number of students enrolled at each grade level.
   a. 6th grade: **b.** 7th grade: **c.** 8th grade:

8. Complete the bar graph to show the *number* of students enrolled in each grade. Draw a vertical bar above each grade label on the horizontal axis.

Middle School Enrollment
(*percent* of total by grade level)

Total Enrollment: 2,000 Students

Middle School Enrollment

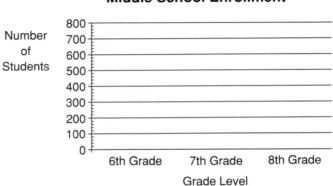

Gridding in Data Analysis Answers

Many data analysis problems involve percent. The standard five-column grid that you see on many tests does not include a percent symbol, so it isn't possible to grid in a percent. However, you know that a percent is another way to express a fractional part of something. Percents have both decimal and fraction equivalencies. For example, 50% is equal to 0.5 and $\frac{1}{2}$.

Read the problem carefully for special instructions about the form the answer should take.

Use these hints to help you fit data analysis answers in the grid:

- Drop unnecessary zeros when entering decimals: $0.500 = .5$.

- Read the problem carefully for instructions about rounding your answer to a certain place value.

- Watch for common repeating decimals. In a repeating decimal, the digit repeats indefinitely. In a calculator display, the digit will repeat until the display is full.

  $0.333333333 = 33\frac{1}{3}\% = \frac{1}{3}$ $0.666666666 = 66\frac{2}{3}\% = \frac{2}{3}$

Filling in the Grid

Example: Out of 125 employees, 60% work full-time. What fraction of the employees work part-time?

Step 1
Solve the problem.
The sum of the full-time and part-time workers is 100%. If 60% work full-time, then $100\% - 60\% = 40\%$ are part-time workers.

Write the answer
as a decimal: $40\% = .4$
or as a fraction: $40\% = \frac{40}{100} = \frac{2}{5}$

Step 2
Write your answer in the top row of boxes. Remember, you can begin in any column as long as your answer fits.

Step 3
Fill in the correct circles on the grid. Both of these answers are correct.

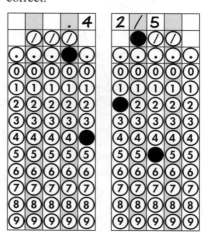

Solve the following problems. Record your answers in the grids.

Problems 1 and 2 refer to the graph below.

Amount of Mei's Monthly Savings Deposit
($2,000 monthly income)

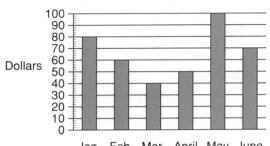

Problems 3 and 4 refer to the following table.

Enrichment Class – Winter Session

Class	Number of Students
Cooking	30
Calligraphy	20
Yoga	35
Woodworking	45
Fitness	70

1. 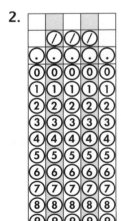 How many more dollars did Mei put in savings in May than she did in March? Grid in your answer as a whole number.

2.  What fraction of her monthly income did Mei put in savings in January?

3. 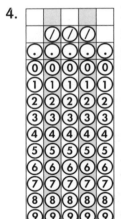 Suppose you are making a pictograph of the information. If each symbol equals 5 students, how many whole symbols would you use to represent the number of students in the yoga class?

4. In a circle graph based on the information, what fraction of the graph should be labeled "Fitness"?

Unit 4 Review

A. Problems 1–3 are based on the circle graph.

1. In 1990 what was the largest criminal justice system expense in the United States?

2. Out of each $1 million spent in 1990 in the criminal justice system, *approximately* how much was spent on the judicial (court) system?

3. In 1990 *about* how much more money was spent on police protection than on legal services?

   (1) 2 times   **(2)** 4 times   **(3)** 6 times

Criminal Justice System Expenditures
(United States, 1990)

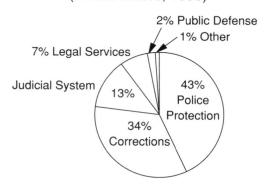

Source: Statistical Abstract of the United States

B. Using the information given below, complete the circle graph.

Beverly, a salesperson, uses a car in her business. Shown below is a list of her estimated yearly car expenses. Using this information, draw a circle graph that shows each expense as a *percent* of her $2,000 yearly expense budget.

Expense	Amount
Insurance	$600
Gas & oil	$800
New tires	$300
Repairs	$300

Yearly Operating Expense
(as a percent of $2,000 total)

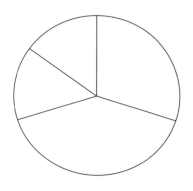

C. Grid in the answer to each problem.

4.

In a circle graph, the entire circle represents a budget of $4,000. A section of the graph is labeled "Supplies 15%." How many dollars does this section represent?

5.

You are creating a pictograph with the following key:

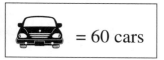 = 60 cars

How many car symbols would you use to represent 330 cars?

146

D. Problems 6–10 are based on the line graph and circle graph below.

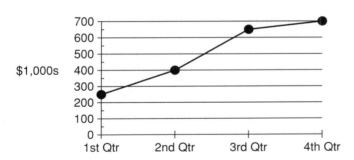

NPX Company Quarterly Sales Revenue
(sales year by quarter)

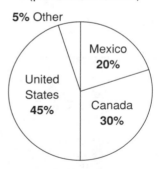

NPX Company Sales
(percent of sales)

6. During the fourth quarter (4th Qtr), *about* how much sales revenue did NPX receive?

7. For each dollar of sales that NPX gets from Mexico, how much does it get from Canada?
   (1) $.50 **(2)** $1.50 **(3)** $3.00

8. What total dollar value of sales did NPX have in the United States in the fourth quarter?

9. **a.** Add the four quarter sales totals to find the total amount of sales revenue earned by NPX during the entire year.

   b. What total amount of sales revenue did NPX receive from Canada during the sales year?

10. **Write** Describe what you think is the most important information provided by each of the two graphs above.

Working Together

To expand your mathematical understanding, do the following with a partner or small group.

Assume your class is given $1,000 to spend on educational supplies or activities. Choose three or more expense categories and draw the two graphs described in **a** and **b** below to display your choices.

Sample expense categories are books, art supplies, science supplies, videotapes, field trips, computer programs, and guest speakers. (You may choose from among these or others you think of.)

   a. Draw a pictograph to show what *dollar amount* (to the nearest $50) you would spend in each category.

   b. Draw a circle graph to show about what *percent* of the $1,000 you would spend in each category.

Unit 5

Analyzing Data

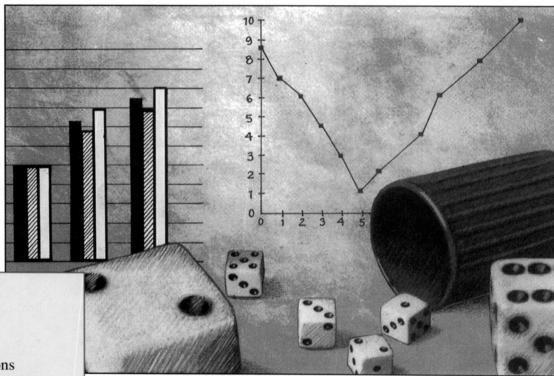

Skills

Interpolating

Extrapolating

Drawing conclusions

Understanding correlation

Determining probability

Understanding margin of error

Tools

Using probability for prediction

Problem Solvers

Analyzing correlation

Identifying needed data

Applications

Gathering more information

Analyzing sales and profit

Sampling a population

You learned how to read data in the last chapter. But it is also important to analyze data—to read between the lines. We want to see what data tells us in addition to the values presented.

Analyzing data involves many skills:

- estimating additional data points—values that aren't directly given on a table or graph
- drawing reasonable conclusions from data
- knowing when data is misleading
- getting additional needed data
- understanding correlation
- working with probability
- using probability for prediction
- working with samples and populations

In this unit, we'll practice each of these data analysis skills.

When Do I Analyze Data?

When do you think about data before making a decision that influences your life?
Check the statements that apply to you.

☐ I read the contents of many food products before I buy them.

☐ I am influenced by medical data about diet and exercise.

☐ I compare store prices before deciding where to shop.

☐ I don't believe all the advertising surveys and claims I hear.

☐ I check to see how political candidates voted on important issues.

☐ I look at interest rates before applying for a loan.

As you begin this unit, describe decisions you've made after thinking about available information.

1. Describe a time you decided not to buy a food product after reading about its contents. Why did you make this decision?

   _____

   _____

2. Describe a situation in which you bought an advertised product, only to find later that the product was not as good as advertised claims led you to believe.

   _____

   _____

3. Describe your reaction to medical findings that show smoking is bad for your health while a balanced diet and exercise are good for you. If you agree, have you changed your lifestyle because of these findings?

   _____

   _____

Throughout this unit, you may use a calculator wherever that would be useful. Information about using a calculator appears on page 219.

Talk About It

Talk with other students about the types of salespeople you've met. As a group, see if you share common opinions on which salespeople tend to be most believable. Which salespeople tend to be least believable? Does the information provided by salespeople seem accurate? How do they use this information? Discuss your experiences that have most influenced how you feel about salespeople.

Interpolation and Extrapolation

Interpolation

Sometimes you want to *estimate* a value that lies between two given values. This is called **interpolating.** For example, consider Oakmont's population shown at right. Population data is given at 10-year intervals, and each number is rounded to the nearest thousand.

Suppose you now want to *estimate* the population of Oakmont in 1975. How do you do this?

First notice that 1975 is halfway between 1970 and 1980. Now *assume* that half the population gain between 1970 and 1980 occurred by 1975. The population increase between 1970 and 1980 is found by subtraction: $56,000 - 42,000 = 14,000$.

1975 population $\approx 42,000 +$ half of the 1970–1980 increase*
$\approx 42,000 + 7,000$
$\approx$ **49,000**

---

* $\approx$ means "is approximately equal to"

Oakmont Population

Year	Population	
1960	30,000	
1970	42,000	
1975*	?	14,000
1980	56,000	
1990	72,000	

*To **interpolate** is to estimate an "in between" value.

Extrapolation

When you **extrapolate,** you *estimate* a value that lies *outside* the given set of values. For example, *estimate* what the population of Oakmont will be in the year 2010. Notice that the population increase has been steadily rising every decade (10 years). Subtract to determine this increase for the past three decades:

1960 to 1970: $42,000 - 30,000 = 12,000$
1970 to 1980: $56,000 - 42,000 = 14,000$
1980 to 1990: $72,000 - 56,000 = 16,000$
1990 to 2000: $90,000 - 72,000 = 18,000$

Let's estimate the next population increase to be 20,000.
2010 population $\approx 90,000 + 20,000 =$ **110,000**

Oakmont Population

Year	Population	
1960	30,000	12,000
1970	42,000	14,000
1980	56,000	16,000
1990	72,000	18,000
2000	90,000	
2010*		

*To **extrapolate** is to estimate a value that lies outside the given set of values.

Notice that when you interpolate or extrapolate, you are estimating values based on given data. You can use both of these skills on data presented on lists, tables, and graphs.

A. Problems 1 and 2 refer to the table on page 150.

1. What was the *approximate* population of Oakmont in 1985?

2. If the present trend continues, in about what year do you think Oakmont's population will hit 100,000? Support your answer.

B. Problems 3–5 refer to the bar graph at right.

3. What was the *approximate* world population in the year 1985?

4. a. By *about* how much did the world's population increase from 1970 to 1980?

   b. By *about* how much did the world's population increase between 1980 and 1990?

5. Assume that the world population growth continues to follow the trend shown on the bar graph. What do you *estimate* the world population will be in the year 2010?

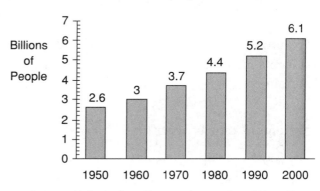

World Population

Source: U.S. Census Bureau, International Data Base

C. Problems 6–9 are based on the line graph at right.

6. If the most recent price rise is repeated, what will be the *approximate* average price of a new home in Lewisburg in the year 2010?

7. In what year would you estimate average new home prices in Lewisburg reached $75,000?

8. *About* how many years after 1980 did it take average new home prices in Lewisburg to double?

   (1) exactly 20

   (2) a little less than 20

   (3) a little more than 20

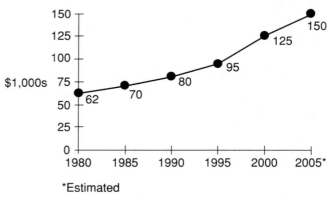

Average New Home Prices in Lewisburg

*Estimated

9. **Explain** Which estimate do you think is likely to be the most accurate: an estimate of average home prices for the year 2010 *or* for the year 2020? Give a reason for your answer.

Drawing Conclusions from Data

When you draw a conclusion from data, you must carefully distinguish between two types of statements:

- statements that are *justified* according to the given data (those that are true or present a reasonable conclusion)

- statements that are *not justified* (those that are false or are not supported by the data)

Examples: Below are examples of four statements students made after looking at the circle graph at right.

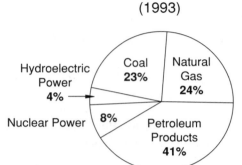

U.S. Energy Consumption
(1993)

Source: Statistical Abstract of the United States

Statement that Is Justified

"In 1993, the United States used twice as much nuclear power as hydroelectric (water) power."

This statement is true and therefore justified because the graph shows nuclear power use at 8%, which is twice as much as hydroelectric use (4%).

Statement that Is Justified

"In 1993, the majority of U.S. energy consumption was supplied by nonrenewable resources."

This statement is reasonable because the graph shows that 88% of U.S. energy consumption was of nonrenewable resources (petroleum, natural gas, coal).

Statement that Is Not Justified

"Petroleum products accounted for more than half of the energy consumption in the U.S. in 1993."

This statement is false because petroleum product use is shown as 41%, which is less than half (50%). It is not justified.

Statement that Is Not Justified

"Wastes from nuclear power plants are so dangerous that we should shut down these plants."

This statement is not supported because the graph does not deal with the hazards of nuclear waste.

A. **Label each statement as follows:**

- *J* if the statement is justified according to the graph above

- *N* if the statement is not justified by the graph above

1. In 1993, Americans used more than their share of the world's oil.

2. About $\frac{1}{4}$ of the energy consumed in the United States in 1993 came from natural gas.

3. The second leading source of energy in the United States in 1993 was coal.

4. In 1993, the cost of obtaining energy from nuclear power was about twice the cost of obtaining energy from hydroelectric power.

B. Problem 5 is based on the bar graph below.

5. Choose the number of each statement that is justified according to the bar graph. Put an *X* through the number of each statement that is not justified according to the bar graph.

(1) Of the three elementary schools, Franklin's budget decreased the least between 1990 and 1994.

(2) Budgets are decreasing in elementary schools because most people think that schools can get by with less money.

(3) Between 1990 and 1994, the average budget decrease for the three elementary schools was *about* 10%.

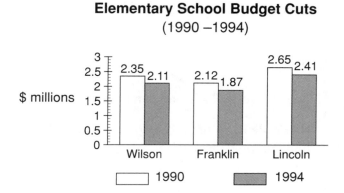

Elementary School Budget Cuts
(1990 –1994)

C. Problem 6 is based on the line graph below.

6. Choose the number of each statement that is justified according to the line graph. Put an *X* through the number of each statement that is not justified according to the line graph.

(1) The average cost of a new car is rising because of improvements such as air bags and antilock brakes.

(2) The average price of a new car in Lincoln City *approximately* doubled between 1980 and 1990.

(3) The estimated average price of a new car in Lincoln City in 1995 is more than $25,000.

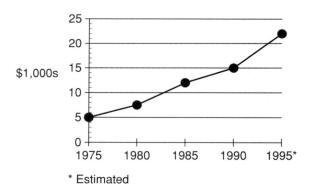

Average Price of a New Car in Lincoln City

* Estimated

D. Discuss Go back through each problem and look at the choices that are not justified. Choose statements that you think are personal opinions. Do you agree or disagree with each of these opinions? Why or why not?

What More Do I Need to Know?

Sometimes a data source doesn't have all the information you need. More data may be required before you can answer certain questions. Being able to identify this needed data is an important skill.

The examples are based on the bar graph below.

Example 1: What *percent* of Blane County registered voters voted in the 1992 presidential election?

The answer is **70%** and can be read on the graph.

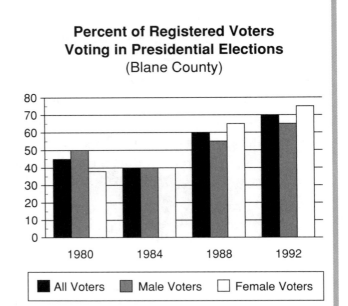

Percent of Registered Voters Voting in Presidential Elections
(Blane County)

Example 2: What more do you need to know to find the *number* of Blane voters who voted in the 1992 presidential election?

   (1) the total number of Blane County residents in 1992

   (2) the total number of registered voters in Blane County in 1992

   (3) the total number of voting-age residents in Blane County in 1992

The answer is **(2) the total number of registered voters in Blane County in 1992.** For example, if Blane County has 200,000 registered voters, the number who voted can be found by multiplication:

70% of 200,000 = 0.7 × 200,000 = 140,000 voters

A. Problems 1–4 are based on the bar graph above.

1. What more do you need to know to find the number of female registered voters in Blane County who voted in the 1984 election?

   (1) the number of female registered voters in Blane County in 1992

   (2) the number of female residents in Blane County in 1984

   (3) the number of female registered voters in Blane County in 1984

2. What more do you need to know to determine which election, 1980 or 1992, drew a greater number of people to the polls in Blane County?

   (1) the population of Blane County in 1980 and in 1992

   (2) the number of registered voters in Blane County in 1980 and in 1992

   (3) the number of voting-age residents in Blane County in 1980 and in 1992

3. **Explain** From data given on the bar graph, can you conclude that the number of registered voters of Blane County increased between 1988 and 1992? Support your answer.

4. **Explain** From data given on the bar graph, can you conclude that more female residents of Blane County voted in the 1992 election than males? Give a reason to support your answer.

B. Problems 5 and 6 are based on the pictograph.

5. What more do you need to know to decide which of the listed states has the most nuclear power plants per 1 million state residents?

   (1) the land area of each state

   (2) the number of cities in each state with a population of 1 million or more

   (3) the population of each state

6. From data given on the graph, can you conclude that Illinois produces more energy from nuclear power than any other state listed? Give a reason to support your answer.

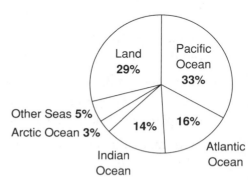

Nuclear Power Plants in the United States
(Selected States, 1991)

◺ = 1 nuclear power plant

Illinois ◺◺◺◺◺◺◺◺◺◺◺◺
Pennsylvania ◺◺◺◺◺◺◺◺
South Carolina ◺◺◺◺◺◺
New York ◺◺◺◺◺
California ◺◺◺◺◺
Arizona ◺◺◺

C. Problems 7 and 8 are based on the circle graph.

7. What more do you need to know to determine how many square miles of the Earth's surface are made up of the Arctic Ocean?

   (1) the average depth of the Arctic Ocean

   (2) the total surface area of the Earth

   (3) the longest distance across the Arctic Ocean

8. **Explain** From the data given on the graph, can you conclude that more than $\frac{2}{3}$ of the Earth's surface is covered by water? Give a reason to support your answer.

Earth's Surface

Land 29%
Pacific Ocean 33%
Other Seas 5%
Arctic Ocean 3%
14%
16%
Indian Ocean
Atlantic Ocean

Getting More Information

You can use your data analysis skills when you talk with salespeople. To get you to buy a service or product, salespeople often use data to back their claims. Data can be very helpful, but it is often limited and can be misleading. Quite often, you need more information before you can make an intelligent decision.

Example

Tony met with an insurance salesperson. She told Tony, "You'll never get a better deal than this. Most of your possessions will be insured against fire and many other types of losses. Your yearly cost is low, starting at just $275 for the first year. Just sign on the dotted line and you're covered."

If you were Tony, would you sign? Certainly not yet!

The problem is that Tony has no data to base a decision on, other than the quoted $275 first-year premium (cost). Without more information he has no way to judge the salesperson's claims of a "good deal." For example, just what does "most of your possessions will be insured" mean? Tony will want to know for sure which possessions are covered and which are not.

Name three other things Tony might want to know before deciding on this insurance.

Your answers will vary, but they may include any of the following:

- Besides fire, what other kinds of losses are covered? For example, what about water damage and theft?
- How much is the premium each year after the first year?
- What yearly premiums do other insurance companies charge for the same type of coverage?
- How much is the deductible (the amount Tony must pay on each claim)? Is there a monetary limit on the coverage? In other words, will the insurance company pay for all of Tony's losses or just part of them?
- Will the insurance company pay *full replacement value* (actual replacement cost) on covered items?
- How soon after a loss will the insurance company pay?

A. For each sales pitch, write two questions you would like to have answered before judging the value of the service or product.

1. "I've got an apartment that you'll just love and it's only $550 per month."

2. "This used pickup is a steal at $7,500. Why, it's only four years old!"

B. For the opinion expressed below, write two questions you'd like to have answered before you could agree or disagree with the speaker.

3. "Education costs here in Newport are rising way too fast! We've got to get them under control. Don't you agree?"

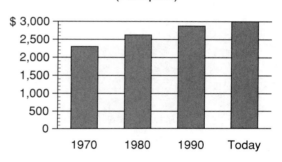

Yearly Cost of Educating a Child
(Newport)

Making Connections: Sources of Information

When you need information about a subject, where do you get it? Often you use a newspaper, an encyclopedia, a newsmagazine, or a library book. Being able to locate needed information is an important skill.

Find answers to the following questions. For each question, identify the source of information you used to find your answer.

1. What is the approximate weight of an adult male lion?

2. About how much do used 1999 Honda Accords sell for in your city?

3. What is the height of Mount McKinley?

4. What is the population of the city in which you live (or live near)?

5. How many acres are in one square mile?

Understanding Correlation

When data values are related to each other in some way, we say there is a **correlation** between those values. Being able to identify correlation is an important data analysis skill.

The graph below shows **positive correlation:** as one value (miles driven) increases, the second value (fare) also increases.

The graph below shows **negative correlation:** as one value (selling price) increases, the second value (number sold) decreases.

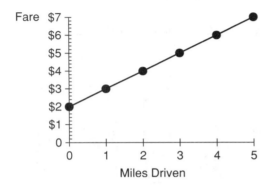

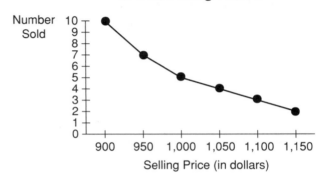

Cab fares usually have a minimum fee plus an added mileage fee.

A higher sales price results in a smaller number of sales of oak dining tables.

A. Write which type of correlation, *positive* or *negative,* is shown on each graph below.

1. _____

2. _____

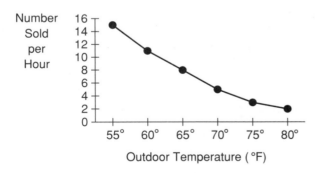

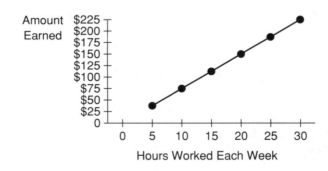

B. Use a check ✓ to indicate what type of correlation would *most likely* be shown by each set of data described below.

3. the price of sandwiches at the County Fair and the number of sandwiches sold

_____ positive correlation

_____ negative correlation

4. outdoor temperature and the number of kids swimming at the local outdoor pool

_____ positive correlation

_____ negative correlation

5. the size of a family's house and the income level of the family

_____ positive correlation

_____ negative correlation

6. home sales and home mortgage (loan) interest rates

_____ positive correlation

_____ negative correlation

Making Connections: Taking a Poll

Is there a correlation between the number of school grades a student has completed and the number of hours the student now spends studying each week? Poll your class to see if this correlation exists for your classmates. (Class time may be included as study time.) Graph your poll results on the scatter diagram below.

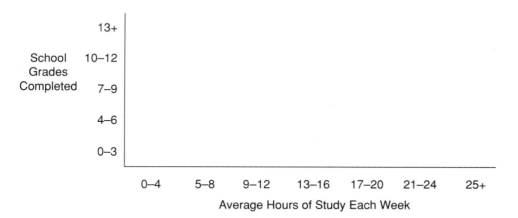

Does your scatter diagram show correlation? If yes, what type? Discuss with your classmates why this correlation exists (if it does).

Note: Data on a scatter diagram shows correlation if the pattern of plotted points tends to rise or fall as you scan across the diagram. No correlation is shown if the pattern of points neither rises nor falls.

Analyzing Correlation

Rainbow Beverage Company conducted a taste-test survey of its new soft drink
Rainbow Gold. The company wanted to determine what amount of added sugar
(measured in teaspoons per gallon) would give the drink the most popular flavor.

A total of 100 participants were asked to rate the taste of each of 12 different mixtures
of Rainbow Gold. For each mixture, the participants scored the drink from 0 to 10, with
10 being the highest possible rating. Each of the 12 mixtures contained a different
amount of added sugar. The average rating obtained for each mixture (sugar level) is
graphed below.

Note: A graph, such as the poll result graph below, can contain some data that shows
positive correlation *and* some data that shows negative correlation.

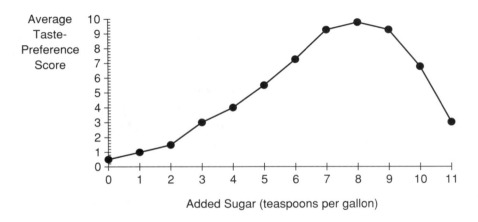

A. Problems 1–4 are based on the graph above.

1. What type of correlation (*positive* or
   negative) is shown between taste preference
   and sugar levels for

   a. 0 to 8 tsp. per gal.?

   b. 8 to 11 tsp. per gal.?

2. a. What sugar level corresponds to the most
      preferred taste?

   b. At the most preferred taste level, how
      much sugar would be in 1 cup (8 fl. oz.)
      of Rainbow Gold?

3. What can you conclude from the data about
   sugar levels higher than 8 tsp. per gal.?

4. What is a reasonable prediction about what
   average taste preference scores would be for
   sugar levels higher than 11 tsp. per gal.?

More on Correlation

The graph below shows data taken on an adult patient during a step exercise as part of a physical examination. As you can see, the graph shows different types of correlation during each stage of the exercise.

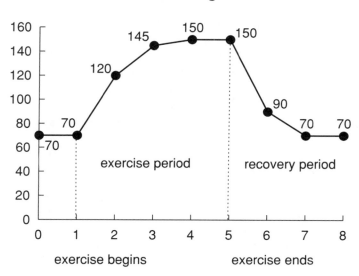

Heart Rate During Exercise

Note: On the heart rate graph at left, the *time* axis (in minutes) is divided into periods of rest and a period of exercise.

B. Problems 5–8 are based on the graph above.

5. What is the patient's heart rate
   a. just before the exercise begins?
   b. at its highest level during the exercise?
   c. at the end of the recovery period?

6. Which type of correlation (*positive* or *negative*) is shown between *heart rate* and *time* during
   a. the first 2 minutes of exercise?
   b. the first 2 minutes of recovery?

7. Suppose the exercise period had been lengthened by 1 minute. Predict what the patient's heart rate would have been at the end of the lengthened exercise period. Give a reason for your answer.

8. **Discuss** Assume that this patient does the step exercise when he is 40 pounds heavier.
   a. How will the patient's extra weight most likely affect his heart rate during each phase of the test?
   b. How will the extra weight most likely affect the patient's recovery rate?
   c. Describe how your answers to **a** and **b** would affect the shape of the heart rate curve shown above.

Profit Analysis

Spikes Toy Company manufactures and sells a toy truck. The total cost of the truck for the manufacturer is $4, and John Spikes can choose the selling price. Before deciding on a selling price, John draws Graphs A and B.

- Graph A shows the **unit profit:** the profit made on the sale of a single truck at each possible selling price.

  (profit = selling price − total cost)

- Graph B shows the **number of unit sales:** the number of trucks John can sell at each possible selling price. This information comes from a market survey of potential customers.

Graph A: Unit Profit

Profit per Unit

At a selling price of $8, John makes a profit of $4 on each truck sold.

Unit Selling Price

Graph B: Number of Unit Sales

1,000s of Units

At a selling price of $8, John can sell **30,000** trucks.

Unit Selling Price

Profit Analysis Graph

To determine the most profitable selling price, John drew a **profit analysis graph** showing **total profit at each selling price.** Each point on the profit analysis graph is found by *multiplying the unit profit by number of unit sales at each possible unit selling price.*

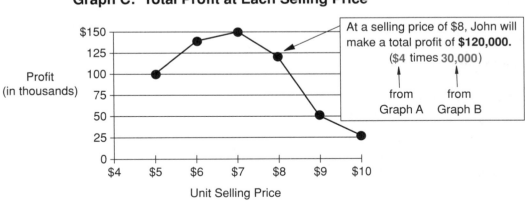

Graph C: Total Profit at Each Selling Price

Profit (in thousands)

At a selling price of $8, John will make a total profit of **$120,000.**
($4 times **30,000**)

from Graph A   from Graph B

Unit Selling Price

A. Problems 1–5 are based on graphs A, B, and C on page 162.

1. What type of data correlation (*positive* or *negative*) is shown on Graph C for unit selling prices of

  a. $4 to $7?

  b. $7 to $10?

2. Looking at Graph A, determine the unit profit on a truck that sells for $6.

3. Looking at Graph B, determine how many trucks will sell at a selling price of $6.

4. Looking at Graph C, estimate the total profit John will make if he chooses a unit selling price of $6.

5. **Write** Looking at Graph C, write a statement about

  a. the maximum profit that John can make from sales of the truck (*Hint:* Look at the highest point on the graphed line.)

  b. the selling price at which John's maximum profit occurs

Imagine that you need to set a price to sell a new mousetrap that you've invented. Your total cost to produce the mousetrap is $2.

- Graph D shows the profit you can make from the sale of each mousetrap at each of several possible selling prices.

- Graph E (from a market survey) shows the number of mousetraps you can sell at each of several possible selling prices.

Graph D: Unit Profit

Graph E: Number of Unit Sales

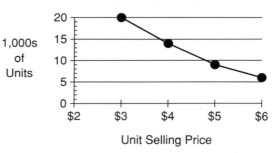

B. Using the information on graphs D and E, complete graph F below, showing the total profit you'd make at each possible selling price.

Graph F: Total Profit at Each Selling Price

Mixed Review

A. Problems 1–3 are based on the line graph at right.

1. What was the *approximate* size of the U.S. civilian labor force in 1988?

2. Assume that the growth rate from the mid-1990s continues. To the nearest million, what would be a reasonable estimated value for the size of the civilian labor force for the year 2005?

3. Can you conclude from information on the graph that the growth rate is occurring because of the growth of the U.S. population? Give a reason to support your answer.

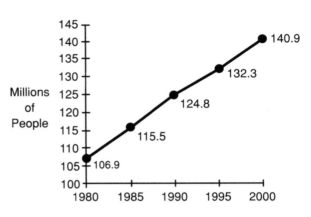

United States Civilian Labor Force

(Source: Statistical Abstract of the United States)

B. Problem 4 is based on the bar graph at right.

4. Which of the following statements is supported by information on the graph?

   (1) Average income rose in the United States between 1970 and 1992.

   (2) For the years shown, the largest increase in the average number of household TV sets took place between 1980 and 1985.

   (3) Between 1970 and 1990, the average number of TV sets in U.S. homes increased about 50%.

   (4) Between 1970 and 1992, the average price of TV sets decreased.

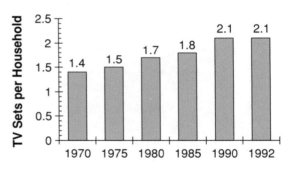

Average Number of TV Sets
(United States Households)

Source: Statistical Abstract of the United States

C. Grid in the answer to each problem.

5.  Refer to the line graph in Part A.

   How many millions more people were part of the U.S. civilian labor force in 1995 than in 1985?

6. Refer to the bar graph in Part B.

   What is the ratio, or fraction, comparing the average number of TV sets per household in 1970 to the average number in 1990?

164

D. Problems 7–9 are based on the line graph at right.

7. In which five-year period shown did the greatest growth take place in the percent of U.S. households getting cable TV service?

8. Out of every 100 U.S. households in 1980, how many had cable TV? Round your answer to the nearest whole number.

9. In order to determine the increase in *number* of U.S. households with cable TV between 1985 and 1990, what more would you need to know?

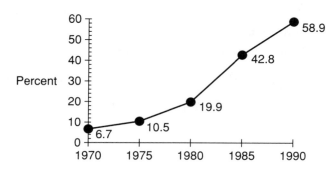

Percent of U.S. Households with Cable TV

Source: Statistical Abstract of the United States

E. Problems 10–15 are based on the bar graph at right.

10. What kind of correlation (*positive* or *negative*) is shown by the graph at right for driver deaths and
    a. the first three age groups?
    b. the last two age groups?

11. According to the graph, in 1990 which age group had the
    a. highest number of driver fatalities per 100,000 drivers?
    b. lowest number of driver fatalities per 100,000 drivers?

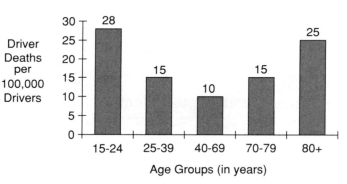

1990 Driver Fatalities by Age of Driver

Source: National Highway Traffic Safety Administration

12. In your opinion, what factors might account for the results shown on the graph? In other words, why do you think driver deaths at first decrease as people get older, and then increase with advanced age?

13. Can you conclude from this graph that all drivers over the age of 80 are poor drivers?

14. What more would you need to know to be able to determine how many fatalities actually occurred in each age group during 1990?

15. **Discuss** How do you think information contained on the graph would influence how car insurance companies set insurance rates?

16. **Discuss** Describe driving habits that, in your opinion, make someone an unsafe driver. What advice would you like to give to drivers who practice the driving habits you listed?

Introducing Probability

Have you heard (or made) statements such as the following:
"There's a forty percent chance of rain tomorrow."
"Ten to one she won't make it to work on time!"
"He hasn't got one chance in a hundred of hitting a home run!"

What you're hearing is the language of **probability,** the likelihood (or chance) of something happening or not happening. Probability, the study of chance, is a useful data analysis tool.

Determining Probability from the Laws of Chance

According to the "laws of chance," the probability that an event will occur (called a *favorable outcome*) depends on two numbers: the number of ways the favorable outcome can occur *and* the total number of outcomes possible.

$$\text{Probability of an event} = \frac{\text{number of favorable outcomes}}{\text{total number of possible outcomes}}$$

Writing Probability as a Number

Example

Suppose you throw a die (one of a pair of dice). What is the chance that the number 6 will come up when the die stops rolling? Since there is only 1 side with 6 dots, the total number of favorable outcomes is 1. Since the die has 6 sides, the total number of possible outcomes is 6.

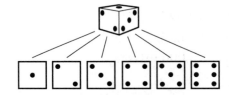

Each of the 6 faces of a die has the same chance of turning up after the die is tossed.

$$\text{Probability of rolling a 6} = \frac{\text{number of favorable outcomes}}{\text{total number of possible outcomes}} = \frac{1}{6}$$

The probability $\frac{1}{6}$ can be written as the percent $16\frac{2}{3}\%$.

The probability of rolling a 6 can be given as $\frac{1}{6}$, as **$16\frac{2}{3}\%$,** or as **1 chance in 6.**

Note: A probability of 0% means that an event cannot happen.
A probability of 100% means that an event will happen for certain.

Example

If you spin the spinner at right, what is the probability that the pointer will stop on a shaded section? (Assume the sections are the same size and that the spinner won't stop exactly on the line between two sections.)

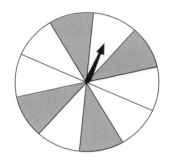

Step 1. Notice that there are 10 possible outcomes, 10 sections on which the spinner can stop. Of these 10 outcomes, 4 are shaded. The number of favorable outcomes is 4.

On the average, 4 spins in 10 will stop on a shaded section. This is the same as saying that 2 spins in 5 will stop on a shaded section.

Step 2. Write the probability as a fraction. Simplify the fraction if possible.

$$\frac{\text{favorable outcomes}}{\text{possible outcomes}} = \frac{4}{10} = \frac{2}{5} \text{ or } 40\%$$

The probability of the pointer stopping on a shaded section is $\frac{2}{5}$, **40%**, *or* **2 chances in 5.**

Solve the following probability problems. You can express each probability in any of the ways shown above.

1. If you toss a die (6 sides), what is the probability of

   a. an even number (2, 4, or 6) coming up?

   b. a number divisible by 3 coming up?

   c. the number 1 *not coming up?*

2. On the spinner above, what is the probability of the pointer landing on an unshaded section?

3. A bag contains colored jelly beans: 8 purple, 12 red, 6 pink, and 4 black. If you shut your eyes and pull out one jelly bean from the bag, what is the probability that the jelly bean is

   a. purple? (*Hint:* First determine how many jelly beans there are in all.)

   b. red?

   c. pink?

   d. black?

4. **Investigate** Suppose, without looking, you draw a card from the group of cards below.

   a. What is the probability that the card you draw will be a face card (a card with a face)?

   b. What is the probability that the card you draw will *not* be a face card?

   c. Assume you do choose a face card on your first draw. Now further assume that you place the chosen face card in your pocket and that again, without looking, you draw another card. What is the probability now that you will draw a face card?

Using Probability for Prediction

On the previous two pages, you saw how probability can be based on the laws of chance. Probability can also be *based on data*.

Basing Probability on Data

Example 1:

Imagine that you work as an assistant at Grove Retirement Center. The graph shows an age breakdown of the center's past applicants.

What is the probability that the next person who applies for residency at the center will be 71 to 80 years old?

Answer: 45%

The graph shows that 45% of past applicants were in the 71–80 years age group. You can *reasonably conclude* (but not prove) that the graph also represents ages of other people who may be interested in Grove but who have not yet applied for residency. Basing probability on available data gives us *the best guess* about future events. It doesn't say what will happen, only what's most likely.

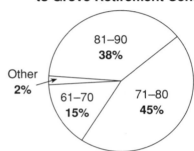

Age Breakdown of Applicants to Grove Retirement Center

81–90 **38%**

Other **2%**

61–70 **15%**

71–80 **45%**

Using Probability for Making Predictions

▶ To predict the number of times something will occur, multiply the probability that it will happen once by the number of times it could happen.

Example 2: If you roll a die 150 times, how many 1s will you probably roll?

Step 1. Determine the probability of rolling a 1 on a single roll:

$$\frac{\text{favorable outcomes}}{\text{total outcomes}} = \frac{1}{6}$$

Step 2. Multiply 150 by $\frac{1}{6}$.

$150 \times \frac{1}{6} = 25$

└ number of rolls

You will probably roll **25** ones.

Example 3: Refer to the circle graph above. Of the next 50 people who apply for residency at Grove, how many will probably be between 61 and 70 years old?

Step 1. You can reasonably conclude that the probability of the next applicant being in the 61–70 years age group is 15%.

Step 2. Find 15% of 50.

15% of 50 = 0.15 × 50 = 7.5

Of the next 50 applicants, **7** or **8** will probably be in the 61–70 age group.

Answer the following probability questions.

1. If you roll a die 100 times, how many 5s will you probably roll? Round your answer to the nearest whole number.

2. Refer again to the graph on page 168.
   a. What is the probability that the next person who applies for residency at Grove will be between 81 and 90 years old?
   b. Of the next 40 people who apply for residency at Grove, how many probably will be between 81 and 90 years old?

Problem 3 is based on the circle graph.

Most Recent 100 Births at Emmanuel Hospital

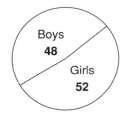

3. Of the next 300 children born at Emmanuel, how many will probably be boys?

4. Hank, a basketball player, has made 40 of his last 200 free-throw shots.
   a. What's the probability that Hank will make his next free throw?
   b. Of the next 50 free throws Hank attempts, how many will he probably make?

5. A recent preference poll of 300 registered voters in King County had the following results in the race for county commissioner.

King County Preference Poll

	Geoff Daniels	Joyce Higgins
Female Voters	70	130
Male Voters	65	35

   a. How many female voters participated in the poll?
   b. Of the next 20 female voters polled, how many will probably prefer Daniels?
   c. What percent of *all voters* polled expressed a preference for Higgins?

Making Connections: Checking Probability

Five students should each flip a penny 10 times. Record the results in the table.

How many students flipped exactly 5 heads and 5 tails? How do you explain this result?

What is the *average* number of heads flipped by the 5 students? Do you think that if 100 students participated, the average would be closer to 5 heads?

	Coin Flips: Heads	Coin Flips: Tails
Student #1		
Student #2		
Student #3		
Student #4		
Student #5		

Probability of Successive Events

Successive events are events that happen one after another. An example is flipping a coin and getting heads and then flipping it again to see if you can get a second heads to follow the first.

▶ To find the probability of successive events occurring, multiply the probability of the first event by the probability of the second event.

Example 1: What is the probability of getting 2 heads in a row when flipping a coin?

Step 1. Remember that the probability of getting heads when you flip a coin is $\frac{1}{2}$. This is because a coin has 2 sides, only 1 of which shows a head.

Step 2. Multiply the equal probabilities of getting heads on each of 2 flips.

Probability of 2 heads on 2 flips in a row $= \frac{1}{2} \times \frac{1}{2} = \frac{1}{4}$ *or* 25%

probability of heads on first flip ⌐
probability of heads on second flip ⌐
probability of 2 heads in a row ⌐

The probability of getting 2 heads in a row is $\frac{1}{4}$ *or* **25%**.

The probability of flipping

followed by

is $\frac{1}{4}$ = 25%

Example 2: The graph at right shows what kind of cars Malcolm's Car Service worked on last year. What is the probability that the next 2 cars Malcolm works on will both be Japanese-made?

Step 1. The probability that a car that comes to Malcolm's for service will be Japanese-made is 20% or $\frac{1}{5}$.

Step 2. Multiply the equal probabilities of Malcolm working on a Japanese-made car twice in a row.

Probability of 2 Japanese-made cars in a row $= \frac{1}{5} \times \frac{1}{5} = \frac{1}{25}$ or 4%

probability of a Japanese-made car as first car ⌐
probability of a Japanese-made car as second car ⌐
probability of 2 Japanese-made cars in a row ⌐

The probability of Malcolm working on 2 Japanese-made cars in a row is $\frac{1}{25}$ *or* **4%**.

Malcolm's Car Service
(types of cars Malcolm works on)

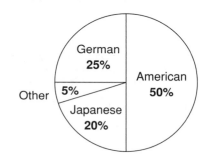

A. Problems 1–3 refer to the graph on page 170.

1. a. What is the probability that the next car Malcolm works on will be American-made?

b. What is the probability that the *next* 2 cars Malcolm works on will be American-made?

2. Explain Can you tell what the probability is that the next car Malcolm works on will be from England? Give a reason to support your conclusion.

3. a. What is the probability that the next car Malcolm works on will be made *somewhere other* than the United States, Japan, or Germany?

b. What is the probability that the *next* 2 cars Malcolm works on will be made *somewhere other* than the United States, Japan, or Germany?

B. Answer each probability question below.

4. a. When rolling a die, what is the probability of rolling two 6s in a row?

b. When rolling a die twice, what is the probability of rolling a 6, followed by rolling a 1?

5. Suppose a game show contestant spins the spinner below 2 times in a row.

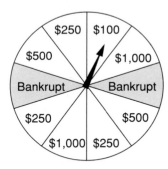

a. What is the probability that the first spin will stop on a $1,000 section?

b. What is the probability that both spins will stop on $1,000 sections?

6. The bar graph below shows the breakdown of registered voters in Jackson County.

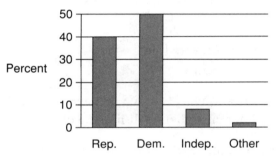

What is the probability that the next 2 residents to register to vote in Jackson County will both be Republicans (Rep.)?

7. Estimate Charlie, a high school football star, scored a touchdown in 60% of the games he played in this year. What is the *approximate* probability that Charlie will score a touchdown in each of his next 2 games?

(1) $\frac{1}{10}$ **(2)** $\frac{1}{3}$ **(3)** $\frac{3}{4}$

Sampling a Population

Population and Sample

Information is often collected about a large group. The large group is called a **population.** Instead of talking with the whole population, though, data collectors usually get information from only a small part of the larger group. This smaller part of the population is called the **sample.** When data about the sample accurately represents the overall population, the sample is said to be a **representative sample.**

Being able to distinguish between a representative sample and a nonrepresentative sample is an important data analysis skill.

Example 1: A supermarket manager wants to know how customers feel about a proposed redesign of the store. To find out, she asks shoppers about the proposed change. She talks with shoppers at different times of the day and in different parts of the store. Her results are as follows:

Number polled: 200
Number in favor: 150
Number against: 50

The question is, "Can the manager reasonably conclude that 75% of all her customers will like the change?"

Yes. The manager chose a representative sample and calculated:

$\frac{150}{200} = \frac{3}{4} = 75\%$ The sample accurately represents the population (all of the store's customers) because it includes a variety of shoppers.

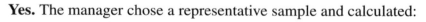

Example 2: A city councilman wants to find out what people in his city think about the proposed expansion of Bevan Chemical Company. To find out, he surveys 200 employees of Bevan Chemical. His results are as follows:

Number polled: 200   Number in favor: 198   Number against: 2

Can the councilman reasonably conclude that 99% of all the city residents favor the expansion?

No. Although he did the math correctly $\left(\frac{198}{200} = \frac{99}{100} = 99\% \right)$, the councilman did not choose a representative sample. A group of workers at the company cannot be said to represent all city residents.

For each group below, identify the *sample* and the *population*. Then tell whether the sample is representative of the population. Give a reason to support your answer.

1. Between 2:30 P.M. and 2:45 P.M., a supervisor checks the rate at which work is being done along a production line. He wants to see if the day crew works at recommended speed.

   Sample: _____

   Population: _____

2. A pickup manufacturer surveys 2,000 owners of the company's new pickup. The manufacturer wants to determine what percent of these owners are satisfied customers. Owners are chosen from every state.

   Sample: _____

   Population: _____

3. A candidate for mayor polls the residents of every 5th apartment in an apartment complex. She wants to find out how these residents feel about the way this city-owned complex is managed.

   Sample: _____

   Population: _____

4. A customer returns a package of stale cookies to Ben's Market. He concludes that all of Ben's packaged cookies are probably stale.

   Sample: _____

   Population: _____

Making Connections: Choosing a Representative Sample

Suppose you want information on each population below. For each situation, tell what you would consider to be a representative sample.

1. You want to know if the students who attend Jackson High School support the school's football coach.

2. You want to compare the food prices at Value Supermarket with the prices at other stores in town.

3. You would like to determine what percent of people who swim at the Aquatic Center think the water temperature is kept too low.

4. You would like to know how city residents feel about recent cutbacks in the number of bus routes as a cost-saving measure.

Sampling and Margin of Error

As you have seen, when you want information about a population, you may actually take data from only a sample of that group. Because of this, there is an amount of uncertainty when you draw conclusions about the population. To account for this uncertainty, you can include a **margin of error** with the results of the survey.

For example, to find how many of the 2,000 Hines Factory employees use public transportation, Oscar surveyed only 200 employees. He found that 50 (25%) of those surveyed do use it. Can you conclude for sure that 500 employees (25% of 2,000) will use public transportation? No, you can't. However, a margin of error will provide a range of possible values that should include the actual number.

▶ Margin of error is often given as a *plus or minus percent.*

Example 1: In the Hines example above, assume a margin of error of plus or minus 5%. You write this margin of error as 500 ±5%, read "500 *plus or minus 5%.*" This means the actual number is within a range of 5% around 500.

$$500 - 5\% \text{ (of 500)} = 475$$

500 ±5% means   (values range from 475 to 525)

$$500 + 5\% \text{ (of 500)} = 525$$

Note: 5% of 500 = 25

A margin of error of ±5% says you can be confident that the number of Hines employees who use public transportation is between 475 and 525.

▶ When a survey result itself is a percent, the margin of error tells the range of probable values for that percent.

Example 2: Suppose a survey reports that 60% of Portland citizens use the city bus service. The margin of error of this survey is ±4%. The margin of error tells you that the actual number of citizens who use the bus is believed to be between 56% and 64% of the city's population.

$$60\% - 4\% = 56\%$$

60% ±4% means   (values range from 56% to 64%)

$$60\% + 4\% = 64\%$$

A. Problems 1–3 refer to the survey information given below.

A total of 200 adults living in Oakdale were surveyed about a proposed library tax. Of those surveyed, 60 (30% of 200) said they are in favor of the tax. The survey concluded that of the 100,000 adults living in Oakdale, 30,000 support the proposed tax. The margin of error is given as ±8%.

1. Identify the *sample* and the *population* in the Oakdale survey.

   Sample: _____

   Population: _____

2. According to the survey, what range of the adult population of Oakdale are in favor of the proposed tax?

   a. between _____ and _____
                 percent   percent

   b. between _____ and _____
                 number   number

3. A larger representative sample gives a smaller margin of error. Because of this, a second survey was done. This larger survey concluded that 28% ±4% are in favor of the proposed tax. According to this second survey, what range of the adult population of Oakdale are in favor of the proposed tax?

   a. between _____ and _____
                 percent   percent

   b. between _____ and _____
                 number   number

B. Problems 4 and 5 are based on the survey results shown on the graph.

4. Suppose 600 Cloverville voters were surveyed to produce this graph. Ignoring the margin of error, determine the

   a. *percent* of surveyed voters who supported the president's policy in February.

   b. *number* of surveyed voters who supported the president's policy in February.

5. Using the margin of error, how many of the 80,000 Cloverville voters can you conclude supported the president's policy in February?

   a. between _____ and _____
                 percent   percent

   b. between _____ and _____
                 number   number

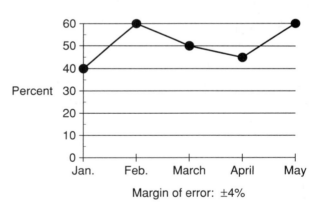

Percent of Cloverville Voters Who Support the U.S. President's Domestic Economic Policy

Margin of error: ±4%

Gridding in Probability Answers

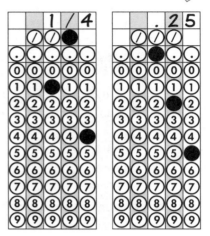

As you know, probability is a ratio comparing the number of favorable outcomes to the number of possible outcomes. The probability ratio can be expressed as a fraction, a decimal, or a percent. Use the fraction or decimal form to enter the probability ratio in a five-column grid. The grids to the right show a 1 out of 4 or 25% chance of a favorable outcome.

Review these basic rules for entering answers in a grid:

- You may start in any column as long as your answer fits within the five columns. Write your answer in the row of boxes at the top of the grid.

- Write only one number or symbol in each box. Do not use commas.

- Do not leave blank columns within your answer. There may be blank spaces at the beginning or end of your answer.

- Always enter mixed numbers as improper fractions or decimals.

As you work with grid-in items, keep in mind that the machine that scores your test will accept either the fraction or decimal form of a number. If you are working a problem on a calculator, you may want to enter the answer as a decimal. Always work with the form that will take the least amount of time.

Filling in the Grid

Example: A game uses an unusual die. The eight sides of the die are shown to the right. If you roll the die once, what is the chance of rolling a side that does not show an arrow?

Step 1
Of the eight sides, five show numbers and three show arrows. The probability of not rolling a side with an arrow is 5 out of 8, or $\frac{5}{8}$.

Step 2
Write your answer in the top row of boxes. Use the slash for the fraction bar.

Step 3
Fill in the correct circles on the grid. Use the digits in the top row as a guide.

Solve the following problems. Record your answers in the grids.

Problems 1 and 2 refer to the drawing below.

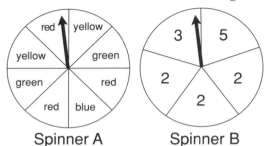

Spinner A   Spinner B

1. 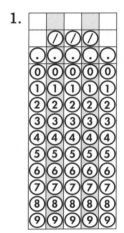 You have a 60% chance of spinning which number on spinner B above?

2.  While playing a game, you spin spinner A and then spinner B. What is the chance of spinning red and the number 3?

3.  Lorie bought 40 raffle tickets at a school fair. If there are 2,600 tickets sold, what is the probability that Lorie will be holding the winning ticket?

4. 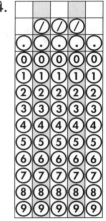 You have the following six cards in your hand:

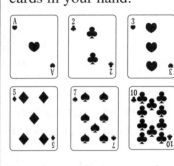

If a player draws a card randomly from your hand, what is the probability that the card will be a heart?

5. 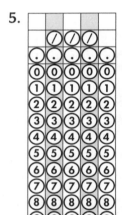 Scott, Stuart, Robin, and Andy work in the same office. One of the workers is chosen at random to work on Saturday. What is the chance that Robin will __not__ be chosen to work on Saturday?

6. 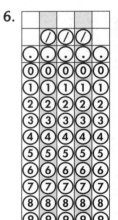 Ten cards are numbered from 1 to 10. One card is randomly chosen and not replaced. A second card is chosen at random. What is the probability that both will be a 5 or less?

Unit 5 Review

A. Problems 1–3 are based on the graph at right.

1. What was Shane's approximate temperature at 2:30 P.M. on the afternoon of April 14?

2. If Shane's temperature decreased at about the same rate as between 3:00 and 4:00 P.M., what would his temperature be at 5:00 P.M.?

3. What more would you need to know to be able to determine how much of a fever Shane still has at 4:00 P.M.?

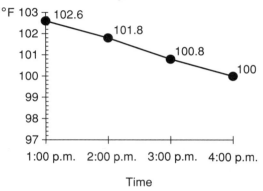

Temperature Record of Shane Nosler April 14

B. Problems 4 and 5 are based on the table at right.

4. Which of the following statements is best supported by information provided on the table?
   (1) In 1982, the United States used more unleaded regular gas than in any other listed year.
   (2) In 1982, the supply of unleaded regular gas was at an all-time low.
   (3) The cost of unleaded regular gas about doubled between 1976 and 1980.

5. What more would you need to know in order to determine the total amount spent in the United States for unleaded regular gas in each listed year?

Average U.S. Gasoline Prices (cents per gallon for unleaded regular)	
1976	61.4
1978	67.0
1980	124.5
1982	129.6
1984	121.2
1986	92.7
1988	94.6
1990	116.4
1992	112.7

Source: United States Department of Energy

C. Answer the following questions.

6. What type of correlation (*positive* or *negative*) would most likely be shown by the number of cold drinks sold at a soda stand and the outdoor temperature? Give a reason to support your conclusion.

7. Describe how a correlation may exist between the amount of education a person has received and the average yearly salary he or she will make throughout life.

178

D. Answer the probability questions below.

8. a. When you roll a die once, what is the probability that you'll roll a 2?

   b. If you roll a die 25 times in a row, how many 2s will you probably roll? Round your answer to the nearest whole number.

9. If you roll a die twice in a row, what is the probability that you'll roll two 5s?

10. On the production line at Del Motors, 6 of the last 150 motors had defective windings.

   a. What is the probability that the next motor checked will also have defective windings?

   b. How many of the next 400 motors made at Del's will probably have defective windings?

E. Grid in the answer to each problem. Refer to the circle graph at right.

11.  What fraction of loan applicants are divorced or never married?

12. Of 4,000 recent loan applicants, the number of those married is between 1,400 and what number?

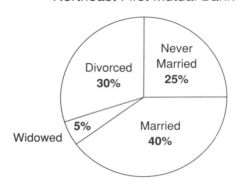

Status of Loan Applicants
Northeast First Mutual Bank

Divorced 30% — Never Married 25% — Married 40% — Widowed 5%

Margin of error: ±5%

Working Together

Do the following activities with other students.

1. As a group, decide whether you feel there is a correlation between a rising poverty rate and rising crime statistics. If you think there is, give opinions on why this correlation exists.

2. Write a list of five changes you or your classmates have made in your lives during the last two years because of statistics you've heard on TV or on the radio. What led you to make these changes?

3. As a group, describe what you consider to be your most reliable sources and your most unreliable sources of data and statistics.

Posttest

Part I: Solve the following problems. You **may** use a calculator.

Problem 1 refers to the drawing below.

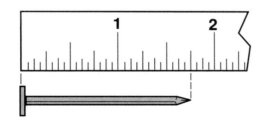

1. To the nearest $\frac{1}{8}$ inch, what is the length of the nail?
   - **(1)** $1\frac{1}{2}$ in.
   - **(2)** $1\frac{5}{8}$ in.
   - **(3)** $1\frac{3}{4}$ in.
   - **(4)** $1\frac{7}{8}$ in.
   - **(5)** 2 in.

2. Arlene made a total of 24 fl. oz. of pudding. If she puts the pudding into snack containers that each hold $\frac{1}{2}$ c., how many containers can she fill?
   - **(1)** 2
   - **(2)** 3
   - **(3)** 4
   - **(4)** 5
   - **(5)** 6

3. Melvin must cut a piece of molding so that it fits along the top of a 5 ft. 6 in. counter. If the molding now measures 7 ft. 2 in., how much must Melvin cut off?
   - **(1)** 1 ft. 4 in.
   - **(2)** 1 ft. 6 in.
   - **(3)** 1 ft. 8 in.
   - **(4)** 2 ft. 6 in.
   - **(5)** 2 ft. 8 in.

4. The living room in Lil's house measures 4 yd. wide and $6\frac{1}{2}$ yd. long. How many square yards of carpet will it take to cover this floor?
   - **(1)** 18
   - **(2)** 21
   - **(3)** 26
   - **(4)** 30
   - **(5)** 34

Problem 5 refers to the following drawing.

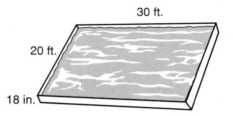

5. What is the volume of the wading pool pictured above?
   - **(1)** 900 cu. ft.
   - **(2)** 1,200 cu. ft.
   - **(3)** 1,500 cu. ft.
   - **(4)** 1,800 cu. ft.
   - **(5)** 2,400 cu. ft.

6. There are three time-zone boundaries between New York City and Seattle. If you place a call to New York City on the east coast from Seattle on the west coast at 9:30 A.M. Seattle time, what time is your called received in New York?
   - **(1)** 5:30 A.M.
   - **(2)** 6:30 A.M.
   - **(3)** 11:30 A.M.
   - **(4)** 12:30 P.M.
   - **(5)** 1:30 P.M.

7. Jenson bought two 1-gal. containers of motor oil. If his truck holds 5 qt. of oil, how many quarts will Jenson have left after changing the truck's oil?

(1) 1 **(4)** 4

(2) 2 **(5)** 5

(3) 3

8. What metric unit is used to measure the *capacity* of a hot water heater?

(1) milliliters **(4)** meters

(2) liters **(5)** grams

(3) kilograms

9. How many 125-ml cream dispensers can be filled with a bottle containing 1 liter of cream?

(1) 4 **(4)** 10

(2) $6\frac{1}{2}$ **(5)** $12\frac{1}{2}$

(3) 8

Problem 10 is based on the following drawing.

Pound Scale

10. Which of the following gives the weight indicated on the scale?

(1) 2 lb. 3 oz. **(4)** 2 lb. 12 oz.

(2) 2 lb. 6 oz. **(5)** 2 lb. 16 oz.

(3) 2 lb. 8 oz.

11. Which of the following weights is equal to 4.7 kg?

(1) 47 g **(4)** 4 kg 70 g

(2) 470 g **(5)** 4 kg 700 g

(3) 4 kg 7 g

Problems 12 and 13 are based on the line plot.

Children Learning to Walk

```
                      X
                 X    X    X
            X    X    X    X    X              X
       X    X    X    X    X    X    X    X    X    X
      ─────────────────────────────────────────────────
       8    9   10   11   12   13   14   15   16   17
                        Age in Months
```

12. In what age range (in months) did most children represented on the graph learn to walk?

(1) 8–10 **(4)** 13–15

(2) 9–11 **(5)** 15–17

(3) 11–13

13. What *percent* of the children represented on the line plot were walking at age 12 months or earlier?

(1) 40% **(4)** 55%

(2) 45% **(5)** 60%

(3) 50%

Problem 14 is based on the table.

	Foreign-Born Students	Total Enrollment
City College	1,000	5,000
Jaynes Learning Center	900	3,000
Whiting Junior College	700	2,000
Edmont Academy	600	2,500
Lynn Community College	900	4,000

14. Which of the five colleges has the largest *percent* of foreign-born students?

(1) City College

(2) Jaynes Learning Center

(3) Whiting Junior College

(4) Edmont Academy

(5) Lynn Community College

15. How many <u>cubic</u> <u>feet</u> does an oven hold if it is 16 inches high, 24 inches wide, and 18 inches deep?

    (1) 3

    (2) $3\frac{1}{2}$

    (3) 4

    (4) $4\frac{1}{2}$

    (5) 5

Problems 16 and 17 refer to the following graph.

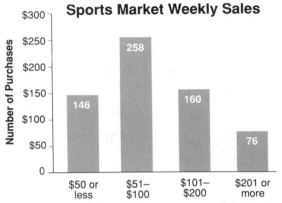

Sports Market Weekly Sales

16. In which of the following ranges would the median purchase for the week belong?

    (1) $50 or less

    (2) $51–$100

    (3) $101–$200

    (4) $201 or more

    (5) Not enough information is given.

17. If the sales manager decided to make a circle graph of the data, what percent would she assign to the range $101–$200?

    (1) 14%

    (2) 16%

    (3) 20%

    (4) 25%

    (5) 62%

18. Kellie orders six identical drapery panels from a catalog. The weight of the total shipment is 11 lb. 10 oz. What is the weight of each panel?

    (1) 1 lb. 4 oz.

    (2) 1 lb. 9 oz.

    (3) 1 lb. 12 oz

    (4) 1 lb. 15 oz.

    (5) 2 lb.

19. 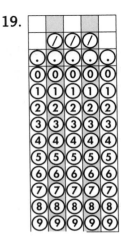 The number of students enrolled in a school's eight music classes are 18, 25, 32, 14, 38, 24, 31, and 34. What is the mean (average) number of students per class?

    Mark your answer in the grid.

20.  Two pieces of plastic pipe are 400 millimeters and 280 centimeters long. If the pieces are joined, what is their total length in <u>meters</u>?

    Mark your answer in the grid.

Part II: Solve the following problems. You <u>may not</u> use a calculator.

Problems 21–25 are based on the table.

Alphonso Trailer Co. Financial Data

Model	Production Cost	Selling Price	Profit
Carrier	$2,400	$4,500	$2,100
Move All	$3,000	$5,800	$2,800
Big Millie	$4,200	$6,800	$2,600
Mighty Moe	$5,700	$7,500	$1,800

21. How much more profit does Alphonso Trailer Company make on each Move All trailer than on each Mighty Moe trailer?

    (1) $1,000   (3) $1,800   (5) $2,800
    (2) $1,400   (4) $2,400

22. What is the *mean* (average) profit that the company makes on its trailers?

    (1) $1,925   (3) $2,175   (5) $2,450
    (2) $2,050   (4) $2,325

23. What is the *median* production cost of the four listed trailer models?

    (1) $3,200   (3) $3,825   (5) $5,700
    (2) $3,600   (4) $4,200

24. What is the *mode,* if any, of the selling prices of the four listed trailer models?

    (1) $4,500   (3) $6,800   (5) no mode
    (2) $5,800   (4) $7,500

25. If the above data were sorted by profit, writing largest profit first, which model would be first on the list and which last?

    (1) Mighty Moe first, Carrier last
    (2) Move All first, Mighty Moe last
    (3) Carrier first, Big Millie last
    (4) Mighty Moe first, Move All last
    (5) Move All first, Carrier last

Problems 26–28 are based on the line graph.

Average Yearly Car Insurance Premiums Western Insurance Company

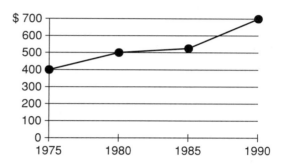

26. In which two years listed were Western's insurance premiums about the same?

    (1) 1975 and 1980   (4) 1980 and 1990
    (2) 1975 and 1985   (5) 1985 and 1990
    (3) 1980 and 1985

27. If the 1985–1990 trend continues, what is the most reasonable *estimate* of Western's average premiums in the year 2000?

    (1) between $400 and $600
    (2) between $575 and $775
    (3) between $750 and $950
    (4) between $1,000 and $1,200
    (5) between $1,300 and $1,500

28. What was the *approximate percent increase* in Western's average premiums between 1975 and 1990?

    (1) 10%   (3) 50%   (5) 100%
    (2) 25%   (4) 75%

Problems 29–31 are based on the bar graph.

Oil Use in the United States 1990
(percent of total used)

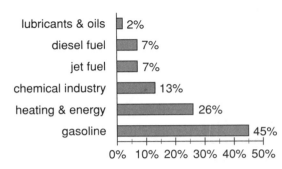

lubricants & oils — 2%
diesel fuel — 7%
jet fuel — 7%
chemical industry — 13%
heating & energy — 26%
gasoline — 45%

0% 10% 20% 30% 40% 50%

Source: Statistical Abstract of the United States

29. Of each 100 gallons of oil used in the United States in 1990, how many gallons were used in the chemical industry (production of plastic, etc.)?

   (1) 2   **(3)** 13   **(5)** 45

   (2) 7   **(4)** 26

30. The phrase that *best describes* gasoline use compared to diesel fuel use in the United States in 1990 is

   (1) about 2 times as much

   (2) almost 3 times as much

   (3) approximately 4 times as much

   (4) nearly 5 times as much

   (5) almost 7 times as much

31. You can conclude from the graph that in 1990

   (1) gasoline was the major use of oil in the United States

   (2) heating and energy costs were higher than in 1980

   (3) gasoline cost more per gallon than diesel fuel

   (4) more air pollution was caused by the use of gasoline than by chemical industries

   (5) diesel fuel and jet fuel were about the same price per gallon

Problems 32–35 are based on the circle graph.

Harper Community College
Age Breakdown of Students in Adult Programs
(7,200 adult students enrolled)

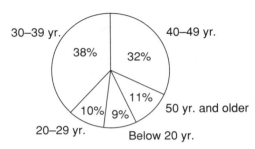

30–39 yr. 38%
40–49 yr. 32%
50 yr. and older 11%
Below 20 yr. 9%
20–29 yr. 10%

Margin of error: ±2%

32. *About* how many students in the adult programs at Harper Community College are in the group identified as *40–49 yr.?*

   (1) between 1,500 and 1,800

   (2) between 2,100 and 2,400

   (3) between 2,500 and 2,800

   (4) between 2,900 and 3,200

   (5) between 3,300 and 3,600

33. What's the probability that the next student who enrolls in an adult program at Harper will be in the *20–29 yr.* age group?

   (1) $\frac{1}{10}$ **(4)** $\frac{1}{3}$

   (2) $\frac{1}{8}$ **(5)** $\frac{1}{2}$

   (3) $\frac{1}{5}$

34. Of the next 200 students who register in the adult programs at Harper, how many probably will be younger than 20 years old?

   (1) 4   **(4)** 18

   (2) 9   **(5)** 23

   (3) 14

35. Taking the *margin of error* into account, you can say that of each 100 students, the number in the *30–39 yr.* age group is probably between

   (1) 28 and 37   **(4)** 49 and 51

   (2) 36 and 40   **(5)** 98 and 102

   (3) 48 and 51

36. Isak plans to use wood molding to make a picture frame. He needs two 26-inch lengths and two 16-inch lengths. If molding is $0.69 per <u>foot</u>, how much will it cost Isak to buy the wood for the frame?

(1) $2.42

(2) $4.83

(3) $22.08

(4) $35.88

(5) $57.96

Problems 37 and 38 refer to the following figure.

**Voter Telephone Survey
on Propositions A and B**

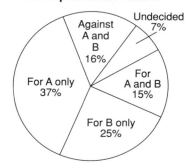

37. Based on the survey results, if you selected a voter at random, what is the probability that he or she is in support of Proposition B?

(1) 1 in 4

(2) 2 in 5

(3) 3 in 4

(4) 3 in 20

(5) 31 in 50

38. Based on the results of the survey, if there are 3,000 registered voters, how many are against both propositions?

(1) 2,550

(2) 2,250

(3) 1,140

(4) 750

(5) 480

39. A package weighs 4.5 kilograms. Which of the following is the best estimate for the weight of the package in pounds?

(1) 2

(2) 7

(3) 10

(4) 12

(5) 13

40.

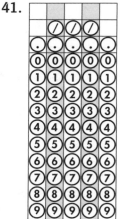

A 2-gallon pitcher is $\frac{3}{4}$ full of orange juice. How many <u>cups</u> of orange juice are in the pitcher?

Mark your answer in the grid.

41.

A baseball pitcher gave up 20 home runs in his first season. During his next four seasons, he gave up 11, 14, 4, and 26 home runs. How many home runs did he give up on average per season?

Mark your answer in the grid.

Part I

1. **(3) $1\frac{3}{4}$ in.** $1\frac{6}{8}$ in. $= 1\frac{3}{4}$ in.

2. **(5) 6** $\frac{1}{2}$ c. $= 4$ fl. oz.; $24 \div 4 = 6$

3. **(3) 1 ft. 8 in.**
$$\begin{array}{c} 7 \text{ ft. } 2 \text{ in.} \\ - 5 \text{ ft. } 6 \text{ in.} \\ \hline \end{array} = \begin{array}{c} 6 \text{ ft. } 14 \text{ in.} \\ - 5 \text{ ft. } 6 \text{ in.} \\ \hline 1 \text{ ft. } 8 \text{ in.} \end{array}$$

4. **(3) 26** Area $= l \times w = 6\frac{1}{2} \times 4 = 26$

5. **(1) 900 cu. ft.**

   Volume $= l \times w \times h = 30 \times 20 \times 1\frac{1}{2} = 900$ Remember to change 18 in. to $1\frac{1}{2}$ ft. before you multiply. All units must be the same.

6. **(4) 12:30 P.M.** One hour must be added for each time zone boundary as you move from west to east. New York is 3 hours later than Seattle.

7. **(3) 3** 2 gallons of oil is equal to 8 quarts: $8 - 5 = 3$

8. **(2) liters** The only two capacity units given as choices are milliliters and liters. Milliliters is too small a unit to be practical for measuring water in a hot water heater.

9. **(3) 8** 1 liter is equal to 1,000 ml: $1,000 \div 125 = 8$

10. **(4) 2 lb. 12 oz.** 1 lb. $= 16$ oz. The scale indicates a weight of 2 lb. plus an additional $\frac{3}{4}$ lb. (3 out of 4 equal divisions): $2\frac{3}{4}$ lb. $= 2$ lb. 12 oz.

11. **(5) 4 kg 700 g** 1 kg $= 1,000$ g, so, 0.7 kg is equal to $0.7 \times 1,000$ g $= 700$ g

12. **(3) 11–13** Of the age ranges given as choices, the range 11–13 contains the most Xs, each X representing one child.

13. **(4) 55%** Of the 20 children represented on the line plot (20 Xs), 11 were walking at age 12 months or earlier. The fraction $\frac{11}{20}$ is equivalent to 55%.

14. **(3) Whiting Junior College** The percent of foreign-born students is found by dividing the number of foreign-born students by the total enrollment. The percents for each college are as follows:

City College	20%
Jaynes Learning Center	30%
Whiting Junior College	35%
Edmont Academy	24%
Lynn Community College	22.5%

15. **(3) 4** $16 \times 24 \times 18 = 6,912$ cubic inches. The number of cubic inches in a cubic foot is $12 \times 12 \times 12 = 1,728$. Divide: $6,912 \div 1,728 = 4$ cubic feet.

16. **(2) $51–$100** Add to find the total number of purchases: $146 + 258 + 160 + 76 = 640$. The median of the sales must be the halfway point, the average of the 320th and 321st sale. There are 146 sales in the category $50 or less. The next 258 sales (sales 147 through 404) are in the second bar. The 320th and 321st sales amounts must fall in the second bar, so the median is in this range.

17. **(4) 25%** The total of the bars is 640. There are 160 sales in the range $101–$200. $160 \div 640 = 0.25 = 25\%$

18. **(4) 1 lb. 15 oz.** Change to ounces for easy division: 11 lb. 10 oz. $= (11 \times 16) + 10 = 186$ oz. Divide: $186 \div 6 = 31$ oz. Convert: $31 \div 16 = 1$ R $15 = 1$ lb. 15 oz.

19. **27**

    The total is 216.

    Divide: $216 \div 8 = 27$

20. **3.2**

    Convert both lengths to meters:

    400 mm $= 0.4$ m, and 280 cm $= 2.8$ m

    Add the lengths:

    0.4 m $+ 2.8$ m $= 3.2$ m

Part II

21. **(1) $1,000** $2,800 - $1,800 = $1,000

22. **(4) $2,325** ($2,100 + $2,800 + $2,600 + $1,800) $\div 4 = $2,325

23. **(2) $3,600** ($3,000 + $4,200) $\div 2 = $3,600

24. **(5) no mode** No two selling prices are the same.

25. **(2) Move All first, Mighty Moe last**

The new list would be

Model	Profit
Move All	$2,800
Big Millie	$2,600
Carrier	$2,100
Mighty Moe	$1,800

26. **(3) 1980 and 1985**

27. **(4) between $1,000 and $1,200** Between 1985 and 1990, Western's premium increased by about $200. If each of the next 2 five-year periods has the same amount of increase, the premium in year 2000 will be about $1,100 ($700 + $200 + $200).

28. **(4) 75%** The percent increase is found by dividing the amount of increase by the original amount: Percent increase = $\frac{700 - 400}{400} = \frac{300}{400} = 75\%$

29. **(3) 13** 13% means 13 out of each 100 gallons.

30. **(5) almost 7 times as much** $7 \times 7\% = 49\%$, which is close to 45%.

31. **(1) gasoline was the major use of oil in the United States** The other choices are not justified because the graph says nothing about fuel costs (choices 2, 3, and 5) and nothing about air pollution (choice 4).

32. **(2) between $2,100 and $2,400** The answer can quickly be estimated by taking 30% of 7,000: $30\% \times 7,000 = 0.3 \times 7,000 = 2,100$

33. **(1) $\frac{1}{10}$** The probability is 10%, which is equivalent to $\frac{1}{10}$.

34. **(4) 18** 9% of 200 is 18.

35. **(2) 36 and 40** $38\% \pm 2\%$ gives a range of possible values of 36% to 40%: $38\% - 2\% = 36\%$, while $38\% + 2\% = 40\%$. For every 100 students: 36% of $100 = 36$ and 40% of $100 = 40$.

36. **(2) $4.83** $(2 \times 26) + (2 \times 16) = 84$ in. 84 in. ÷ 12 = 7 ft., and $7 \times \$.69 = \$4.83$

37. **(2) 2 in 5** Add: $25\% + 15\% = 40\%$ $\frac{40}{100} = \frac{2}{5}$ or 2 in 5

38. **(5) 480** $3,000 \times 0.16 = 480$

39. **(3) 10** 1 kilogram ≈ 2.2 pounds. $4.5 \times 2.2 = 9.9$ pounds, which is close to 10 pounds.

40.  **24**

1 gal. = 4 qt. and 1 qt. = 4 c. Therefore, 1 gal. = 16 c. and 2 gal. = 32 c. $32 \times \frac{3}{4} = 24$ cups

41.  **15**

Add: $20 + 11 + 14 + 4 + 26 = 75$ Divide: $75 \div 5 = 15$

Posttest Evaluation Chart

Make note of any problems you answered incorrectly. Review the skill area for each of those problems, using the unit number given.

Problem Number	Skill Area	Unit
1, 3, 4, 5, 6, 15, 20, 36	Distance, space, and time	1
2, 7, 8, 9, 10, 11, 18, 39, 40	Capacity, weight, and temperature	2
12, 13, 14, 16, 19, 21, 22, 23, 24, 25, 41	Organizing and summarizing data	3
17, 26, 28, 29, 30, 32, 38	Displaying data on a graph	4
27, 31, 33, 34, 35, 37	Analyzing data	5

Answer Key

Unit 1

When Is Measuring Important to Me? p. 13

Answers will vary. Any reasonable answers are acceptable.

English Units of Length pp. 14–15

Part A

Estimates will vary. Any reasonable estimate is acceptable.

1. 1 ft. 7 in.   **2.** 4' 5"
1 yd. 3 in.   2 yd. 20 in.
2 yd. 2 ft.   5 yd. 2 ft.

Part B

Estimates will vary.

3. 48"   **4.** 102 in.
11 ft. $19\frac{1}{2}$ ft.
180 in.   84 in.
3,520 yd.   6,864 ft.

The English Ruler pp. 16–17

Part A

1. $\frac{7}{8}$ in. $2\frac{1}{4}$ in. $3\frac{1}{2}$ in. $4\frac{15}{16}$ in.

Part B

2. $1\frac{3}{8}$ in. $1\frac{1}{4}$ in. $1\frac{7}{16}$ in.

Part C

3.

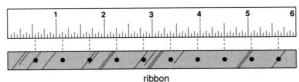

ribbon

Making Connections: Tape Measures p. 17

1. $29\frac{3}{4}$ in.   **2.** $17\frac{7}{8}$ in.

Metric Units of Length pp. 18–19

Part A

Estimates will vary.

1. 2 cm 1 mm = 2.1 cm
1 m 89 cm = 1.89 m
1 km 150 m = 1.150 km = 1.15 km

2. 4 cm 8 mm = 4.8 cm
3 m 25 cm = 3.25 m
5 km 950 m = 5.950 km = 5.95 km

Part B

Estimates will vary.

3. 80 mm   **4.** 300 cm
620 mm   525 cm
115 mm   5,000 m
47.5 mm   6,100 m

The Metric Ruler pp. 20–21

Part A

1. 41 mm = 4 cm 1 mm   **3.** 6 cm 3 mm = 6.3 cm
2. 39 mm = 3.9 cm   **4.** 2 cm 4 mm = 2.4 cm

Part B

5. 107 mm = 10 cm 7 mm = 10.7 cm
6. 43 mm = 4 cm 3 mm = 4.3 cm
7. 119 mm = 11 cm 9 mm = 11.9 cm

8. 14

Making Connections: English Decimal Rulers p. 21

0.7 in.   2.2 in.   3.5 in.   5.9 in.

Adding and Subtracting Lengths pp. 22–23

Part A

Estimates will vary.

1. 12 ft. 2 in.   7' 7"   11 yd.
2. 16 yd. 4 in.   4 mi. 190 yd.   6 mi. 1,720 ft.
3. 12 cm 1 mm   20 cm 2 mm   9 m 55 cm

Part B

Estimates will vary.

4. 4 ft. 11 in.   1' 9"   1 ft. 3 in.
5. 1 yd. 2 ft.   2 yd. 20 in.   2 yd. 1 ft.
6. 2 m 80 cm = 2.8 m
2 m 77 cm = 2.77 m
8 cm 8 mm = 8.8 cm

Multiplying and Dividing Lengths pp. 24–25

Part A

Estimates will vary.

1. 22 ft. 2 in.   26 ft. 9 in.   29' 8"

2. 6 yd. 2 ft.   31 yd. 29 in.   46 yd. 2 ft.

3. 33 cm 2 mm = 33.2 cm   27 m 63 cm = 27.63 m

Part B

Estimates will vary.

4. 1 ft. 5 in.   2 ft. 9 in.   1' 7"

5. 2 yd. 14 in.   2 yd. 20 in.   2 yd. 32 in.

6. 1 cm 9 mm = 1.9 cm   4 m 96 cm = 4.96 m

Mixed Problem Solving pp. 26–27

1. **9 ft. 3 in.**

   6 ft. 4 in. + 2 ft. 3 in. + 8 in. = 9 ft. 3 in.

2. **500 m**

   2.5 km ÷ 5 = 0.5 km = 500 m

3. **72 cm**

   14 cm 4 mm × 5 = 70 cm 20 mm = 72 cm

4. **53 cm = 0.53 m**

   1 m 65 cm – 1 m 12 cm = 53 cm *or*
   1.65 m – 1.12 m = 0.53 m

5. **33 ft. 10 in.**

   15 ft. 11 in. + 15 ft. 11 in. + 2 ft. =
   32 ft. 22 in. = 33 ft. 10 in.

6. Estimates will vary. To estimate the length of ribbon needed, Esther can assume that each of the 75 bows takes about $1\frac{1}{2}$ ft. of ribbon.

   75×1 ft. = 75 ft., so $75 \times \frac{1}{2}$ ft. is about 38 ft.

   75 ft. + 38 ft. = 113 ft.

7. **2 ft. 8 in.**

   12 ft. – 9 ft. 4 in. = 2 ft. 8 in.

8. **5 ft. 9 in.**

   17 ft. 3 in. ÷ 3 = 5 ft. 9 in.

9. a. **13 ft. 6 in.**

      2 ft. 3 in. × 6 = 13 ft. 6 in.

   b. **6 in.**

      14 ft. – 13 ft. 6 in. = 6 in.

10. **4 cm 2 mm**

    2 cm 4 mm + 1 cm 8 mm = 3 cm 12 mm =
    4 cm 2 mm

11. **2.78 cm**

    27 cm 8 mm ÷ 10 *or* 27.8 cm ÷ 10

12. a. **17 to 18 yd.**

       Estimates will vary.

       0.8 mi. ≈ 1 mi.; 1 mi. = 1,760 yd.

       106 ≈ 100

       1,760 yd. ÷ 100 = 17.6 yd.

b. The exact answer is probably less than this estimate because the length of the train was rounded up to a greater length and divided into fewer parts (the number of cars rounded down).

Converting Length pp. 28–29

Part A

Estimates will vary.

1. 30 cm ≈ 12 in.   5.2 m ≈ 17 ft. $8\frac{1}{2}$ m ≈ 9 yd.

2. 6 m ≈ 234 in.   3 km ≈ 2 mi.   90 km ≈ 54 mi.

Part B

Estimates will vary.

3. 24 in. ≈ 60 cm   4. 2 yd. ≈ 2 m

   4.5 ft. ≈ 135 cm $1\frac{1}{2}$ mi. ≈ 2,400 m

   3 yd. ≈ 273 cm   9.4 mi. ≈ 15 km

Part C

Estimates will vary.

5. No. The paper is approximately 12 in. wide.

6. a. approximately 42 mi.

   b. approximately 27 mi.

   c. approximately 71 mi.

7. approximately 15 cm

8. Runners would have faster times in the metric mile because it is about 100 meters (110 yards) shorter than the mile run.

9. 1 m ≈ 39 in.

   3 m ≈ 3 × 39 in. = 117 in. = **9 ft. 9 in.**

   or

   1 m ≈ 1.1 yd.

   3 m ≈ 3 × 1.1 yd. = 3.3 yd. ≈ **9 ft. 11 in.**

Making Connections: English and Metric Measurements p. 29

Estimates will vary.

1. **27,000 ft.**

   8,848 ≈ 9,000; 3.3 ≈ 3

   9,000 × 3 = 27,000

2. **10.2 miles**

   16.9 ≈ 17; 17 × 0.6 = 10.2

3. **50,000 km**

   25,048 ≈ 25,000; 1.6 ≈ 2

   25,000 × 2 = 50,000

   (Actual distance is closer to 40,000 km.)

4. 33,000 ft.

10,915 ≈ 11,000; 3.3 ≈ 3

11,000 × 3 = 33,000

5. 240,000 mi.

384,000 ≈ 400,000

400,000 × .6 = 240,000

6. 186,000,000 km

92,900,000 ≈ 93,000,000; 1.6 ≈ 2

93,000,000 × 2 = 186,000,000

(Actual distance is closer to 150,000,000 km.)

Gridding in Answers pp. 30–31

1.  **8**

   2.5 × 3.3 = 8.25,
   which rounds to 8 feet.

2.  **6.25 or $\frac{25}{4}$**

   9 in. × 25 = 225 in.
   Using the fact 1 yd. = 36 in., divide:
   225 ÷ 36 = 6.25 yd.
   As a fraction:
   $6.25 = 6\frac{1}{4} = \frac{25}{4}$ yd.

3.  **1.5 or $\frac{3}{2}$**

   Subtract: 6 ft. 4 in. − 4 ft.
   10 in. = 1 ft. 6 in.
   As a decimal: 1 ft. 6 in. = 1.5 ft.
   As a fraction: $1\frac{6}{12} = 1\frac{1}{2} = \frac{3}{2}$ ft.

4.  **6**

   8 ft. × 12 = 96 in. and
   96 in. ÷ 16 = 6 in.

Mixed Review pp. 32–33

Part A

1. 84 in.   54 in.   6 yd.   5'

2. 500 cm   4,000 m   9 cm   8 km

3. **a.** 3 ft. 9 in.   **b.** 5 yd. 2 ft.   **c.** 1 m 38 cm = 1.38 m

Part B

4. 4 ft. 5 in.   4 yd. 2 ft.   5 yd.   2' 4"

5. 10 cm 1 mm *or* 10.1 cm
   750 m
   21 m
   1 m 60 cm *or* 1.6 m

Part C

6. **a.** $4\frac{9}{16}$ in.   **b.** 11 cm 6 mm *or* 116 mm

7. **a.** $5\frac{5}{8}$ in.   **b.** 14 cm 4 mm *or* 14.4 cm

Part D

8. $\frac{13}{16}$ in.

9. $\frac{6}{16}$ in. = $\frac{3}{8}$ in.

10. $\frac{9}{16}$ **in.**

    The bottom edge of the door will end up being
    $\frac{15}{16}$ in. from the floor. ($\frac{15}{16}$ in. − $\frac{6}{16}$ in. = $\frac{9}{16}$ in.)

Part E

11. No. (8 ft. = 96 in.)

12. **1 ft. 9 in.**

    7 ft. 8 in. − 5 ft. 11 in. = 1 ft. 9 in.

13. A 440-yd. run is about 2 m 34 cm (2.34 m) longer
    than a 400-m run.

14. **74 yd. 2 ft.**

    4 yd. 2 ft. × 16 = 64 yd. 32 ft. = 74 yd. 2 ft.

15. Sheila can count the number of steps it takes her to
    walk around her school. She can then multiply by $\frac{1}{2}$
    or .5 m since her stride is 50 cm ($\frac{1}{2}$ of 1 m).

16. Answers will vary.

Part F

17. **6.5 or $\frac{13}{2}$**

    33 in. = 2 ft. 9 in.
    Add: 3 ft. 9 in. + 2 ft. 9 in. =
    5 ft. 18 in. = 6 ft. 6 in.
    As a decimal: 6.5 ft.
    As a fraction: $6\frac{6}{12} = 6\frac{1}{2} = \frac{13}{2}$ ft.

18.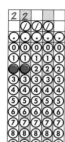

22

6 in. = $\frac{1}{2}$ ft.

Divide: $11 \div \frac{1}{2} = 11 \times \frac{2}{1} = 22$ boards

Finding Perimeter pp. 34–35

Part A

1. 36 cm
2. 8.8 mi.
3. 27 in.

Part B

4. **69 ft.** $18 \times 4 = 72; 72 - 3 = 69$

5. a. **880 yd.**

   $2(250 \text{ yd.} + 190 \text{ yd.}) = 2(440) = 880$

   b. **6 laps**

   Each lap is 880 yd.; 2 laps = 1,760 yd. = 1 mile

6. **68 ft. 6 in.**

   The perimeter of each tablecloth is 22 ft. 10 in.

   22 ft. 10 in. × 3 = 66 ft. 30 in. = 68 ft. 6 in.

7. **108 yd. $\frac{1}{2}$ ft. = 108 yd. 6 in.**

   432 yd. 2 ft. ÷ 4 = 108 yd. 6 in.

Making Connections: Discovering Pi p. 35

Estimates will vary. Estimates should be a little over 3. (An estimate close to $3\frac{1}{8}$, which equals 3.125, is very close to the usual approximation of π ≈ 3.14.) The value of π is the same no matter what the size of the circle.

Finding the Area of a Rectangle pp. 36–37

Part A

1. 24 sq. yd.
2. 8 cm^2
3. $7\frac{1}{2}$ cm^2
4. a. First figure: $P = 28$ ft., $A = 40$ sq. ft.

   Second figure: $P = 28$ ft., $A = 49$ sq. ft.

   b. Two figures that have the same perimeter do not necessarily have the same area.

5. Answers will vary. Below are examples.

   a. The lake should be approximately square with each side being about 3 miles in length.

   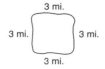

b. The lake should be long and narrow, the longer sides of the lake being close to 6 miles long and the shorter sides being a small fraction of a mile.

Making Connections: Unusual Units of Measure p. 37

1. Answers will vary.
2. Answers will vary.
3. Answers vary because students have different size arms and hands.

Finding Volume pp. 38–39

Part A

1. 24 cu. yd.
2. 42 cu. ft.
3. 100 m^3

Part B

4. **Yes.**

   The actual storage volume of the freezer is $21\frac{1}{3}$ cu. ft. $(4 \times 2 \times 2\frac{2}{3})$.

5. **$3\frac{3}{4}$ cu. ft.**

   $2\frac{1}{2} \times 1\frac{1}{2} \times 1 = 3\frac{3}{4}$

6. a. **20 cu. ft.**   b. **1,240 lb.**

   $6 \times 5 \times \frac{2}{3} = 20$ $62 \times 20 = 1,240$

Making Connections: Decisions with Area and Volume p. 39

1. **Both boxes hold 512 cu. in. of sand.**

   $16 \times 8 \times 4 = 512$ and $8 \times 8 \times 8 = 512$

2. **Box A takes more cardboard to make.**

   Box A takes 448 sq. in. of cardboard:

   2 sides are 16 × 4 = 64 sq. in. each

   2 sides are 16 × 8 = 128 sq. in. each

   2 sides are 8 × 4 = 32 sq. in. each

   Box B takes 384 sq. in. of cardboard:

   Each of the six sides are 8 × 8 = 64 sq. in.

3. Since both boxes hold the same amount of sand, choose Box B in order to save money on the cost of cardboard.

Using Units of Time pp. 40–41

Part A

1. **3,600 seconds in an hour**

   $60 \times 60 = 3,600$

2. **120 minutes in 2 hours**

   $60 \times 2 = 120$

3. 168 hours in a week

$24 \times 7 = 168$

4. $52\frac{1}{2}$ weeks (52 weeks and 1 day) in a common year

$365 \div 7 = 52\frac{1}{7}$

Part B

5. 6:30 A.M. **7.** 11:17 A.M.

6. 9:13 P.M. **8.** 11:46 A.M.

Part C

9. 9/14/57 **11.** 0 2 2 6 6 7

10. 7/4/94 **12.** 1 2 0 9 8 6

Making Connections: Military Time p. 41

1. 5:00 **3.** 15:00 **5.** 20:45

2. 8:20 **4.** 19:00 **6.** 23:17

Working with Time Schedules pp. 42–43

Problems 1 and 2 refer to the calendar filled in below.

November

Sunday	Monday	Tuesday	Wednesday	Thursday	Friday	Saturday
	1	2 Work 9 A.M.–3 P.M.	3	4 Work 11 A.M.–5 P.M.	5	6 Work 8 A.M.–noon
7	8	9 Work 9 A.M.–3 P.M.	10	11 Work 11 A.M.–5 P.M.	12	13
14	15	16 Work 9 A.M.–3 P.M.	17 Aunt Rosie's Birthday	18 Work 11 A.M.–5 P.M.	19 Office Party 4–7 P.M.	20 Work 8 A.M.–noon
21	22	23 Work 9 A.M.–3 P.M.	24 Lou Peterson's Birthday	25 Work 11 A.M.–5 P.M.	26	27
28	29	30 Work 9 A.M.–3 P.M.				

1. 7:45 A.M.

2. $489

(54 weekday hours at $7.50 per hour and 8 Saturday hours at $10.50 per hour)

3.

Sunday Work Schedule		
Employee	Start Time	Leave Time
Juanita	10:30 A.M.	2:30 P.M.
Frank	10:00 A.M.	2:00 P.M.
Viola	11:30 A.M.	3:30 P.M.

4. 6 minutes

5. 31 minutes

6. 7:39 A.M.

7.

Time Card			
	In	Out	Total Hours
Tuesday	8:30 A.M.	5:15 P.M.	8 hr. 45 min.
Wednesday	8:00 A.M.	4:45 P.M.	8 hr. 45 min.

Using the Distance Formula pp. 44–45

1. 275 miles

$55 \times 5 = 275$

2. 45 miles per hour

$270 \div 6 = 45$

3. $5\frac{1}{3}$ hours (or 5 hours 20 minutes)

$240 \div 45 = 5\frac{15}{45} = 5\frac{1}{3}$

4. 150 miles

$60 \times 2\frac{1}{2}$ or $60 \times 2.5 = 150$

5. 100 miles per hour

2.5 miles $\times$ 50 laps $= 125$ miles

1 hour 15 minutes $= 1\frac{1}{4}$ hr. $= 1.25$ hr.

$125 \div 1.25 = 100$

6. a. 6 miles per hour

$60 \div 10 = 6$

b. 4 hours 20 minutes

$26 \div 6 = 4\frac{1}{3}$ hr. $= 4$ hr. 20 min.

Making Connections: Speedometers and Odometers p. 45

1. 33,121.8

4 hours 30 minutes $= 4\frac{1}{2}$ hours

$4\frac{1}{2}$ hours $\times$ 40 miles per hour $= 180$ miles

$32,941.8 + 180 = 33,121.8$

2. About 4 hours

Estimates will vary.

$220 \approx 240$ and $62 \approx 60$

$240 \div 60 = 4$

Working with Time Zones pp. 46–47

1. 5:00 P.M.

2. 8:00 P.M.

3. 7:00 P.M.

Oregon and California are in the same time zone.

4. breakfast

5. 6:45 A.M.

6. 5:00 P.M.

Jeff's watch will show 2:00 P.M. when he lands because of the flight time. Then he will set it 3 hours *later* to account for the time zone changes.

7. Portland: 9:30 A.M.; Philadelphia: 12:30 P.M.

8. 4:00 P.M.

Kali's watch will show 7:00 P.M. when she lands because of the flight time. Then she will set it 3 hours *earlier* to account for the time zone changes.

Making Connections: International Date Line p. 47

1. **12:00 noon on Thursday**

   (7 hours earlier plus 1 day)

2. **7:00 P.M. on Thursday**

   (7 hours later minus 1 day)

3. **1:00 A.M. on Monday**

   (9 hours earlier plus 1 day)

4. **11:00 P.M. on Saturday**

   (10 hours later minus 1 day)

Unit 1 Review pp. 48–49

Part A

1. 24 in.   24 in.   150 minutes   21 days

2. 4,600 m   8 yd. 2 ft.   1 m 75 cm = 1.75 m

Part B

3. 9 ft. 4 in.   1 yd. 2 ft.   18 yd. 2 ft.   1 ft. 10 in.

4. 13 cm 5 mm = 13.5 cm
   1 km 225 m = 1.225 km
   43 m 75 cm = 43.75 m
   1 m 50 cm = 1.5 m

Part C

5. a. $16\frac{1}{2}$ sq. yd.

   b. **$156.75** $9.50 × 16.5 = $156.75

6. a. $3\frac{3}{4}$ cu. ft.

   $2\frac{1}{2} × \frac{3}{4} × 2 = 3\frac{3}{4}$

   b. **About 28 gal.**

   $7.5 × 3.75 = 28.125 \: or \: 28\frac{1}{8}$ gal.

Part D

7. **168**

   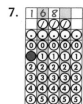

   $d = 48 × 3.5$
   $d = 168$ miles

8. $\frac{5}{2}$ **or 2.5**

   $t = \frac{30}{12} = 2\frac{1}{2} = \frac{5}{2}$ hr.
   or $t = 30 ÷ 12 = 2.5$ hr.

Part E

9. a. $3\frac{4}{8} = 3\frac{1}{2}$ in.   c. 8 cm 8 mm = 8.8 cm

   b. $3\frac{7}{16}$ in.

Part F

10. 11/6/56

    5/29/73

    | 1 | 0 | 0 | 4 | 9 | 4 |

    | 0 | 4 | 0 | 1 | 8 | 0 |

Working Together

Answers will vary.

Unit 2

When Do I Measure These Things? p. 51

Answers will vary. Any reasonable answer is acceptable.

English Units of Capacity pp. 52–54

Part A

1. fluid ounce   2. gallon   3. Answers will vary.

Part B

Estimates will vary. Any reasonable estimate is acceptable.

4. 1 c. 7 fl. oz.   5. 5 c. 7 fl. oz.
   1 qt. 3 fl. oz.   2 qt. 11 fl. oz.
   3 gal. 1 qt.   7 gal. 1 qt.

Part C

Estimates will vary.

6. 24 fl. oz.   7. 7 fl. oz.
   144 fl. oz.   40 fl. oz.
   11 c.   192 fl. oz.
   21 qt.   7.6 qt.

Part D

8. $6\frac{1}{2}$ **bottles of dressing**

   1 c. = 8 fl. oz.

   $52 ÷ 8 = 6\frac{4}{8} = 6\frac{1}{2}$

9. **about 33 oil changes. This estimate is probably high since Leon collects *more than* 3 qt. per oil change.**

   Estimates will vary.

   4 qt. = 1 gal.

   25 gal. = 25 × 4 = 100 qt.

   100 qt. ≈ 99 qt.

   99 ÷ 3 = 33

10. Answers will vary.

193

English Cups and Spoons p. 55

Part A

$\frac{3}{8}$ c. = 3 fl. oz.

Part B

5 fl. oz. = 10 tbsp. = 30 tsp.

Part C

1. **2 fl. oz. remain**

   $\frac{1}{2}$ c. = 4 fl. oz.

   4 tbsp. = 4 × $\frac{1}{2}$ fl. oz. = 2 fl. oz.

   4 − 2 = 2

2. **a.** a teaspoon or a measuring cup

   b. 12 tsp. of mustard *or* $\frac{1}{4}$ **c. (2 fl. oz.)**

   1 tbsp. = 3 tsp.

   4 × 3 = 12

Metric Units of Capacity pp. 56–57

Part A

1. liters
2. milliliters
3. liters
4. milliliters

Part B

5. 0.05 liter   0.03 liter   0.7 liter

Part C

Estimates will vary.

6. 3.180 liters (*or* 3.18 liters) = 3 liters 180 ml

   1.875 liters = 1 liter 875 ml

   6.250 liters (*or* 6.25 liters) = 6 liters 250 ml

Part D

7. 600 ml   900 ml   5,000 ml
8. 2,300 ml   3,500 ml   4,125 ml

Metric Cups and Spoons p. 58

Part A

150 ml = $\frac{3}{5}$ cup

Part B

25 ml; 5 teaspoons *or* 1 tablespoon plus 2 teaspoons

Part C

1. **a.** teaspoon
   b. cup
   c. tablespoon
   d. cup or tablespoon
   e. teaspoon

2. 10 teaspoons
3. 10 tablespoons

Metric Containers p. 59

1. 125 ml
2. 500 ml
3. 2 liters
4. 250 ml
5. 1 liter
6. 4 liters

Making Connections: Shopping for Metric Sizes p. 59

Answers will vary. Sample answers are given below.

1. 4 liters
2. 2 liters
3. 500 ml
4. 4 liters

Working with Capacity pp. 60–61

Estimates will vary. Any reasonable estimate is acceptable.

Part A

1. 4 c. 1 fl. oz.

   5 qt. 7 fl. oz.

   15 gal. 1 qt.

Part B

2. 1 c. 6 fl. oz.

   3 qt. 3 c.

   3 gal. 2 qt.

Part C

3. 2.400 liters (or 2.4 liters)

   4.125 liters

   1.750 liters (or 1.75 liters)

   5.125 liters

Part D

4. 3 liters 250 ml

   1 liter 850 ml

   2 liters 875 ml

   4 liters 525 ml

Part E

5. 10.915 liters = 10 liters 915 ml

   8.025 liters = 8 liters 25 ml

   7 liters

6. 1.650 liters = 1 liter 650 ml

   1.800 liters = 1 liter 800 ml

   4.425 liters = 4 liters 425 ml

On the Job pp. 62–63

Part A

1. 250 ml
2. 100 ml
3. 500 ml
4. 250 ml should be removed.
5. 1 ml change between each pair of shortest lines
6. 30 ml would need to be added.
7. 1 ml
8. 0.3 ml have been removed.

Part B

Estimates will vary.

9. **Estimate: 2 gal.**
   $600 \div 300 = 2$
   Exact (to nearest $\frac{1}{4}$ gallon): $1\frac{3}{4}$ gal.
10. **Estimate: 8 liters**
    $64 \div 8 = 8$
    Exact (to nearest 0.1 liter): 7.9 liters

Making Connections: The United States and the Metric System p. 63

1. a. **1 ft. 6$\frac{5}{6}$ in.**
   4 ft. 8$\frac{1}{2}$ in. $\div$ 3 = 1 ft. 6$\frac{5}{6}$ in.
   b. **0.52 m (52 cm)**
   $1.56 \div 3 = 0.52$
2. a. **332.8 fl. oz.**
   $2.6 \times 128 = 332.8$
   b. **9,700 ml**
   $9.7 \times 1,000 = 9,700$
3. Most students will answer **1b** and **2b**.
4. Problems **1b** and **2b** are easiest because metric units are simpler to calculate with than English units.

Mixed Review pp. 64–65

Part A

1. 24 fl. oz.
   200 fl. oz.
   20 qt.
   3 c.
2. 4 qt.
   3 gal.
   4,000 ml
   2,900 ml
3. 2 qt. 1 c.
   4 gal. 1 qt.
   1 c. 6 fl. oz.
4. a. 0.700 liter (or 0.7 liter)
   b. 4 liters 750 ml
   c. 5 liters 400 ml = 5.4 liters

Part B

5. 4 c. 1 fl. oz.
   8 qt. 6 fl. oz.
   5 gal. 1 qt.
   8.525 liters
6. 1 c. 6 fl. oz.
   2 qt. 26 fl. oz.
   1 gal. 2 qt.
   1.750 liters (or 1.75 liters)

Part C

7. a. $\frac{5}{8}$ c.
   b. 5 fl. oz.
   c. 150 ml

8.

Part D

9. 1 gal. 1 qt. *or* 1$\frac{1}{4}$ gal.
10. 1 liter 200 ml *or* 1.2 liters

Part E

11. Don't pour it all in, only most of it. (A liter is slightly larger than a quart.)
12. **125 ml**, which is $\frac{1}{2}$ of a metric cup
    (4 fl. oz. is $\frac{1}{2}$ of an English cup, and an English cup ≈ a metric cup)

Part F

13. **9**
    1 c. = 8 fl. oz.
    Divide:
    75 fl. oz. $\div$ 8 fl. oz. = 9 c. 3 fl. oz.
    Ignore the remainder since Josh needs to completely fill the 1-cup containers.

14. **1.2**
    350 milliliters $\times$ 8 = 2,800 milliliters.
    Change to liters:
    2,800 milliliters = 2.8 liters.
    Subtract:
    4 liters − 2.8 liters = 1.2 liters.

Part G

15. fl. oz., ml
16. gal., liter
17. fl. oz., ml
18. gal., liter

English Units of Weight pp. 66–68

Part A

1. capacity, weight
2. 16; 2,000

Part B

3. pounds   5. ounces

4. tons   6. pounds

Part C

Estimates will vary. Any reasonable estimate is acceptable.

7. 1 lb. 15 oz.   8. 2 tn. 125 lb.

    1 lb. 1 oz.   4 tn. 1,800 lb.

    10 lb. 7 oz.   1 tn. 1,075 lb.

Part D

Estimates will vary.

9. 80 oz.   10. 6,400 lb.

   1 lb 2 oz. = 18 oz.   1,800 lb.

   150.4 oz.   3,800 lb.

Part E

11. **24 treat bags**

    $4 \frac{1}{2}$ lb. = 72 oz.

    $72 \div 3 = 24$

12. *about* **400; This estimate is a little low because each bag weighs less than 40 lb.**

    Estimates will vary.

    1 tn. = 2,000 lb.

    8 tn. × 2,000 lb. = 16,000 lb.

    38 ≈ 40

    16,000 ÷ 40 = 400

English Weight Scale p. 69

Part A

1. 2 lb. 8 oz. = $2 \frac{1}{2}$ lb.   2. 4 lb. 12 oz. = $4 \frac{3}{4}$ lb.

   8 oz. = $\frac{1}{2}$ lb.   3 lb. 12 oz. = $3 \frac{3}{4}$ lb.

   2 lb. 14 oz. = $2 \frac{7}{8}$ lb.   5 lb. 6 oz. = $5 \frac{3}{8}$ lb.

Part B

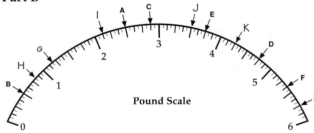

Pound Scale

Metric Units of Weight pp. 70–72

Part A

1. metric ton   2. kilogram   3. 1,000

Part B

4. kilograms   6. metric tons

5. grams or kilograms   7. milligrams

Part C

8. *0.006 kg*

   0.020 kg *or* 0.02 kg

   0.750 kg *or* 0.75 kg

Part D

Estimates will vary.

9. 2.900 g *or* 2.9 g = 2 g 900 mg

   4.100 kg *or* 4.1 kg = 4 kg 100 g

   8.750 t *or* 8.75 t. = 8 t. 750 kg

10. 3.100 g *or* 3.1 g = 3 g 100 mg

   5.800 kg *or* 5.8 kg = 5 kg 800 g

   2.250 t *or* 2.25 t. = 2 t. 250 kg

Part E

11. *600 kg*

   300 kg

   5,200 kg

12. 500 g

   900 g

   3,400 g

13. 900 mg

   150 mg

   6,700 mg

Part F

14. a. **19,950 kg**

    14 × 1,425 = 19,950

   b. **19.950 t**

    19,950 ÷ 1,000 = 19.950

15. **500 kg too much**

   8.5 t = 8,500 kg

   9,000 − 8,500 = 500

16. milligrams

Metric Weight Scale p. 73

Part A

1. *0.8 kg = 0 kg 800 g*   2. *4.9 kg = 4 kg 900 g*

   2.1 kg = 2 kg 100 g   3.5 kg = 3 kg 500 g

   2.9 kg = 2 kg 900 g   5.6 kg = 5 kg 600 g

Part B

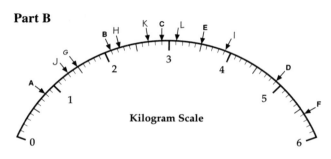

Kilogram Scale

Working with Weight pp. 74–75

Part A

Estimates will vary. Any reasonable estimate is acceptable.

1. 18 oz. = 1 lb. 2 oz.

   20 lb. 13 oz.

   4 lb. 11 oz.

2. 2 tn. 2,400 lb. = 3 tn. 400 lb.

   4 tn. 2,450 lb. = 5 tn. 450 lb.

   14 tn. 2,390 lb. = 15 tn. 390 lb.

Part B

Estimates will vary.

3. 2 lb. 5 oz.   4. 1,600 lb.

   2 lb. 12 oz.   1 tn. 1,750 lb.

   2 lb. 14 oz.   3 tn. 1,800 lb.

Part C

5. 2.300 kg *or* 2.3 kg

   5.250 kg *or* 5.25 kg

   1.500 t *or* 1.5 t

   3.680 g *or* 3.68 g

Part D

6. 4 kg 275 g

   6 g 500 mg

   2 t 650 kg

Part E

Estimates will vary.

7. 9.2 mg   8. 3.55 g

   8.3 kg   6.85 kg

   3.4 t   1.555 t

Volume, Capacity, and Weight pp. 76–77

Part A

1. 2 kg   3. 8 kg   5. 15 g

2. 4 kg   4. 250 g   6. 5 g

Part B

7. 1 kg   8. 250 g   9. 4 kg

Part C

10. approximately 2.2 lb.

11. approximately 8.8 lb.

12. **approximately 0.5 lb.** $2.2 \div 4 \approx 0.5$

Part D

13. Volume = 30,000 cm^3

    Weight = 30,000 g = 30 kg ≈ 66 lb.

14. Volume = 400 m^3

    Weight = 400 t

Measuring Temperature pp. 78–79

Part A

1. **a.** 86°F *or* 30°C   2. **a.** cool

   b. 32°F *or* 0°C   **b.** hot

Part B

3. 68°F ≈ 20°C   5. 26°F ≈ –3°C

4. 100°F ≈ 38°C

Part C

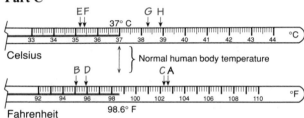

Part D

6. 99.8°F   7. 37.3°C

Gridding in Measurement Answers pp. 80–81

1.  **12.5**

   250 milligrams = 0.25 gram

   0.25 g × 50 tablets = 12.5 grams

2. 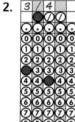 $\frac{3}{4}$ **or .75**

   Divide the number of gallons by the number of times the tank is filled:

   $5 \div 6\frac{2}{3} = \frac{3}{4}$ gal. = .75 gal.

3.  $\frac{1}{2}$ **or .5**

Divide the ounces in the bottle by the number of weeks the product lasts: 32 oz. ÷ 8 = 4 oz. Find how many cups 4 oz. equals: 4 oz. ÷ 8 oz. = $\frac{1}{2}$ c. or .5 c.

4.  **.05**

1 kilogram = 1,000 grams
Divide: 50 ÷ 1,000 = 0.05 kilograms

5.  $\frac{17}{4}$ **or 4.25**

6 lb. − 1 lb. 12 oz. = 4 lb. 4 oz.
4 lb. 4 oz. = $4\frac{4}{16}$ = $4\frac{1}{4}$ = $\frac{17}{4}$ lb. or 4.25 lb.

6.  **1.725**

Change 475 milliliters to liters:
475 ÷ 1,000 = .475.
Add .475 + 1.25 = 1.725 liters.

Unit 2 Review pp. 82–83

Part A

1. 16 fl. oz.
32 oz.
2 gal.
6,000 lb.

2. 3,000 ml
4,000 g
2,900 ml
3,500 mg

3. 4 gal. 1 qt.
1 lb. 8 oz.
1 tn. 800 lb.

4. 4 liters 750 ml
5,400 g or 5.4 g
3 kg 500g

Part B

5. 5 lb.
4 tn. 1,100 lb.
22.250 kg or 22.25 kg
10 g 700 mg

6. 1 lb. 12 oz.
2 tn. 200 lb.
1.650 g or 1.65 g
2 kg 500 g

Part C

7.  **9**

3 qt. 20 fl. oz. = 116 fl. oz.
116 ÷ 12 = $9\frac{2}{3}$ dispensers
Nine dispensers can be completely filled.

8. **4.7**

Subtract:
102.1° − 97.4° = 4.7°

Part D

9. c. 0.95 liter
10. b. 3.8 liters
11. a. 0.48 liter
12. c. 0.91 kg
13. a. 142 g
14. b. 3.41 kg

Part E

15. lb., kg
16. tn., t
17. oz., g
18. lb., kg

Part F

19. $\frac{3}{8}$ c. *or* 3 fl. oz.
20. 2.8 kg *or* 2 kg 800 g
21. 97.4°F

Working Together

Answers will vary.

Unit 3

When Is Data Important to Me? p. 85

Answers will vary.

How Is Data Used? pp. 86–87

Answers will vary. Sample answers are given below.

Part A

1. finding public opinion

2. to provide information

3. information for your own use or to support their interests

4. information for your own use or to provide information

Part B

5. You would probably want to know how many customers visit the restaurant during different time periods and what hours people are able to work.

6. You would want to know how many children live in the neighborhood and how many adults would use the proposed park.

7. You would want to know the repair records of cars like the ones you're thinking about buying. Consumer magazines carry this information.

Making Connections: Designing a Questionnaire p. 87

Answers will vary.

Writing a Data Summary pp. 88–89

Part A

1. 50 people

2. food prices

Answers to the second question will vary.

Part B

Television Data Summary

1. Number of TV movies watched each month
   a. 0 to 4   5
   b. 5 to 8   4
   c. 9 to 12   3
   d. more than 12   2

2. Number of TV news shows watched each month
   a. 0 to 4   3
   b. 5 to 8   3
   c. 9 to 12   3
   d. more than 12   5

3. Number of TV sporting events watched each month
   a. 0 to 4   7
   b. 5 to 8   4
   c. 9 to 12   2
   d. more than 12   1

Using a Tally Sheet pp. 90–91

Part A

Voting Summary

Male Responses		Female Responses	
a. For Darrel Jenkins	92	a. For Darrel Jenkins	53
b. For Beverly Myers	46	b. For Beverly Myers	98
c. Undecided	58	c. Undecided	28

Part B

Transportation Data Summary

Method of Transportation Used	
a. bus	58
b. car	49
c. carpool	32
d. other	18

Making Connections: Working with Data p. 91

Answers will vary.

Displaying Data on a Line Plot pp. 92–93

Part A

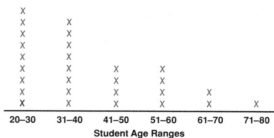

Student Age Ranges

Part B

Hourly Wage Ranges

Comparing Sets of Data pp. 94–95

Part A

1. a. **ABC Computers with 10 women managers**

   b. **Davis Hardware**

   $\frac{3}{10} \times 100\% = 30\%$

2. a. Davis Hardware with 3 women managers

   b. **ABC Computers**

   $\frac{10}{50} \times 100\% = 20\%$

Part B

3. a. 103   b. 148

4. Estimates will vary but should be close to the samples given below.

   a. **approximately 50%**

   $\frac{50}{103} \approx \frac{50}{100} \times 100\% = 50\%$

   b. **approximately 40%**

   $\frac{61}{148} \approx \frac{60}{150} \times 100\% = 40\%$

Part C

5. a. **40%**

   $\frac{4}{10} \times 100\% = 40\%$

   b. **50%**

   $\frac{10}{20} \times 100\% = 50\%$

6. a. **Both classes have 20%.**

   $\frac{2}{10}$ and $\frac{4}{20}$

   b. **Mr. Johnson's class**

   $\frac{3}{10} \times 100\% = 30\%$

Sorting a List of Data pp. 96–97

Part A

Sorted by Date of Birth	Sorted by Last Name
10/6/84 - Peg Swanson	Bissell, Jade - 4/6/90
9/14/85 - Erik Hoefler	Hoefler, Erik - 9/14/85
3/9/87 - Shelley Lewis	Lewis, Shelley - 3/9/87
4/6/90 - Jade Bissell	Petersen, Joey - 2/17/91
2/17/91 - Joey Petersen	Swanson, Peg - 10/6/84

Part B

Sorted by Amount Owed	Sorted by Last Name
$243 - Twyla Green	Green, Edith - $78
$240 - Tom Larsen	Green, Twyla - $243
$185 - Israel Putnam	Larsen, Tom - $240
$129 - Kitty Powers	Powers, Kitty - $129
$78 - Edith Green	Putnam, Israel - $185

Note: If you sorted the first list in part B from least to greatest, your new list would be in the exact opposite order.

Making Connections: Collecting and Sorting Data p. 97

Answers will vary.

Mixed Review pp. 98–99

Part A

1.

Survey Summary
(number of people in each category)

Hours spent on household chores
a. 0 to 2 __2__
b. 3 to 4 __3__
c. 5 to 6 __2__
d. more than 6 __1__

Hours spent with friends
a. 0 to 2 __0__
b. 3 to 4 __4__
c. 5 to 6 __2__
d. more than 6 __2__

Hours spent with family members
a. 0 to 2 __3__
b. 3 to 4 __2__
c. 5 to 6 __1__
d. more than 6 __2__

2.

Tally Summary	
Source	Number
Newspaper	47
Newsmagazine	23
Radio	19
Television	68

Part B

3.

```
                            x      x
x        x       x          x      x       x
x        x       x          x      x       x        x
$200–$300 $301–$400 $401–$500 $501–$600 $601–$700 $701–$800 more than
                                                              $800
              Monthly Rental Rates
```

Part C

Note: Estimation can help in answering **b** in problems 4 and 5.

4. a. Harden High School with 22 male employees

  b. Harrison Elementary

    about 50%; $\frac{10}{22} \approx \frac{10}{20} = 50\%$

5. a. Harrison Elementary with 10 male employees

  b. Harden High School

    about 33%; $\frac{22}{62} = \frac{11}{31} \approx \frac{10}{30} = \frac{1}{3} \approx 33\%$

Part D

6. Sorted by Name

  a. chisel   #153
  b. drill   #124
  c. hammer   #94
  d. screwdriver #137
  e. wrench   #87

Sorted by Code Number

  a. #87   wrench
  b. #94   hammer
  c. #124   drill
  d. #137   screwdriver
  e. #153   chisel

Finding the Mean pp. 100–101

Part A

1. $78.50

  $314 ÷ 4 = $78.50

2. $234.20

  $1,171 ÷ 5 = $234.20

3. 5 ft. 10 in.

  17 ft. 6 in. ÷ 3 = 5 ft. 10 in.

Part B

Answers on **a** and **c** will vary.

Commonsense Average	Mean	Difference Between
4. between $55 and $60	**$75** $300 ÷ 4 = $75	$15–$20
5. about 13 kg	**10.9 kg** 43.6 ÷ 4 = 10.9	about 2 kg
6. about $85,000	**$91,000** $455,000 ÷ 5 = $91,000	about $6,000

Finding the Median and the Mode pp. 102–103

Part A

1. 5 lb. 2 oz.

2. 5 ft.

  $\frac{5 \text{ ft. 1 in.} + 4 \text{ ft. 11 in.}}{2} = \frac{10 \text{ ft.}}{2}$

3. 1.4 mi.

4. $6.00

  $\frac{\$6.00 + \$6.00}{2} = \frac{\$12}{2}$

Part B

5. 23 (occurs 3 times)

6. $375 (occurs 3 times)

Part C

7. median: 25 MPG

  mode: 24 MPG

8. median: 10 years 1 month

$$\frac{(10 \text{ years } 3 \text{ months} + 9 \text{ years } 11 \text{ months})}{2}$$

mode: This data *does not* have a mode.

Choosing a Typical Value pp. 104–105

Part A

1. **(1)** mean
2. **(2)** median
3. **(4)** commonsense
4. **(3)** mode

Part B

Answers will vary slightly.

5. **a.** $2,700 **b.** $5,160

Choose the answer to **a.**

6. **a.** 38.5 **b.** 30

Choose the answer to **a.**

Part C

7. **a.** at $.60: 13 **b.** $1.20
   at $.90: 16 **c.** $1.50
   at $1.20: 17
   at $1.50: 33
   at $2.00: 18

8. **a.** $1.24 **b.** $1.20

9. sales mode; The drink that sells for $1.50 is the sales mode.

Part D

10. Mean: 349
    Median: 395
    Mode: none
    Choose the median of 395.

11. Mean: $29,000
    Median: $35,000
    $$\frac{\$36,000 + \$34,000}{2}$$
    Mode: $12,000
    Choose the median of $35,000.

Reading a Table pp. 106–107

Part A

1. 90 calories

2. Mushrooms have the smallest amount of calcium.

3. **15 more grams**
   $20 - 5 = 15$

4. **180 g**
   $90 \times 2 = 180$

5. **28 oz. of water**
   $32 \text{ oz.} \times 0.89 = 28.48$

6. **a.** 89% (onions)
   b. 84%
   $419\% \div 5 = 83.8\%$

Part B

7. $.40

8. Radio Walker (25%)

9. $18.90

10. $2.40 savings

11. Radio Walker ($6.00)

12. **a.** First find the average discount rate:
    $25\% + 10\% + 15\% + 20\% + 10\% = 80\%$
    $80\% \div 5 = 16\%$
    Then compare each of the discount rates with 16%.
    The discount rate for compact discs is 15% and is closest to the average.

    b. First, find the mode: 10% is the discount rate that occurs most frequently. Then choose the items with discount rates of 10%: videotapes and cassettes.

13. Answers will vary.

Sorting Data in a Table p. 108

1.

Name	Net Sales	Commission Rate	Weekly Salary	Gross Pay
Pritchett, Stephanie	$1,500	9.0%	$410.00	$545.00
Crawford, Elaine	$1,776	7.5%	$340.00	$473.20
Zarate, Ephran	$1,625	7.5%	$340.00	$461.88
Kitazawa, Kazuyo	$2,250	6.0%	$325.00	$460.00

2.

Name	Net Sales	Commission Rate	Weekly Salary	Gross Pay
Pritchett, Stephanie	$1,500	9.0%	$410.00	$545.00
Zarate, Ephran	$1,625	7.5%	$340.00	$461.88
Crawford, Elaine	$1,776	7.5%	$340.00	$473.20
Kitazawa, Kazuyo	$2,250	6.0%	$325.00	$460.00

Completing a Table p. 109

Part B

1. $240.00

2. Jennie Thompson

3. $9.00 more

4. $1,240 total regular pay

5. Median overtime rate is **$11.25**.
   $$\frac{\$12.00 + \$10.50}{2}$$

6. At Smith Furniture the overtime pay rate is 1.5 times the regular pay rate.

Computer Spreadsheets pp. 110–111

1. | 3 Toaster | | $19.49 | =B3*C3 | =0.05*D3 | =D3+E3 |

2. | 4 Waffle Iron | | $39.79 | =B4*C4 | =0.05*D4 | =D4+E4 |

3. Sales tax rate is 5%. (0.05 = 5%)

4.

	A	B	C	D	E	F
	Item	**Quantity**	**Item Cost**	**Subtotal**	**Sales Tax**	**Total Cost**
2	Blender	3	$29.95	$89.85	$4.49	$94.34
3	Toaster	5	$19.49	$97.45	$4.87	$102.32
4	Waffle Iron	4	$39.79	$159.16	$7.96	$167.12

Gridding in Mean, Median, and Mode pp. 112–113

1.  **1.4**

0.2 + 1.5 + 3.6 + 1.8 + 0.8 + 0.5 = 8.4, and 8.4 ÷ 6 = 1.4 in.

2.  **97**

Arrange the five values in order and find the middle number:

64, 80, 97, 128, 135.

3.  **71.5**

The average is the mean.

Add: 74 + 69 + 71 + 72 = 286.

Divide: 286 ÷ 4 = 71.5.

4.  **11**

The mode is the value that occurs most often. Size 11 occurs three times, which is more than any other size occurs.

Unit 3 Review pp. 114–115

Part A

1. Mean: 2,200 sq. ft.

Median: 2,275 sq. ft.

Mode: 2,400 sq. ft.

2. Mean: $2.30

Median: $2.29

Mode: $2.29

Part B

Answers to **a** will vary.

3. a. about 5 years old

b. 6 years old

36 ÷ 6 = 6

4. a. about 13 seconds

b. 13.3 seconds

Choose **a** in both problem 3 and problem 4.

Part C

5. a. Production (237)

b. Marketing & Sales

$\frac{7}{10}$ is 70%.

6. a. Mean: 27.4 employees

b. The mean is misleading because none of the employee numbers in this category is even close to this amount. Four of the five numbers are between 6 and 8, while the fifth number is 110.

Part D

Name	Total Sales (a)	Commission Rate (b)	Commission (c = a × b)	Salary (d)	Total Earnings (e = c + d)
Kathy Lehrer	$6,500.00	9%	$585.00	$1,240.00	$1,825.00
Ernst Netz	$4,650.00	10%	$465.00	$1,080.00	$1,545.00
Judi Garcia	$3,280.00	8%	$262.40	$1,200.00	$1,462.40

7.  **1,545**

The total earnings of the three employees are $1,462.40, $1,545, and $1,825. The median is the middle value of $1,545.

8.  **1,173**

Add: $1,080 + $1,200 + $1,240 = $3,250, and $3,250 ÷ 3 = $1,173.33, which rounds to $1,173. Do not grid in the comma.

Working Together

Answers will vary.

Unit 4

Why Are Graphs Important? p. 117

Answers will vary.

Graphing and Estimating pp. 118–119

Part A

1. **d.** *about* five hundred thousand
2. **f.** *a little less than* two hundred fifty thousand
3. **b.** *almost* one hundred twenty-five thousand
4. **a.** *slightly more than* two hundred fifty thousand
5. **c.** *a little over* one hundred twenty-five thousand
6. **e.** *approximately* four hundred thousand

Part B

Answers will vary. Sample answers are given below.

7. $420.00   9. 810   11. 190

8. 40   10. $350.00   12. $3,500.00

Part C

13. ✂ ✂ ✂

16. ✂ ✂

14. ✂ ✂

17. ✂ ✂ ～

15. ✂ ✂ ✂ ✂ ～

18. ✂ ✂ ✂

Part D

19. **(4)** $1\frac{1}{2}$ in.
20. **(5) 3 in.**

Problem 20 was easier. Without a ruler it is difficult to know which of these two estimates is closest to the actual length of the bar.

Part E

Answers will vary but should be similar to the sample answers shown.

21. 0 ——— 1 ——●— 2 →
22. 2 —— 3 —●—— 4 →
23. 0 ——————— ●—— 10 →
24. 5 ——●———————— 30 →

Part F

Answers will vary but should be similar to the sample answers shown. Problem 25 was easiest to shade because one-half is easier to mark than three-fifths or 29%.

25.   26.   27.

Reading a Pictograph pp. 120–121

Part A

1. 1,000,000 (1 million) cars
2. *approximately* 2 million
3. *about* $4\frac{1}{2}$ million
4. 500,000 per year (6 million ÷ 12)

Part B

5. **(3) 5,000,000**

   Totals are rounded to the nearest 5 million ($\frac{1}{2}$ of a symbol).

6. **(1) 3 times**

   1950: 4 symbols

   1990: 12 symbols

   $4 \times ? = 12$

   3 times as many

7. **(3) 20 million**

   $5\frac{1}{2}$ symbols $- 3\frac{1}{2}$ symbols $= 2$ symbols

   2 symbols $= 20$ million

8. No. Numbers on the graph are rounded to nearest 5 million cars.

Displaying Business Data pp. 122–123

Part A

State	Rounded Total	State	Rounded Total
California	$650,000	New Jersey	$450,000
Delaware	$200,000	New York	$800,000
Illinois	$450,000	Pennsylvania	$600,000
Michigan	$350,000	Texas	$550,000

Part B

State   Sales Total

California 🖥 🖥 🖥 🖥 🖥 🖥 🖥

Delaware 🖥 🖥

Illinois 🖥 🖥 🖥 🖥 🖥

Michigan 🖥 🖥 🖥 🖥

New Jersey 🖥 🖥 🖥 🖥 🖥

New York 🖥 🖥 🖥 🖥 🖥 🖥 🖥 🖥

Pennsylvania 🖥 🖥 🖥 🖥 🖥 🖥

Texas 🖥 🖥 🖥 🖥 🖥 🖥

Part C

1. $1\frac{1}{2}$ more symbols, which represents a difference in sales of $150,000

2. **a.** Delaware had the least amount of sales.

   b. New York had the greatest amount of sales.

3. **a.** You can't tell from the graph. Both have 4 symbols.

   b. According to the original data, Illinois had more sales than New Jersey.

   c. No. The difference between the sales totals disappears on the graph due to rounding.

4. Answers may vary. Sample answers are given below.

   a. A pictograph uses pictures to stand for data.

   b. Comparisons can be made much more quickly on a pictograph than on a list or table.

5. Answers may vary. Sample answers are given below.

   a. A list or table is much more accurate than a pictograph.

   b. A list or table is easier to produce (write or draw) than a pictograph.

Making Connections: Finding and Graphing Data p. 123

Answers will vary.

Reading a Bar Graph pp. 124–125

Part A

1. *about* 250 million

2. **by *about* 100 million**

   250 million − 150 million = 100 million

3. by *about* 50 million

4. Answers will vary. Suggested answer is 10 million.

Part B

5. *about* 45%

6. between 1970 and 1990

7. between 1910 and 1930

8. **(4) 750**

   75% of 1,000 = 750

9. Answers will vary. A sample answer is given below.

   The shift of the population to cities has occurred because jobs are now more readily available in cities. Problems associated with the population growth of cities include crowded living, traffic congestion, and air pollution.

Graphing Research Data pp. 126–127

Part A

Paper: **24%**	Food: *10%*	Metal: *7%*	Plastic: *13%*
Yard waste: *17%*	Glass: *9%*	Wood: *15%*	Other: *5%*

Part B

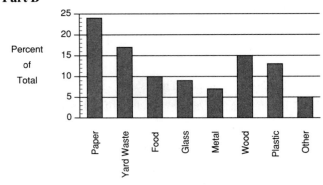

Part C

1. paper, yard waste, and wood

2. plastic

3. *about* **16% or 17%**

   paper + glass = 24% + 9% = 33%

   $\frac{1}{2}$ of paper + glass = $\frac{1}{2}$ × 33% = between 16% and 17%

4. 1st: paper   5th: food

   2nd: yard waste   6th: glass

   3rd: wood   7th: metal

   4th: plastic   8th: other

Making Connections: Taking a Poll and Graphing p. 127

Answers will vary.

Scatter Diagrams pp. 128–129

Part A

1. $25,000; $30,000; 3 children

2.

Number of Children of Selected Families

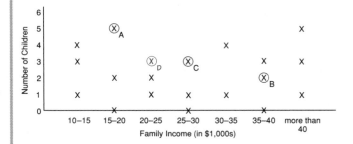

3. The poll does *not* indicate a relationship between family income and family size. There are small and large families at all income levels.

Part B

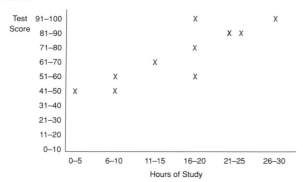

4. The pattern of data on the scatter diagram indicates that there is a relationship between the two sets of data. In most cases, test scores seem to improve as the number of hours of study increases.

Mixed Review pp. 130–131

Part A

1. 100,000 eggs

2. **550,000 eggs**

9 symbols $-$ 3$\frac{1}{2}$ symbols $=$ 5$\frac{1}{2}$ symbols

5 symbols $=$ 5 $\times$ 100,000 $=$ 500,000

$\frac{1}{2}$ symbol $=$ 50,000

500,000 $+$ 50,000 $=$ 550,000

3. **9$\frac{1}{2}$ symbols**

960,000 $\approx$ 950,000

950,000 $\div$ 100,000 $=$ 9.5 $=$ 9$\frac{1}{2}$

Part B

4. *about* 33 million two-job families

5. 1980

6. between 1985 and 1990

7. Yes, at least for the years shown on the graph. As you move from left to right across the graph, each bar is higher than the previous bar. This indicates a steady increase.

Part C

8. 12 applicants

9. 4 applicants (2 who sent out between 21 and 25, and 2 who sent out between 26 and 30)

10. 7 applicants (all *X*s at 3 or higher as measured on the vertical scale)

Part D

Answers will vary. A good choice is to use a symbol to equal 2,000 pets. Here's an example of a pictograph representing the data.

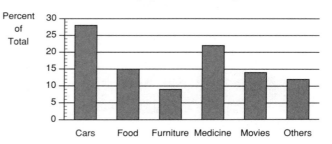

Estimated Pet Population of Harney County

Part E

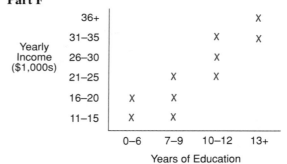

Part F

36+					X
31–35				X	X
26–30				X	
21–25			X	X	
16–20		X	X		
11–15		X	X		

Yearly Income ($1,000s)

0–6   7–9   10–12   13+

Years of Education

As the number of years of education increases, yearly income increases.

Reading a Line Graph pp. 132–133

Part A

1. **(2) $1,000**

2. *about* $23,000
   (from about $7,000 to about $30,000)

3. 1985

4. **(3) 6 times**

1990: $30,000
1950: $5,000
$30,000 $\div$ $5,000 $=$ 6

Part B

Answers will vary.

5. **$5,000**

   for men: approximately $13,000
   for women: approximately $8,000
   $13,000 − $8,000 = $5,000

6. 1980

7. *about* **$20,000**

   $30,000 − $10,000 = $20,000

8. *about* **$15,000**

   $20,000 − $5,000 = $15,000

9. In recent years there has been a lot of social and political pressure to pay equal salaries to women and men for equal work performed This has led to a slow rise in the salaries of women.

Drawing a Growth Curve pp. 134–135

Part A

Birthday	Birth	1st	2nd	3rd	4th	5th	6th	7th
Rounded Height	19 in.	32 in.	37 in.	40 in.	43 in.	46 in.	48 in.	49 in.

Part B

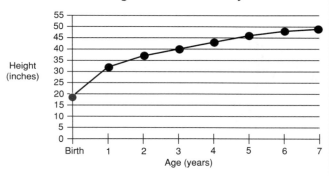

Height Record of Jeremy Barnes

Part C

1. *about* **30 in.**

   49 in. − 19 in. = 30 in.

2. during his first year of life

3. between his sixth and seventh birthdays

4. *about* $1\frac{1}{2}$ inches per year

5. between his sixth and seventh birthdays

6. Answers will vary. One advantage is that the line graph gives you a much quicker view of Jeremy's growth pattern than the table does.

Making Connections: Measurements and Graphing p. 135

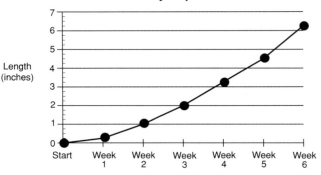

Growth History Maple Tree Branch

Using Two Data Sources pp. 136–137

Part A

1. **(2)** bar graph; $20,000

2. **(3) both; $2,060**

   from table: $1,100 salary;
   6% commission from
   graph: $16,000 sales total
   6% × $16,000 = $960
   $1,100 + $960 = $2,060

3. **(2)** bar graph: Clarke

4. **(1) table; $475**
   $1,975 − $1,500 = $475

Part B

5. **(2) line graph; $1,400**

   $2,300 − $900 = $1,400

6. **(1) pictograph; 20%**

   $400 ÷ $2,000 = .2 = 20%

7. **(3) both; 33%**

   $700 ÷ $2,100 = $\frac{1}{3}$ = $33\frac{1}{3}$%

8. **(3)** both; average monthly income

9. Answers may vary. A sample answer is given below.

   Many residents of Stryker County may find that rapidly rising housing costs cause them economic hardship, whether they rent or own the place where they live.

Reading a Circle Graph pp. 138–139

Part A

1. excise taxes

2. individual income taxes *and* Social Security receipts account for 71% (almost = 75%) of revenue sources in the 1995 budget.

3. (2) about 3 times as much

$$32\% \div 11\% \approx 33\% \div 11\% = 3$$

Part B

4. $.18

5. $.33

$$\$0.48 - \$0.15 = \$0.33$$

6. direct benefit payments for individuals

7. $14.00

8. $.05

$$\$1.00 - \$.95 = \$.05$$

└─ the sum of the other segments

9. median

The median is $.15 which is close in value to $.14, $.15, and $.18. The mean is $.20, and there is no mode.

Graphing Family Expenses pp. 140–141

Part A

1. 40%

2. 25%

$$\frac{\$500}{\$2,000} \times \frac{100\%}{1} = 25\%$$

3. 5%

$$\frac{\$100}{\$2,000} \times \frac{100\%}{1} = 5\%$$

4. 10%

$$\frac{\$200}{\$2,000} \times \frac{100\%}{1} = 10\%$$

5. 6%

$$\frac{\$125}{\$2,000} \times \frac{100\%}{1} = 6.25\%$$

Round 6.25% down to 6%.

6. 14%

$$\frac{\$275}{\$2,000} \times \frac{100\%}{1} = 13.75\%$$

Round 13.75% up to 14%.

Part B

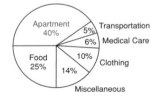

Sanderson Family Expenses

Part C

7. 10%

$$\frac{1}{4} \times \frac{40\%}{1} = 10\%$$

8. a. Apartment: $.40

b. Food: $.25

c. Transportation: $.05

d. Clothing: $.10

e. Medical Care: $.06

f. Miscellaneous: $.14

9. (3) 4 times as much

$$25\% \div 6\% \approx$$
$$24\% \div 6\% = 4$$

10. Answers will vary. Some sample answers are:

A circle graph is better than other types of graphs in presenting a divided whole. A circle graph does not use either vertical or horizontal axes.

Making Connections: Choosing an Appropriate Graph p. 141

Answers will vary. Suggested answers are given below.

1. line graph: shows changes over time

2. scatter diagram: compare two different groups of data

3. bar graph: show side-by-side comparisons

4. circle graph: show part of a whole

5. pictograph: compare number of symbols

Data in Different Forms pp. 142–143

Part A

1. circle graph

2. bar graph

3. With a bar graph, it is easier to find numerical sums or differences. With a circle graph, it is easier to determine sums or differences in percents. Size comparisons are easily made on both graphs.

Part B

4. 2,000

$$380 + 640 + 440 + 540 = 2,000$$

5. a. Thomas: 19%

$$380 \div 2,000 = 19\%$$

b. Tioga: 32%

$$640 \div 2,000 = 32\%$$

c. Highland: 22%

$$440 \div 2,000 = 22\%$$

d. Worth: 27%

$$540 \div 2,000 = 27\%$$

6.

Middle School Enrollment
(*percent* of students in each school)

Part C

7. a. 6th grade: 760 students

38% of 2,000 is 760.

b. 7th grade: 680 students

34% of 2,000 is 680.

c. 8th grade: 560 students

28% of 2,000 students is 560.

8.

Middle School Enrollment

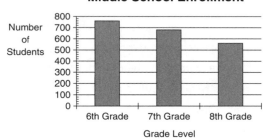

Gridding in Data Analysis Answers pp. 144–145

1. **60**

Subtract: $100 − $40 = $60

2.  $\frac{2}{50}$ or $\frac{1}{25}$

$\frac{$80}{$2,000} = \frac{2}{50}$

3.  **7**

Divide: 35 ÷ 5 = 7

4.  $\frac{7}{20}$

Add to find the total number of students: 30 + 20 + 35 + 45 + 70 = 200. Find the fraction for Fitness: 70 ÷ 200 = $\frac{7}{20}$.

Unit 4 Review pp. 146–147

Part A

1. police protection

2. **$130,000**

13% of $1 million = 13% × $1,000,000 = $130,000

3. **(3) 6 times**

43 ÷ 7 ≈ 42 ÷ 7 = 6

Part B **Yearly Operating Expense**
(as a percent of $2,000 total)

Part C

4.  **600**

$4,000 × 0.15 = $600

5. **5.5 or $\frac{11}{2}$**

330 ÷ 60 = 5.5 or $5\frac{1}{2}$ = $\frac{11}{2}$

Part D

6. $700,000

7. **(2) $1.50**

30% is 1.5 times 20%.

8. **$315,000**

45% of $700,000 = 45% × $700,000 = $315,000

9. a. $2,000,000 ($2 million)

$250,000 + $400,000 + $650,000 + $700,000 = $2,000,000

b. $600,000

30% of $2 million = 30% × $2,000,000 = $600,000

10. Answers may vary. Sample answers are given below.

The line graph shows the growth of sales during four quarters of the sales year. The circle graph shows where sales were made.

Working Together

Answers will vary.

Unit 5

When Do I Analyze Data? p. 149

Answers will vary.

Interpolation and Extrapolation pp. 150–151

Answers will vary on all estimates. Any reasonable answers are acceptable.

Part A

1. **approximately 64,000**

   $56,000 + \frac{1}{2}$ of $16,000 =$

   $56,000 + 8,000 = 64,000$

2. **in about 2005**

   Oakmont's population will be about 90,000 in the year 2000 and growing at the rate of about 20,000 each 10 years. So the population should increase about 10,000 more between 2000 and 2005.

Part B

3. **approximately 4.8 billion**

   Growth from 1980 to 1990: $5.2 - 4.4 = 0.8$

   1985 is halfway between 1980 and 1990, so growth between 1980 and 1985 = $0.8 \div 2 = 0.4$

   $4.4 + 0.4 = 4.8$

4. a. **approximately 0.7 billion**

   $4.4 - 3.7 = 0.7$

   b. **approximately 0.8 billion**

   $5.2 - 4.4 = 0.8$

5. **approximately 7.1 billion**

   Past trend shows a 0.7 billion increase from 1970 to 1980, a 0.8 billion increase from 1980 to 1990, and a 0.9 billion increase from 1990 to 2000. Estimated increase from 2000 to 2010: 1.0 billion

   2000: 6.1 billion
   $6.1 + 1.0 = 7.1$

Part C

6. **approximately $175,000**

   2005: $150,000
   estimated increase: $25,000
   $150,000 + $25,000 = $175,000

7. approximately 1987 or 1988

8. **(2) a little less than 20**

   In 20 years prices had slightly more than doubled.

9. An estimate for 2010 is likely to be more accurate. A lot of unforeseen circumstances between 2010 and 2020 could change the home price trend in Lewisburg.

Drawing Conclusions from Data pp. 152–153

Part A

1. **N** The graph does not provide information on world oil consumption.

2. **J** According to the graph, natural gas accounted for 24% ($\approx 25\% = \frac{1}{4}$) of energy in the United States in 1993.

3. **N** According to the graph, natural gas was the second leading source of energy in the United States in 1993.

4. **N** The graph says nothing about energy costs.

Part B

5. **(1)** is false and should be crossed out.

   (2) should be crossed out. The graph provides no information about possible reasons.

   (3) is true and should be the one you chose. Taking data from the graph, you can calculate the average budget decrease to be about 10.3%.

Part C

6. **(1)** should be crossed out. The graph provides no information about possible reasons.

   (2) is true and should be the one you chose.

   (3) is false and should be crossed out.

Part D

Opinions are given in problem 1, statement **(2)** in problem 5, and statement **(1)** in problem 6. Answers may vary about agreeing with these opinions. Any reasonable answers are acceptable.

What More Do I Need to Know? pp. 154–155

Part A

1. **(3)** the number of female registered voters in Blane County in 1984

2. **(2)** the number of registered voters in Blane County in 1980 and in 1992

3. No. The bar graph says nothing about the *number* of registered voters, only about what percent of those registered actually voted.

4. No. The number of females and males who voted depends on the number of females and males who are registered voters. This information is not given on the graph.

Part B

5. **(3)** the population of each state

6. No. To determine which state produces the most nuclear power, you would need to know how much power each nuclear plant in each state produced. The graph does not tell this.

Part C

7. **(2)** the total surface area of the Earth

8. Yes. The total surface area covered by water is equal to 71% (100% − 29%). This is more than two-thirds ($66\frac{2}{3}$%). You may also have used this approach: You know that 29% of the Earth's surface is land. This is *less than* $\frac{1}{3}$ ($33\frac{1}{3}$%). Therefore, you know that *more than* $\frac{2}{3}$ is not land—that is, is covered by water.

Getting More Information pp. 156–157

Answers may vary. Example answers are given. Any reasonable answers are acceptable.

Part A

1. How large is the apartment? In what kind of neighborhood is the apartment located?

2. How many miles has the pickup been driven? Has the pickup ever been wrecked?

Part B

3. How do the education costs in Newport today compare with the education costs in other cities in the state? How does the education of children in Newport compare with education gotten by children in other cities in the state?

Making Connections: Sources of Information p. 157

Sources may vary.

1. An adult male lion weighs about 350 to 400 pounds.

2. The price of used Honda Accords will depend on where you live.

3. Mount McKinley is about 20,300 feet high.

4. Your city's population will depend where you live.

5. There are 640 acres in 1 square mile.

Understanding Correlation pp. 158–159

Part A

1. negative correlation   2. positive correlation

Part B

3. **negative correlation**

   As prices rise, sales tend to decrease.

4. **positive correlation**

   As temperature increases, more kids are likely to head for the swimming pool.

5. **positive correlation**

   Families with higher incomes are likely to have larger, more expensive houses.

6. **negative correlation**

   High mortgage rates mean higher payments, which leads to fewer sales.

Making Connections: Taking a Poll p. 159

Answers will vary.

Analyzing Correlation pp. 160–161

Part A

1. **a.** positive correlation

   b. negative correlation

2. **a.** The most popular sugar level is 8 tsp. per gal.

   b. At 8 tsp. per gal. (16 c.), 1 c. of Rainbow Gold would contain $\frac{1}{2}$ tsp. of sugar.

3. When the sugar level increases above 8 tsp. per gal., the drink becomes too sweet for many people's taste.

4. A reasonable prediction is that taste preference scores would be even lower than for 11 tsp.

Part B

5. **a.** 70 beats per minute

   b. 150 beats per minute

   c. 70 beats per minute

6. **a.** positive correlation   **b.** negative correlation

7. After an additional minute of exercise the heart rate would most likely have remained at 150 beats per minute. By the 4th minute, the heart rate had reached a constant rate for this level of exercise.

8. Discussion will vary but should be similar to the sample answers given below.

   a. The patient's heart rate will probably be higher during each phase of the test.

   b. The patient's recovery time will probably be longer.

   c. The curve of the graph between minute 1 and minute 5 will most likely be steeper. In addition, the curve between minute 5 and minute 8 will not be as steep as the curve shown, indicating a longer recovery period.

Profit Analysis pp. 162–163

Part A

1. **a.** positive correlation
   b. negative correlation

2. $2

3. 70,000 trucks

4. approximately $140,000

5. **a.** The maximum profit John can make from the sale of the toy truck is about $150,000.
   b. The maximum profit occurs at a selling price of $7.

Part B

Graph F: Total Profit at Each Selling Price

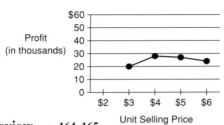

Mixed Review pp. 164–165

Part A

1. approximately 120 million

2. **approximately 149 million**

   Assuming that the labor force continues growing at the same rate, which is 8 million people every 5 years: $141 + 8 = 149$

3. **No.** Although that may be part of the reason, the graph says nothing about growth in the U.S. population.

Part B

4. **(3)** Between 1970 and 1990, the average number of TV sets in U.S. homes increased about 50%.

Part C

5.  **16.8**

   $132.3 - 115.5 = 16.8$ million

6. 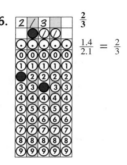 $\frac{2}{3}$

   $\frac{1.4}{2.1} = \frac{2}{3}$

Part D

7. 1980–1985 (the steepest part of the curve)

8. 20 out of 100 families (19.9 rounds to 20.)

9. The *number* of U.S. households in the years 1985 and 1990.

Part E

10. **a.** negative correlation
    b. positive correlation

11. **a.** the 15–24 years age group
    b. the 40–69 years age group

12. Answers may vary. Examples are: Drivers gain experience and take fewer chances as they get older. On the other hand, as adults become 70 or older, their reactions may become slower and their senses (sight and hearing) may deteriorate. In addition, older people may be less likely to survive a serious car accident.

13. No. A graph can't tell you anything about all the people of a particular group.

14. the total number of drivers in each age group in 1990

15. Answers may vary. In general, car insurance companies set the highest insurance rates for groups most likely to be involved in serious accidents. This means the rates are likely to be highest for the 15–24 years age group and the 80+ age group. The rates are likely to be lowest for the 40–69 years age group.

16. Answers will vary.

Introducing Probability pp. 166–167

1. **a.** $\frac{1}{2}$ *or* **50%**
   simplify $\frac{3}{6}$

   b. $\frac{1}{3}$ *or* **33** $\frac{1}{3}$ **%**
   simplify $\frac{2}{6}$ because two numbers (3 and 6) are divisible by 3

   c. $\frac{5}{6}$ *or* **83** $\frac{1}{3}$ **%**
   If the probability of a 1 coming up is $\frac{1}{6}$, the probability of it not coming up is $1 - \frac{1}{6} = \frac{5}{6}$.

2. $\frac{3}{5}$ *or* **60%**
   simplify $\frac{6}{10}$

211

3. **a.** $\frac{4}{15}$ or $26\frac{2}{3}\%$ **c.** $\frac{1}{5}$ or **20%**

     simplify $\frac{8}{30}$ simplify $\frac{6}{30}$

   b. $\frac{2}{5}$ or **40%**   **d.** $\frac{2}{15}$ or $13\frac{1}{3}\%$

     simplify $\frac{12}{30}$ simplify $\frac{4}{30}$

Notice that if you add the answers in **a** through **d**, the total is 1 (or 100%). This means that when you pick a jelly bean, you must get one of the colors in the bag!

4. **a.** $\frac{3}{5}$ *or* **60%**

   b. $\frac{2}{5}$ *or* **40%**

   c. $\frac{1}{2}$ *or* **50%**

The second time you draw, there are only 4 cards on the table, 2 of which are face cards.

Using Probability for Prediction pp. 168–169

1. **17**

   $16\frac{2}{3}$ rounded to the nearest whole number is 17.

2. **a. 38%**

   b. about 15 or 16

     38% of 40 ≈ 15

3. **about 144**

   48% of 300 = 144

4. **a. 20% or $\frac{1}{5}$**

     simplify $\frac{40}{200}$

   b. 10

     20% of 50 = 10

5. **a. 200 female voters**

     70 + 130 = 200

   b. 7

     $\frac{70}{200}$ = 35%

     35% of 20 = 7

   c. 55%

     165 ÷ 300 = .55 = 55%

Making Connections: Checking Probability p. 169

Answers will vary. The average number of heads flipped by the 5 students probably will be close to 5. If 100 students participated, the average would normally be very close to 5 heads and 5 tails.

Probability of Successive Events pp. 170–171

Part A

1. **a.** 50% *or* $\frac{1}{2}$

   b. 25% *or* $\frac{1}{4}$ ($\frac{1}{2} \times \frac{1}{2}$)

2. No. You know there is a 5% chance the next car Malcolm works on will be from other countries (including England). The most you can say is that the probability that the next car will be from England is less than 5%.

3. **a.** 5% *or* $\frac{1}{20}$

   b. 0.25 (5% of 5%) *or* $\frac{1}{400}$ ($\frac{1}{20} \times \frac{1}{20}$)

Part B

4. **a.** $\frac{1}{36}$ ($\frac{1}{6} \times \frac{1}{6}$)

   b. $\frac{1}{36}$ ($\frac{1}{6} \times \frac{1}{6}$)

5. **a.** $\frac{1}{5}$ *or* **20%**

     simplify $\frac{2}{10}$

   b. $\frac{1}{25}$ *or* 4% ($\frac{1}{5} \times \frac{1}{5}$)

6. 16% (40% of 40%)

7. $\frac{1}{3}$

   60% of 60% = 36% ≈ $\frac{1}{3}$

Sampling a Population pp. 172–173

Supporting reasons will vary.

1. Sample: the work rate of the day crew between 2:30 P.M. and 2:45 P.M.

   Population: the work rate of the day crew for the whole day work shift

   Sample is not representative. Check should be made at several times during the day.

2. Sample: 2,000 surveyed owners

   Population: all new pickup owners

   Sample is representative. A variety of owners were surveyed.

3. Sample: residents of every 5th apartment

   Population: all residents of apartment complex

   Sample is representative. Residents were randomly chosen.

4. Sample: one package of stale cookies

   Population: all packaged cookies

   Sample is not representative. Not enough packages of cookies were looked at.

Making Connections: Choosing a Representative Sample p. 173

Answers may vary. Example answers are given.

1. **Perhaps 50 to 100 students.**

   Students should be chosen from each class, some of whom are athletes and some of whom aren't. Both male and female students should be surveyed.

2. **The prices of perhaps 20 different food items found in Value Supermarket and several other stores.**

   These items should be chosen from several departments such as vegetables, meats, etc.

3. **A sample of about 40 people of all ages who swim at the Aquatic Center.**

   Both males and females should be questioned, as should people who swim at different times of the day.

4. A sample of 75 people.

Some of those questioned should be riders who are affected directly. Some questioned should be people who don't ride the bus at all. (You should find out why they don't ride the bus.) Of the riders questioned, riders from different routes should be included. Both male and female riders, and riders of all ages, should be questioned.

Sampling and Margin of Error pp. 174–175

Part A

1. Sample: 200 surveyed Oakdale adult residents

   Population: the 100,000 adult residents of Oakdale

2. **a.** between 22% and 38% (30% ±8%)

   b. between 22,000 and 38,000

3. **a.** between 24% and 32% (28% ±4%)

   b. between 24,000 and 32,000

Part B

4. **a.** 60% (read off the graph)

   b. 360

   60% of 600 = 360

5. **a.** between 56% and 64% (60% ±4%)

   b. between 44,800 and 51,200

Gridding in Probability Answers pp. 176–177

1. 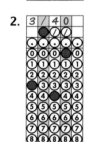 **2**

   There are five equal sections on the spinner, and 60% of 5 is 3. The number 2 appears in 3 out of 5 sections. Since $\frac{3}{5} = 3 \div 5 = 60\%$, you have a 60% chance of spinning a 2.

2.  $\frac{3}{40}$

   There is a $\frac{3}{8}$ chance of spinning red and a $\frac{1}{5}$ chance of spinning a 3.

   Multiply: $\frac{3}{8} \times \frac{1}{5} = \frac{3}{40}$. There is a 3 out of 40 chance of both events occurring.

3.  $\frac{2}{130}$ or $\frac{1}{65}$

    $\frac{40}{2,600} = \frac{2}{130}$

4. 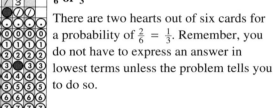 $\frac{2}{6}$ or $\frac{1}{3}$

   There are two hearts out of six cards for a probability of $\frac{2}{6} = \frac{1}{3}$. Remember, you do not have to express an answer in lowest terms unless the problem tells you to do so.

5. 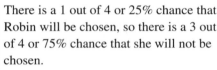 $\frac{3}{4}$ or .75

   There is a 1 out of 4 or 25% chance that Robin will be chosen, so there is a 3 out of 4 or 75% chance that she will not be chosen.

6.  $\frac{4}{18}$ or $\frac{2}{9}$

   The chance that the first card will be a 5 or less is $\frac{5}{10} = \frac{1}{2}$. Assuming the first card is 5 or less, there are 4 cards remaining out of 9 that are equal to or less than 5. Multiply: $\frac{1}{2} \times \frac{4}{9} = \frac{4}{18} = \frac{2}{9}$

Unit 5 Review pp. 178–179

Part A

1. 101.3°F (halfway between 101.8°F and 100.8°F)

2. 99.2°F (At 4:00 P.M. Shane's temperature is dropping at the rate of about 0.8°F per hour.)

3. Shane's normal body temperature

Part B

4. **(3)** The cost of unleaded regular gas about doubled between 1976 and 1980.

5. the total number of gallons of unleaded regular gas purchased in the United States in each listed year

Part C

6. **positive correlation**

   Cold drinks tend to sell better when the weather is hot than when it is cold: as temperature increases, so do sales.

7. Answers will vary. You probably said there is a positive correlation between amount of education and salary level. (And in fact, statistics show that a positive correlation does exist.)

Part D

8. **a.** $\frac{1}{6}$ or $16\frac{2}{3}\%$

   b. 4

   $\frac{1}{6}$ of $25 = 4\frac{1}{6} \approx 4$

9. $\frac{1}{36}$

   $\frac{1}{6} \times \frac{1}{6} = \frac{1}{36}$

10. **a. 4% or $\frac{1}{25}$**

   simplify $\frac{6}{150}$

   b. 16

   4% of 400 or $\frac{1}{25} \times 400$

Part E

11.  $\frac{11}{20}$

   $30\% + 25\% = 55\% = \frac{55}{100} = \frac{11}{20}$. You must reduce the fraction to fit the answer in the grid.

12. **1,800**

   Consider the margin of error noted beneath the graph. The percent of married loan applicants is actually between 35% and 45%. $4{,}000 \times .35 = 1{,}400$ and $4{,}000 \times .45 = 1{,}800$

Working Together

Answers will vary.

Glossary

area the amount of surface within a *two-dimensional figure* (p. 36)

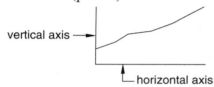

area = $l \times w$
= 25 square yards

The most common area units are square foot, square yard, and square meter.

axes the sides of a graph along which data values are written (p. 124)

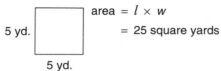

vertical axis →
horizontal axis

bar graph a graph that shows data as side-by-side vertical or horizontal bars (p. 124)

Vertical Bar Graph   Horizontal Bar Graph

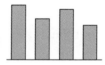

capacity the amount of liquid (such as milk) or granular substance (such as sugar) that a container can hold (p. 52)

1 gallon   1 liter   1 cup

Celsius the temperature scale of the *metric system* of measurement (p. 78)

100°C = boiling point of water
0°C = freezing point of water

centimeter a metric unit of length. One centimeter (cm) is a little less than one-half inch (p. 18).

centimeter
inch

circle graph a graph that shows data as parts of a divided circle. A circle graph is sometimes called a *pie graph* (p. 138).

circumference the distance around a circle (p. 35)

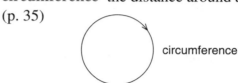

circumference

column a vertical list of numbers or words that is read from top to bottom (p. 106)

column of numbers	column of words
145	Emma Jones
419	Bruce Overton
207	Eunice Hawthorne
382	Al Johnson

correlation a relationship of one set of data values to another. *Positive correlation* means that as one value increases, the second value also increases. *Negative correlation* means that as one value increases, the second value decreases (p. 158).

data a group of numbers or words that are related in some way (p. 84)

Number data: 12, 17, 6, 14, 8
Word data: carrots, peas, radishes, cabbage

diameter the distance through a circle's center (p. 35)

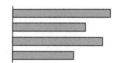

diameter

distance formula the formula $d = r \times t$ that relates distance (d), rate (r), and time (t). The distance formula can also be written as a rate formula and a time formula (p. 44).

Rate formula: $r = \frac{d}{t}$ Time formula: $t = \frac{d}{r}$

English system the system of measurement most commonly used in the United States (p. 14)

extrapolate to estimate a data value that lies outside a given set of values (p. 150)

Fahrenheit the temperature scale of the *English system* of measurement (p. 78)

212°F = boiling point of water
32°F = freezing point of water

fluid ounce an English unit of capacity equal to one-eighth of a cup (p. 52)

gram a metric unit of weight; about the weight of a raisin (p. 70)

≈ 1 gram (g)

interpolate to estimate a data value that lies between two given values (p. 150)

kilogram a metric unit of weight; about the weight of a quart of milk (p. 70)

≈ 1 kilogram (kg)

kilometer a metric unit of distance. One kilometer (km) is a little longer than one-half mile (p. 18).

kilometer
mile
to scale

line graph a graph that displays data as points along a graphed line (p. 132)

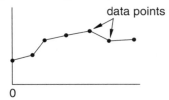

data points

0

line plot a visual display of data on which values are written as Xs. Each X is placed above a value or range of values written below a horizontal line (p. 92).

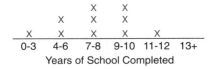

```
                  X    X
           X      X    X
   X    X    X    X    X
  0-3  4-6  7-8  9-10 11-12 13+
       Years of School Completed
```

liter a metric unit of capacity. One liter is slightly larger than one quart (p. 56).

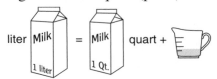

liter Milk 1 liter = Milk 1 Qt. quart +

margin of error the range of most often obtained values around the predicted value (p. 174)

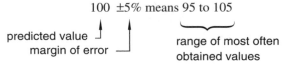

100 ±5% means 95 to 105
predicted value
margin of error
range of most often obtained values

mean the *average* of a set of numbers, found by dividing the sum of the set by the number of numbers in the set (p. 100)

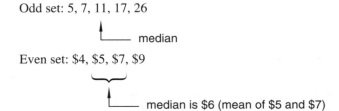

$14 + $8 + $11 = $33 $11 ⟵ mean
                       3)$33
number of numbers ⎤   ⎿ sum of numbers

median the middle number of an odd set of numbers or the mean of the two middle numbers of an even set of numbers (p. 102)

Odd set: 5, 7, 11, 17, 26
                ⎿ median

Even set: $4, $5, $7, $9
              ⎿ median is $6 (mean of $5 and $7)

meter a metric unit of length. A meter is a little longer than a yard (p. 18).

meter
yard
to scale

metric system a system of measurement based on the decimal system. The metric system is also called the *international system,* abbreviated *SI* (after the French spelling) (p. 18).

milligram a metric unit of weight; about the weight of a grain of sand (p. 70)

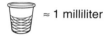

milliliter a metric unit of capacity; about the amount that could be held by a small thimble (p. 56)

millimeter a metric unit of length; about the thickness of a dime (p. 18)

≈ 1 millimeter

mode the value in a set of data that occurs most often (p. 102)

$4, $5, $6, $7, $7, $8
mode

ounce an English unit of weight; about the weight of a standard envelope with enclosed one-page letter (p. 66)

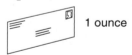
1 ounce

perimeter the distance around a *two-dimensional figure* (p. 34)

8 ft.
3 ft. | | 3 ft.   Perimeter = 3 + 8 + 3 + 8
8 ft.   = 22 ft.

pi (pronounced "pie") the number of diameters contained in a circumference (p. 35)

Pi has the approximate value 3.14 or $\frac{22}{7}$.

pictograph a graph that displays data as a row or column of symbols. Each symbol stands for a number of objects (p. 120).

Allison Farms Egg Production

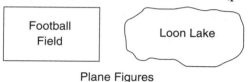

plane figure a flat or *two-dimensional figure;* a figure that has surface but not volume (p. 34)

Football Field   Loon Lake

Plane Figures

population a large group of people, places, or things about which information is being gathered (p. 172)

probability the likelihood (or chance) of something happening or not happening (p. 166)

radius half of the diameter; the distance from the center of a circle to the edge (p. 35)

radius

rectangle a four-sided figure that contains four right angles (p. 34)

rectangle

rectangular solid a *three-dimensional figure* in which all lines meet at right angles (p. 38)

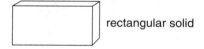
rectangular solid

right angle the 90° angle formed when two perpendicular lines meet. A right angle is often called a corner angle (p. 36).

right angle

row a horizontal list of numbers or words that is read from left to right across a table (p. 106)

row of numbers: $4.50 $3.75 $6.19 $5.50
row of words: robins sparrows ducks geese

sample a small part of a larger group (*population*) (p. 172)

scatter diagram a graph that shows the relationship between two different groups of data. A scatter diagram is also known as a *scattergram* (p. 128).

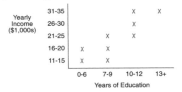

sorting arranging data in a specific order. The most common types of sorting are alphabetic, numeric, and date (p. 96).

spreadsheet a table (part of a computer program) on which calculations are done automatically (p. 110)

square a four-sided figure having four equal sides and four right (90°) angles (p. 34)

square

successive events events that happen one after another. Flipping a coin twice in a row is an example of two successive events (p. 170).

followed by

table a display of data organized in rows (read from left to right) and columns (read from top to bottom) (p. 106)

Name of Company	Women Managers	Total Managers
Thompson Elec.	4	16
Davis Hardware	3	10
ABC Computers	10	50

row →

column

tally to count or record individual responses to a poll or questionnaire. Each response is recorded as a slash (tally mark) on a tally sheet. A group of 5 marks is written as 卌 (p. 90).

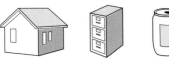
tally marks

tally sheet

three-dimensional figure a figure that has length, width, and height; a figure that has both surface area and volume (p. 38)

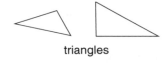

three-dimensional figures

time zone one of 24 regions of Earth. All points in each time zone are at the same clock time. Time zones next to each other differ in time by one hour (p. 46).

triangle a three-sided figure (p. 34)

triangles

two-dimensional figure a plane or flat figure. See *plane figure* (p. 34).

volume the amount of space taken up or enclosed by a *three-dimensional figure* (p. 38)

3 in.
4 in.
5 in.

volume = $l \times w \times h$
= 60 cubic inches

Common volume units are the cubic foot, cubic yard, and cubic meter.

weight the amount an object weighs. Weight is a measure of how heavy an object feels when lifted. Common weight units are the ounce, pound, ton, gram, and kilogram (p. 66).

Tool Kit

Using a Four-Function Calculator

A calculator is a valuable math tool that can help you calculate quickly and accurately. The calculator pictured at right is likely similar to one you've seen or used before.

It is called a four-function calculator because you use it to add, subtract, multiply, or divide. On page 221, you will see how to use a scientific calculator.

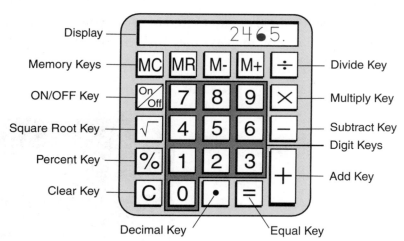

To enter a number on a calculator, you press one digit key at a time. The entered number 2,465 is shown on the display above. As you look at the calculator keys and display, notice these features:

- Most calculators display a decimal point to the right of a whole number.
- Most calculators *do not* display a comma to separate groups of digits.
- A calculator does not have a comma (,) key or a dollar sign ($) key.

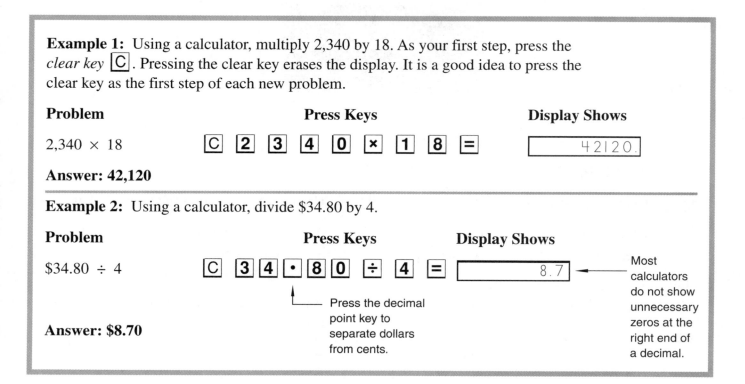

Example 1: Using a calculator, multiply 2,340 by 18. As your first step, press the *clear key* [C]. Pressing the clear key erases the display. It is a good idea to press the clear key as the first step of each new problem.

Problem	Press Keys	Display Shows
2,340 × 18	C 2 3 4 0 × 1 8 =	42120.

Answer: 42,120

Example 2: Using a calculator, divide $34.80 by 4.

Problem	Press Keys	Display Shows
$34.80 ÷ 4	C 3 4 • 8 0 ÷ 4 =	8.7

Press the decimal point key to separate dollars from cents.

Most calculators do not show unnecessary zeros at the right end of a decimal.

Answer: $8.70

Tool Kit

Scientific Calculator Basics

Some tests allow you to use a scientific calculator for part of the test. A scientific calculator has many functions. You will use only the basic functions for your work in this text. Study the diagram to find the keys you will need. If you are using a different scientific calculator, the keys may be located in a different place, but they will have the same purpose.

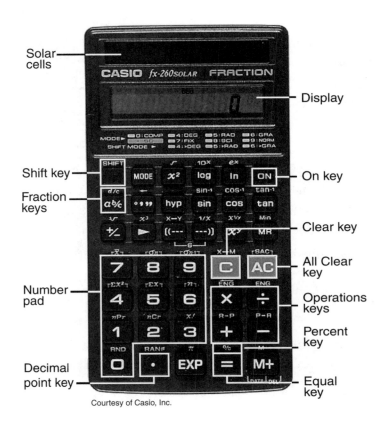

Courtesy of Casio, Inc.

Explanation of Special Keys

ON Resets the calculator.

AC All Clear key erases all numbers and operations from the current calculation.

C The clear key erases only the last number or operation you entered.

a% Used to enter fractions and mixed numbers. Press a second time to change fractions to decimals.

SHIFT Used to access second function of a key.

d/c A second function above the fraction key **a%** used to change mixed numbers to improper fractions and back.

% A second function above the equal sign **=** used to enter percents.

Tool Kit

Basic Functions

A scientific calculator works much like the basic calculator described on page 219. Before beginning a calculation, make sure the display reads 0. The letters DEG should also appear in the display window. You can reset the display by pressing $\boxed{\text{ON}}$.

Fractions

You can enter fractions on some scientific calculators. The display shows fractions by separating the parts of the fraction using the $\lrcorner$ symbol. For example, $4\frac{3}{8}$ will be displayed as $\boxed{\qquad 4 \lrcorner 3 \lrcorner 8.}$

To enter a fraction, use the fraction key $\boxed{a\frac{b}{c}}$ to separate the parts of a fraction. Then press $\boxed{=}$ to display the fraction in lowest terms. Press $\boxed{a\frac{b}{c}}$ again to change the fraction to a decimal.

Use $\boxed{\text{SHIFT}}$ $\boxed{a\frac{b}{c}}$, or d/c, to change a mixed number to an improper fraction. Use this function when entering a mixed number on a five-column grid.

Example 1: Reduce $\frac{14}{56}$ to lowest terms. Then change to a decimal.

Press: $\boxed{1}$ $\boxed{4}$ $\boxed{a\frac{b}{c}}$ $\boxed{5}$ $\boxed{6}$ $\boxed{=}$ Your display reads: $\boxed{\qquad 1 \lrcorner 4.}$, which means $\frac{1}{4}$.

Press: $\boxed{a\frac{b}{c}}$ Your display reads: $\boxed{\qquad 0.25}$

Example 2: Find the sum of $3\frac{3}{4}$ and $\frac{7}{8}$. Write the answer as an improper fraction.

Press: $\boxed{3}$ $\boxed{a\frac{b}{c}}$ $\boxed{3}$ $\boxed{a\frac{b}{c}}$ $\boxed{4}$ $\boxed{+}$ $\boxed{7}$ $\boxed{a\frac{b}{c}}$ $\boxed{8}$ $\boxed{=}$ $\boxed{\quad 4 \lrcorner 5 \lrcorner 8.}$, which means $4\frac{5}{8}$.

Change to an improper fraction. Press $\boxed{\text{SHIFT}}$ $\boxed{a\frac{b}{c}}$, or d/c.

The display reads: $\boxed{\qquad 3 7 \lrcorner 8.}$, which means $\frac{37}{8}$.

Percents

Example 1: Find 40% of 55.

Press: $\boxed{5}$ $\boxed{5}$ $\boxed{\times}$ $\boxed{4}$ $\boxed{0}$ $\boxed{\text{SHIFT}}$ $\boxed{=}$ Your display reads $\boxed{\qquad 22.}$.

Example 2: 12 is 10% of what number?

Press: $\boxed{1}$ $\boxed{2}$ $\boxed{\div}$ $\boxed{1}$ $\boxed{0}$ $\boxed{\text{SHIFT}}$ $\boxed{=}$ Your display reads $\boxed{\qquad 120.}$.

Tool Kit

Most Often Used Measurement Units

English System

Length

1 foot (ft. or ') = 12 inches (in. or ")

1 yard (yd.) = 3 feet

  = 36 inches

1 mile (mi.) = 1,760 yards

  = 5,280 feet

Weight

1 pound (lb.) = 16 ounces (oz.)

1 ton (tn.) = 2,000 lb.

Capacity

1 tablespoon (tbsp.) = 3 teaspoons (tsp.)

1 cup (c.) = 8 fluid ounces (fl. oz.)

1 pint (pt.) = 2 cups

  = 16 fluid ounces

1 quart (qt.) = 2 pints

  = 4 cups

  = 32 fluid ounces

1 gallon (gal.) = 4 quarts

  = 128 fluid ounces

Metric System

Length

1 centimeter (cm) = 10 millimeters (mm)

1 meter (m) = 100 cm

  = 1,000 mm

1 kilometer (km) = 1,000 m

Weight

1 gram (g) = 1,000 milligrams (mg)

1 kilogram (kg) = 1,000 g

1 metric ton (t) = 1,000 kg

Capacity

1 metric tablespoon = 3 metric teaspoons

  = 15 milliliters (ml)

1 metric cup = 250 milliliters

1 liter = 1,000 milliliters

  = 4 metric cups

1 kiloliter (kl) = 1,000 liters

Comparing English and Metric Units

(English units are written first.)

Length

1 inch = 2.54 centimeters (exactly)

1 yard ≈ 0.91 meters

1 mile ≈ 1.6 kilometers

Capacity

1 teaspoon ≈ 4.9 milliliters

1 cup ≈ 0.94 metric cup

1 fluid ounce ≈ 30 milliliters

1 quart ≈ 0.94 liter

1 gallon ≈ 3.8 liters

Weight

1 ounce ≈ 28 grams

1 pound ≈ 0.45 kilogram

1 ton ≈ 0.91 metric ton

Tool Kit

Estimation

Estimation is an important math tool that enables you to answer questions such as the following:

- What is the approximate answer to this problem?
- Am I using the right operation to solve this problem?
- Did I place the decimal point in the correct place in the answer?
- Is my exact answer accurate/reasonable?

Rounding Whole Numbers

One way to estimate is to round whole numbers before doing a calculation. *To round a whole number is to replace it with a number (usually ending in one or more zeros) that is easier to work with.* Whole numbers are most often rounded to multiples of 10 (10, 100, 1,000, etc.).

Nearest Ten

32 rounds to 30

— less than 5
(round down)

Nearest Hundred

796 rounds to 800

— 5 or more
(round up)

Nearest Thousand

6,594 rounds to 7,000

— 5 or more
(round up)

Using Estimation in Whole-Number Problem Solving

Round each whole number before beginning a calculation.

Add	Estimate	Subtract	Estimate	Multiply	Estimate	Divide	Estimate
219	200	4,936	5,000	52	50		**400**
+ 87	+ 100	− 2,135	− 2,000	× 38	× 40	$19\overline{)8,376}$	$20\overline{)8,000}$
	300		**3,000**		**2,000**		

Using Estimation with Fractions and Decimals

Round each fraction or decimal to a whole number before beginning a calculation.*

Add	Estimate	Subtract	Estimate	Multiply	Estimate	Divide	Estimate
$5\frac{2}{3}$	6	$8\frac{3}{4}$	9	$4\frac{7}{8} \times 3\frac{1}{5}$	$5 \times 3 = \mathbf{15}$	$9\frac{1}{3} \div 2\frac{3}{4}$	$9 \div 3 = \mathbf{3}$
$+ 2\frac{1}{4}$	+ 2	$- 3\frac{1}{8}$	− 3				
	8		**6**				

---

* If a fraction is equal to $\frac{1}{2}$ or larger, round to the next largest whole number.

Tool Kit

Rounding to Compatible Numbers

A second way to estimate a quotient is to round so that the dividend and divisor are **compatible numbers.** Compatible numbers are based on the basic division facts. These numbers divide evenly (have no remainder).

Example: Divide: $8\overline{)624}$

Method 1. Estimate by rounding all numbers to numbers ending in zero.

Divide	Estimate
$8\overline{)624}$	$\overset{60}{10\overline{)600}}$

Method 2. Estimate by rounding to compatible numbers: 8 and 64 are compatible numbers.

Divide	Estimate
$8\overline{)624}$	$\overset{80}{8\overline{)640}}$

Note: The exact answer is 78. In this case, rounding to compatible numbers gives an estimate much closer to the exact answer than rounding to multiples of 10.

Estimating with Measurement Units

Problems involving measurement units often ask you to change a number of smaller units into a number of larger units.

Example 1: Write 38 in. as a number of feet and inches.

To estimate the answer, first remember that 1 ft. = 12 in. Then round 38 in. to 36 in. and divide. (*Note:* 36 and 12 are compatible numbers.)

Estimate: $36 \div 12 = $ **3 ft.**

Example 2: Write 26 ft. as a number of yards and feet.

To estimate, first remember that 1 yd. = 3 ft. Now round 26 to 27 and divide.

Estimate: $27 \div 3 = $ **9 yd.**

Estimating with Dollar and Cents

When estimating with dollars and cents, round small amounts to the nearest $1. Round larger amounts to the nearest $10 or $100.

Nearest $1

$2.78 rounds to $3.00

Round up if $.50 or more.

Nearest $10

$32.95 rounds to $30.00

Round down if less than $5.

Nearest $100

$291.75 rounds to $300.00

Round up if $50 or more.

Contents

Throughout the book, look for this logo 🐷 for smart financial tips and this logo 🐷 for bad choices to avoid. Also, don't forget to "Do the Math" at the end of each chapter.

Two Ways to Look at Debt

As a college student, Robyn B. loved using credit cards. They let her go out often with friends. They also let Robyn buy new clothes and travel during school breaks. By the time Robyn graduated, though, she owed almost $7,000.

Eventually, Robyn had to start to repay this money. Otherwise, she would face mounting fees, interest charges, and debt collectors. Now, Robyn had to scrimp and save. She made credit card payments. In addition, she had to pay for rent, food, gasoline, and other expenses. Robyn tells her story in a video on the Texas Guaranteed Student Loan Corporation "Adventures in Education" public service Web site.

Bad debt problems don't go away overnight. Suppose Robyn paid $300 per month and her interest rate was 18 percent. Paying off $7,000 in credit card debt would take twenty-nine months. If instead she paid only $200 per month, it would take fifty months—more than four years!

Three percent of college students carry credit card balances greater than $4,000, reports a 2012 Sallie Mae survey. More than 21 million students attended American colleges and universities that year, so that is more than 630,000 young adults!

The average amount of debt on a college student's credit card is $755, says the survey. Only 33 percent pay off outstanding balances every month. The other two-thirds incur interest and other fees.

Why Borrow?

Credit and debt can either help or hurt your financial life. Much depends on why, where, and how much you use them. Of course, how you follow through with paying matters, too.

A debt is a legal obligation to pay money. Americans' two biggest forms of personal debt are home mortgages and student loans. These types of debt help millions of people enjoy home ownership and going to college.

A credit agreement is a contract in which one party agrees to advance money for another. If you get a credit card, the company that issues the card agrees to pay when you present it at a store or for cash advances. In return, you agree to repay those funds, plus any interest or other fees. If you don't pay the bill on time, you owe more fees and interest.

Interest is a charge for the temporary use of money. Usually, interest is a percentage of the principal, which is the amount someone borrows. Fees are other charges for things, such as late payments or ATMs (automated teller machines). Credit card companies make money by charging interest and fees. Often, businesses that honor the card also pay a small percentage to the credit card company. In their view, credit cards boost customer spending.

Used properly, credit can be very convenient. Credit card holders rarely need to carry cash. Credit cards also make payments easier for air travel, hotels, online purchases, and some regular expenses.

Credit cards can ease temporary cash shortages, too. Suppose your car breaks down a week before payday. With a credit card, you can have repairs done right away. You would then pay when the credit card bill arrives.

Credit and debt are not available to everyone. Creditors want to know they can get their money back—preferably at a profit. Thus, companies investigate customers' creditworthiness. Creditors review applicants' credit history. For secured loans or credit agreements, they also investigate any property someone might surrender for failing to pay. If someone is a bad credit risk, he or she may be unable to get credit or a loan. Or, that person may have to pay higher interest or fees.

Learn about credit and debt now. You'll make smarter financial choices later.

Plan ahead. Save as much as possible for big-ticket items, such as college, a home, or a car. Every dollar saved is a dollar you won't have to borrow and pay interest on later.

Borrowing isn't a magic well for all your wants and needs. Sources of lending aren't always available. You eventually must pay back everything anyway.

Evaluate items you might borrow money for in comparison to other items in your budget. In general, limit debt to necessities that you can't otherwise buy with cash or savings.

Be Smart About Credit

Now it's your turn to "Do the Math." The end of each chapter features a math or word problem. Use what you learned in the chapter to help you answer the questions. The right math will help you make the right financial decisions.

Do the Math

Here are one year's costs for the state university you want to attend:

Expense	Amount
Tuition (resident)	$13,067
Dorm & Meal Plan	$10,596
University Health Fee	$862
Other Fees	$480
Books**	$1,438
Personal Expenses**	$4,130
Transportation**	$420
Total**	$30,993
**=estimate	

After talking with your parents, you estimate the following resources will be available:

Source of Funds	Amount
Savings	$8,500
Parents' Contribution	$11,900
Scholarship Award	$2,500
Summer Job	$2,250

1. If all expenses and resources are as shown, how much money would you still need?
2. Suppose you borrow that amount for each of the first three years of college, plus 112 percent of that amount for a fourth year. Not counting interest and fees, what would you owe?

Kinds of Credit and Debt

While forms of credit and debt vary, some basic concepts apply to them all. The principal is the amount someone borrows. If you borrow $10,000 for college, the principal of the loan is $10,000.

Interest is the cost for using someone else's money. Credit card interest and other fees make up the card's finance charge. Suppose you charged a $500 plane ticket on your credit card with an 18 percent annual interest rate. If you only paid $200 when the bill came, you would owe interest on the remaining $300. You'd probably owe interest on new charges, too. Contract terms might also let lenders and creditors collect late fees or other charges.

The term is how long you have to pay back a loan. Generally, the shorter a loan's term is, the larger payments will be. The longer a loan's term is, however, the more interest you'll probably pay.

Credit vs. Debit Cards

Until 2009, credit card companies aggressively courted teens' business. They wanted teens to charge—full steam ahead! As credit card companies raked in profits, teens paid high interest and fees.

Pitches to students included direct mail offers, T-shirt giveaways, and other promotions. Aletha B. filled out her name and address to redeem a free sandwich coupon. The next week, a credit card arrived in the mail with a $2,000 credit limit. Less than a year later, *CNN Money* reported, the naïve teen was in debt.

The Credit Card Accountability and Responsibility Disclosure Act of 2009 (Credit CARD Act) now restricts credit cards for young people under the age of twenty-one. Most teens under eighteen cannot get credit cards in their own names. From then until age twenty-one, young adults usually need a source of income to get credit on their own.

Prepaid or secured credit cards are an exception for teens and college students under age twenty-one. For those credit cards, the cardholder keeps the credit limit in a bank account. If the cardholder doesn't pay on time, the credit card company can automatically take money from that bank account.

Another exception is to have a cosigner. Another person—usually a parent or guardian—is on the account with the teen or college student. Then both people are responsible for any charges.

Most credit card companies offer revolving credit. Each credit card charge adds to the cardholder's debt, up to the card's dollar limit. A college student's card might allow charging up to $500 or $1,000, for example. Payments make more of the credit limit available for borrowing again.

Suppose a college student charges $450 on a credit card with a $500 limit. That person can only charge $50 more before hitting the limit. If the cardholder pays off the $450, the $500 credit limit is available again.

Debit cards are not the same as having debt. Rather, using a debit card contract authorizes withdrawals from a bank account. If you "charge" $90 for new clothes, for example, the money comes out of your account as soon as you use the card.

Debit cards require you to track your spending carefully. Otherwise, you risk overdrawing your account and incurring fees. Debit card purchases also don't carry all the safeguards that credit card purchases do. On the plus side, debit cards provide some convenience for online shopping, travel, or other purposes.

Student Loans

A student loan is a form of term loan. You borrow funds for an approved educational program. The lender usually pays the funds directly to the school. You agree to pay back the loan according to the contract.

Student loans generally offer lower interest rates than other loans. The Free Application for Federal Student Aid, or FAFSA, lets college financial aid offices and banks or other lenders determine how much you need. It also determines how much of your loans qualify for lower rates under different federal programs.

For example, information on the FAFSA may show that you need $4,000 in addition to money from your parents and savings. Perhaps a bank or student loan company might lend you that amount at a special rate of 3.4 or 5 percent. If you wanted to borrow more, the rate might be 7 or 8 percent. This is just an illustration. Programs' actual rates vary from year to year.

As a rule, students may defer, or postpone, repayment of the principal while they are enrolled in school more than half time. Some student loans also allow deferred payment of interest.

Your college education is a serious matter. Your financial obligations to pay for college are serious, too. Be sure you understand all the loan's terms. In most cases, you will need to repay the loans and interest, regardless of whether you finish college or get a high-paying job. Young adults usually cannot discharge student loans in bankruptcy, either.

Some lenders might also ask parents to guarantee student loans. Then, if students don't pay after graduation, the parents must pay. Such loans can put financial and emotional stress on families if parents are stuck with the bills.

Mortgages

A mortgage is a security interest in real property. The property owner borrows money from a bank or other lender. If the property owner fails to pay according to the loan's terms, the lender may take the property in a process called foreclosure.

People often use mortgages when buying a home. Most home loans have long terms—anywhere from ten to thirty years.

In many cases, borrowers must make a substantial down payment of 10 to 25 percent of the purchase price. Loans guaranteed by the Federal Housing Administration (FHA) require smaller down payments. As of 2013, FHA minimum down payments were as low as 3.5 percent.

Other Types of Credit and Debt

People also borrow money for other purposes. Car loans help people buy cars. Home improvement loans let people expand or repair houses. Like mortgages, both types of loans are usually secured loans. If borrowers don't pay on time, lenders may take the collateral—the property that secures the loan. A car dealer might repossess a car, for example.

Loans and credit also help people start and run businesses. Depending on the circumstances, lenders may require collateral for such loans.

Still, other types of loans provide cash for a short term. Examples include payday loans from check-cashing services and refund anticipation loans from tax return preparers. Both loans typically have high interest rates.

Cosigning loans and guaranteeing credit arrangements or loans count as debt, too. Don't enter into either arrangement lightly. You may become fully liable if the other person doesn't pay on time.

On the flip side, having a parent cosign for your first credit card or car loan can help get credit you couldn't get on your own. If that happens, don't abuse the cosigner's trust. Make timely payments so that person won't have to pay your bills or get a lower credit rating.

Take an active role in managing credit and debt. Keep your financial documents organized. Review bills or other financial materials right away. Mark due dates on a calendar so you don't accidentally miss payments.

Tracking and paying bills on time will help avoid unnecessary fees and debts. These practices will also aid in overall budgeting and financial planning.

Paying the minimum on credit card bills is not the same as paying off your debts. A minimum payment of $20 on a $1,000 credit card bill may avoid late charges. However, you'll still owe $980, plus interest and any new charges. Even if you made no new charges, paying off the balance could take eight years. Over that time, you'd pay hundreds of dollars in interest!

Instead, aim to pay the full balance of all credit card bills within the grace period. You'll avoid interest charges. Meanwhile, you'll build a good credit record.

Do the Math

Terry uses a credit card to buy a computer at the college bookstore. The computer costs $500, including tax. The credit card charges 21 percent interest. The minimum monthly payment is the greater of (a) $20 or (b) interest plus 2 percent of the outstanding balance. If less than $20 is owed, the entire amount is due.

1. Suppose Terry does not charge anything else and makes only the minimum payments of $20 on time each month. Paying off the debt will take thirty-four months, and the total interest paid will be $163.32. What percentage would the total interest be of the computer's $500 purchase price?

2. Suppose Terry makes ten monthly payments of $50, plus one more payment of $54.39. If Terry makes all payments on time, the debt will be paid off in eleven months, and the total interest will be $54.39. How much less interest would Terry pay this way than if he paid just $20 per month?

Be Smart About Credit

The Costs of Credit and Debt

Interest is the most obvious cost for credit and debt. Calculating that cost isn't always obvious, however. Other fees and charges may apply, too. Understand all the costs of credit and debt so you can make smart choices.

Fixed vs. Variable Rate

A fixed interest rate stays the same for the term of a loan or credit agreement. The advantage of fixed rates for borrowers is certainty. Fixed rates lock in an interest rate. Borrowers know what their costs are and can plan accordingly. If rates fall a lot, they can consider refinancing the loan. As discussed later, refinancing involves costs, but it's sometimes worth it.

Variable interest rates can change. The lender still gets the going rate for interest, even if market conditions change. Borrowers may benefit by paying a lower rate at first. However, borrowers risk

having to pay more as rates rise. Both term loans and revolving credit agreements can have variable interest rates.

Mortgages and other term loan contracts with variable interest rates spell out what happens when rates change. In some cases, monthly payments go up if rates rise. For example, a $750 monthly mortgage payment might go up to $800. Other contracts might keep the same monthly payments but change how long the debtor must keep making those payments. A borrower might make the same $750 monthly payment, for example, while additional interest is added to the loan's balance. Then paying off the loan might take another year or more.

Most credit cards charge interest on the average daily balance. The card issuer calculates the average owed on each day of the billing period. It then multiplies that by the monthly interest rate.

Sometimes, the average daily balance includes finance charges from a prior billing cycle. Then the new finance charge will include compound interest—interest charged on the interest. Compounding makes credit cards' effective annual rate higher than the simple annual percentage rate. For instance, a credit card's stated interest rate might be 18 percent. Compound interest might bring the effective annual rate up to 21 percent.

Credit cards with grace periods let cardholders avoid new finance charges by paying off all amounts within twenty days or whatever the contract says. Smart consumers only use credit cards with grace periods.

Be Smart About Credit

Other Credit Card Fees

Interest isn't the only way credit card companies make money. Annual fees for having a card can range from $15 to nearly $300. An airline might charge $100 each year for a credit card that earns frequent flier miles, for example. Occasionally, the benefits might substantially exceed any annual fee. Usually, though, credit cards without annual fees offer better deals.

Low-use or low-activity fees are another trap. These fees impose charges on people who don't use credit cards very often. In effect, they encourage people to incur debt.

Watch out for credit card limits, because exceeding them will cost you. Suppose you charge $1,600 on a card with a $1,500 credit limit. Federal law says companies need your approval before letting you exceed the credit limit. You may think the credit card company is being nice if it lets you charge another $100 of charges. However, you could then owe a $25 fee. Going over the credit limit again within six months might cost another $35.

If you pay your bill late, watch out! As of 2013, companies can collect up to $25 as a late fee. Another late payment within six months raises the fee to $35. Meanwhile, finance charges mount up.

That's not all! Foreign transaction fees on credit cards might add 1 to 3 percent to purchases made abroad. Even "free" credit card rewards sometimes charge fees to redeem rewards, such as gift cards, or to reinstate points after missing a payment. If you pay for something, it isn't really free, is it?

Points, Fees, and Other Loan Costs

Mortgages also involve costs besides interest. Application fees and loan origination fees pay someone to review your application. There's another application fee for federal home loan guaranty programs, such as those for the FHA or Veterans Benefits Administration.

Appraisal fees let lenders learn how much property is worth. Inspection fees make sure any building's structure is sound and satisfies safety codes. A survey confirms the property's legal description. Title insurance protects the lender if someone else claims he owns rights in the property. Attorney fees and court filings can be extra. All these costs can run several thousand dollars. Homeowners usually must pay these costs at the closing—the time when the property sale officially takes place.

Lenders may also charge fees called points. Each point equals 1 percent of the loan's principal. Two points on a $100,000 loan would be $2,000, for example. In theory, points pay the lender's administrative costs in making the loan. In practice, points are another way that lenders make money.

In 2012, the Consumer Financial Protection Bureau proposed rules that would require lenders to give borrowers a no-point, no-fee option. The option's interest rate would build in costs that fees would otherwise cover. Then customers could compare costs from different lenders more easily.

Be Smart About Credit

In any case, do the math. Online loan calculators provide worksheets that can help. Consider all the costs and loan terms. Then decide what's best for your short- and long-term goals.

Whenever possible, avoid any mortgage or other loan with a prepayment penalty. Paying an extra one to six months' interest makes it harder to cut down outstanding debt.

Shop around before signing up for any credit card, mortgage, or other loan. Just as you'd compare prices and features for clothes, electronics, or other products, investigate the terms and true costs for credit and debt. Credit and debt are financial products. Try to get the best value for your hard-earned money.

Some credit cards waive the annual fee for the first year. That may sound like a good deal to earn airline miles or other rewards. But the thirteenth month's bill could charge you a $100 fee. That's usually not such a good deal.

Other credit cards offer low introductory rates. Maybe the annual interest rate for the first year is just 6 percent. You might run up charges but then find yourself owing an annual rate of 20 percent after the first year.

Read all the fine print before accepting any deal. Can you live with all the terms after the introductory period ends?

Be Smart About Credit

Do the Math

To finance their home, Kerry and Edward get a mortgage loan of $100,000. The fixed interest rate for their twenty-year loan is 6 percent a year. Payments are due in equal monthly installments of $716.43 for 239 months, with one final payment of $716.92.

This chart shows the loan's amortization over the twenty-year period. Amortization breaks down how much of each loan payment goes toward principal and interest. As the outstanding principal decreases over time, the interest share of each payment also goes down.

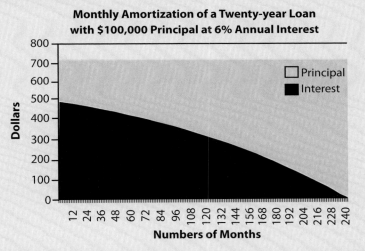

Monthly Amortization of a Twenty-year Loan with $100,000 Principal at 6% Annual Interest

1. About what fraction of the first year's payments goes toward interest?
2. About how long will it take before a majority of each payment goes toward principal?
3. If Kerry and Edward make all payments on time without any prepayments, they will pay $71,943.69 in interest over twenty years. What percentage is that of the loan's initial principal?

The Costs of Credit and Debt

Credit Ratings and Reports

Even if you don't currently have credit cards or loans, you'll probably need or want them sometime in the future. Get your financial house in order now, so you won't face unexpected glitches later.

What's Your Score?

Equifax, Experian, and Trans Union are the three main credit bureaus in the United States. The companies collect detailed information about people's credit history. They then calculate credit scores. Credit card companies and other potential lenders get these scores when they investigate your creditworthiness. Employers and property owners might also review your credit history.

Credit scores are also called FICO scores. Previously known as Fair Isaac Corporation, FICO developed the first computer software to analyze creditworthiness. FICO's credit scores range from 300 to 850. The higher the score, the more creditworthy someone is.

For most people, payment history makes up just over a third of the FICO score. A history of late payments hurts someone's FICO score. Nearly another third of the FICO score comes from how much people owe. Someone whose charges often approach his or her credit card limits is likely a higher credit risk.

The last third of the FICO score looks at several factors. A long credit history can boost someone's score. Conversely, many recent credit card applications can damage the score. Also, having many unsecured credit cards appears riskier than having a few credit cards and a secured mortgage or other installment loan .

How a FICO score breaks down

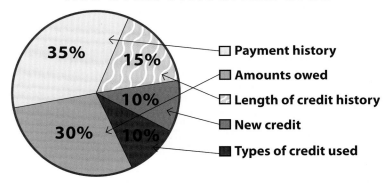

Of course, the final decision on any credit or loan application rests with each potential creditor. Besides your credit score, companies may also consider other factors, such as current income.

Check Your Report Card

Federal law lets you get one free credit report per year from each major credit bureau. Stagger requests every four months or so. Then you can check your credit situation three times per year, instead of just once.

Beware of TV and Internet promotions that require fees or memberships to get your free credit report. Use the Federal Trade Commission's (FTC) sponsored Web site instead: <www .annualcreditreport.com>.

Free credit reports usually don't include the actual FICO score, but they do contain important details about your credit history. That data includes your creditors and loans, payment history, and other information. Correct any errors right away. Even if there are no errors, see how your credit report stacks up against the FICO scoring factors.

Improve Your Score

Regular studying can help you do better on a pop quiz. Likewise, regular attention to your credit and debt situation can improve your credit score.

First and foremost, pay bills on time. A poor record marks you as a bad risk. The lower you can keep any outstanding balances, the better. Getting too close to your credit limit signals potential problems. Better yet, pay debts in full!

Resist the urge to move debts around from card to card. Using credit and debt isn't a shell game. Companies might offer low introductory rates if you transfer outstanding balances to new credit cards. However, those rates usually jump up after a short time. In any case, you still owe your debts and interest.

Apply for new loans or credit accounts only when you need them. You don't get points for having a wallet full of credit cards. Having fewer credit cards means fewer potential credit limits to max out.

If you have no credit history and limited income, consider getting a low-limit student credit card when you go to college. A $500 or $1,000 credit card would be enough to handle most emergencies or large necessary purchases, such as textbooks.

If you don't get a low-limit student credit card when you're in college, consider getting a debit card or secured credit card. Both options limit your spending to money in the bank. Be extra careful to avoid overdrafts and late payments.

Watch Out for Identity Theft

Identity theft happens when criminals use credit information and other personal data for financial gain. While identity thieves enjoy ill-gotten goods, you may find yourself left in the lurch. Bill collectors may pester you for crooks' debts. Meanwhile, crooks can ruin your credit rating.

The FTC fielded 279,156 complaints about identity theft in 2011. Eight percent of those cases involved teens. That's 19,563 young people who lost money or had to correct their credit history. You can't always prevent identity theft. However, you can make it less likely by following some guidelines:

- Keep private information private. Don't disclose your social security number, account number, or other financial data unless you know exactly who gets the information and why.
- Avoid easy-to-guess passwords. Use mixtures of uppercase and lowercase letters, numbers, and symbols.
- Use different passwords for different Web sites. Hackers have broken into many databases, including LinkedIn, Best Buy, Sony, and Yahoo! Contributor Network. When people always use the same password, identity thieves get more chances to commit fraud.
- Change passwords for e-mail and online accounts every sixty to ninety days.
- Shop or make payments only on secure Web sites.
- Don't fall for phishing expeditions. Any e-mail or phone call asking for your account number, social security number, or other personal information could be bogus. If someone raises a real concern, call back the phone number listed on your credit card or account papers.
- Don't share too much on social media. Your birthday, anniversary, pet's name, and other personal information can clue criminals into possible passwords.

Be Smart About Credit

GOOD ¢

Request your free credit report even if you don't have a credit card or other debt yet. Check for any credit cards, loans, or other accounts that you didn't open. If you see potential identity theft problems, act promptly:

- Notify law enforcement.

- Put a fraud alert in your credit files.

- Write to credit institutions or debt collectors about disputed accounts and charges.

- Review your credit reports regularly to follow up.

NON ¢

Don't fall for credit repair scams. Some companies may try to charge you for services that you could do yourself for free.

Even worse, some people may pressure you to break the law. Trying to erase accurate information in your credit history is illegal. Inventing a new credit identity is also illegal.

Do the Math

Pat's credit history shows the following:

- Buy! Buy! Revolving credit card since 2007 with three late payments per year. Current balance on the account is $5,899. Credit limit is $6,000.

- GasGoCo credit card since 2006 with all payments on time. Credit limit is $1,500 and current balance is $49.

- ShopMore, PayBuddy, and Bricks & Mortar revolving credit cards. Outstanding balances on these cards are $4,000, $4,400, and $4,800, respectively. Each card's credit limit is $5,000.

- Revolving credit cards issued within the last six months by ClassyStuff, Pampered, and Prestige stores with credit limits of $8,000 each. None of the cards has been used.

- Secured car loan with an outstanding balance of $2,000.

1. How much does Pat currently owe?

2. What advice might you give for improving Pat's credit score?

Be Smart About Credit

Know Your Rights and Responsibilities

Chapter 5

Smart consumers follow the rule of *caveat emptor*: buyer beware! When it comes to money matters, watch out!

Shop around carefully. Read all financial documents and understand what you're getting into. If there's any doubt, don't use credit or incur more debt.

The Legal Landscape

Detailing all the law's requirements is beyond this book's scope. In general, the law provides some protection against predatory practices. That term includes many types of abusive, unfair, and fraudulent conduct. Hiking credit card fees without notice is one example. Misleading customers into buying unnecessary services, such as payment insurance, is another example.

The Truth in Lending Act and Regulation Z set out the main federal rules dealing with credit and loan agreements. The FTC, the Consumer Financial Protection Bureau, and federal banking authorities enforce the law. In general, all customers have basic rights:

- Lenders and credit card companies must provide detailed disclosures. Among other things, they must clearly state what the customer must pay and when. They must explain interest rates, fees, penalties, and other contract terms.
- Creditors must give notice if certain terms change.
- Creditors must state how customers can dispute charges.
- Creditors can use customers' confidential information only in certain ways.
- Creditors cannot discriminate because of factors such as race, religion, sex, national background, or marital status.
- Creditors face limits on whom they may deal with and what terms they can impose. For example, most teens cannot currently get unsecured credit cards in their own name.
- Creditors and collection agencies cannot improperly harass customers. For example, bill collectors can't call at all hours of the day and night.
- Subject to some exceptions, creditors cannot collect on debts that customers did not actually incur.

Unfortunately, the law does not enforce itself. Report any potential violations to the FTC or Consumer Financial Protection Bureau.

Be Smart About Credit

Do Your Homework!

Sadly, the law does not prevent people from making bad deals. Remember to consider all the costs of any deal, including tacked-on fees. Slick salespeople often sound like they're offering a great service. In fact, they're out to make a profit.

Get all promises in writing. Then read documents carefully. If you don't understand any deal, don't do it!

File all credit and loan information so it's handy. Keep hard copies of contracts, statements, and receipts organized in a safe place. Store any computer data only on removable media that no one else can access.

Review all billing statements promptly. If you need to dispute a charge, follow the creditor's procedures. Failure to do so could waive your rights and cost you money!

Call card issuers immediately if credit or debit cards are lost or stolen. Doing so preserves your rights and helps limit liability.

Never deal with a loan shark—a lender that operates outside the law. Loan sharks practice usury (unethical or immoral loans) by charging far more interest than the law allows. Even worse, they may threaten violence for late payments. Inform law enforcement immediately if anyone approaches you for such arrangements.

Do the Math

- As a smart consumer, you promptly review your latest PayU$ Credit Card statement and see two problems. (See statement shown on page 35.) First, you only dined once at Del's Deli on January 16. Your bill was $23.41.
- Second, you returned a defective video game to Big Box Department Store on January 8. The statement does not show the store's credit of $29.46.

- Write a letter contesting the errors to PayU$ Credit Card Company. State how much you will remit before the due date to pay the uncontested balance in full.

Be Smart About Credit

Pay U$ Credit Card Statement

Account Information		Payment Summary	
Account	123456789	Previous Balance (+)	$223.66
Name	Your Name	Payments/Credits (–)	–$223.66
Billing Period	01/02/16–02/01/16	Purchases/Debits (+)	$730.42
Statement Date	February 3, 2016	Finance Charges/Fees (+)	0
Payment Due Date	February 27, 2016	Cash Advances (+)	0
		Current Amount Due	$730.42
		Minimum Payment	$20.00

Reference	Transaction Date	Post Date	Description	Charges	Credits
xxxx11	01/02/16	01/05/16	Big Box Dept Store	$76.76	
xxxx22	01/02/16	01/05/16	Build It Yourself	$24.15	
xxxx33	01/03/16	01/05/16	Go Go Gasoline	$48.14	
xxxx44	01/07/16	01/08/16	Internet Provider	$15.00	
xxxx55	01/12/16	01/12/16	Tacky Taxi	$18.00	
xxxx66		01/14/16	PAYMENT		$223.66
xxxx77	01/16/16	01/18/16	Del's Deli	$23.41	
xxxx88	01/16/16	01/18/16	Del's Deli	$45.22	
xxxx99	01/16/16	01/18/16	Del's Deli	$30.66	
xxxx10	01/16/16	01/18/16	Del's Deli	$18.98	
xxxx20	01/23/16	01/25/16	FlyBy Airlines	$243.56	
xxxx30	01/25/16	01/26/16	Designer Duds	$186.54	

Know Your Rights and Responsibilities

Troubleshooting Tools

Smart money management is the best way to avoid getting into financial trouble. Have a budget and update it regularly. Distinguish between needs and wants in your budget. Make paying for necessities a priority. If your budget doesn't balance, find ways to curb spending.

Schedule a weekly time to pay bills. Make sure your records reflect all automatic payments, check payments, and online transactions.

Beyond this, remember the most important rule for managing credit and debt: Never charge or borrow more than you can readily pay back! Don't spend more money for current expenses, including any long-term debt payments, than you have coming in.

If problems do crop up, don't ignore them! The more you let debt grow, the longer it will take to pay off.

A Nation of Debtors

Sadly, trouble with debt happens too often. As of December 2012, 46.7 percent of American households carried balances on their credit cards. Among those households, NerdWallet.com says, the average outstanding credit card debt was $15,325.

Delinquent debt can lead to hassles with bill collectors. Some creditors may also garnish wages. They can get your employer to pay them directly.

Nonpayment of secured loans can entitle creditors to seize collateral. On a car loan, for example, they might repossess the car. For home loans, creditors can foreclose on the mortgage.

Bad mortgage debts were one factor behind the financial crisis that hit in 2008. Many people had borrowed money on terms they couldn't afford. While housing prices kept rising, people kept refinancing their loans. After housing prices peaked in 2007, the bubble burst. Many people who couldn't refinance defaulted on their debts.

Meanwhile, banks and others had sold securities based on bundles of bad mortgage debts. As some businesses failed, companies became more reluctant to make loans. Many businesses' cash flow suffered. The economy slumped, and high unemployment followed. Thousands more people had problems paying their mortgages. Foreclosure filings exceeded 2.8 million in both 2009 and 2010. Banks repossessed more than 1 million homes in 2010.

By 2012, more than one-fourth of all mortgage owners were still "underwater," says the real estate database company Zillow. That means those homeowners owed more than their homes were worth. Even selling the home wouldn't pay off the mortgage.

Getting Help

Mortgage foreclosures cause massive upheavals for families. Yet all debt problems can become serious.

Suppose you were usually good about paying bills on time. Then a family member gets sick or you are laid off from a job. If a situation seems temporary, some companies may waive fees or change the payment plan.

In other cases, problems result from relying on credit and debt too often. If that happens to you, you need more than a payment plan. You also need to stop the bad practices that produced the problem.

The National Foundation for Credit Counseling has an online database of nonprofit organizations. Also, check out agencies with the Better Business Bureau.

Beware of anyone who guarantees you'll only pay pennies on the dollar. Also, avoid any agencies that ask for huge up-front fees or demand detailed financial data before saying what they can do.

Reputable credit counselors provide free information about the scope and cost of their services, their licensing and qualifications, and confidentiality. Get details in writing. If you can't afford the fees, see if the agency can modify them. If not, seek help elsewhere. Read everything before signing!

Credit counselors should help you review your budget. In some cases, they may also recommend a debt management plan. Basically, you pay money into an account. The credit counselor then pays creditors with those funds. In return for regular payments, creditors may reduce interest charges or waive certain fees.

Before agreeing, get assurance that the credit counselor will make all payments on time. Also, don't just take an agency's word that all creditors are on board. Double-check with your creditors. Unless they confirm their agreement, keep paying creditors directly.

Whether you use a debt management plan or not, don't expect business as usual for future credit card use. If you're facing huge debts, you probably should not use credit at all except for dire emergencies. New debts make it even harder to get back on track financially.

Bankruptcy—The Last Resort

If all else fails, consider personal bankruptcy. With some exceptions, the court takes jurisdiction over a debtor's property. Federal law determines which types of creditors are paid before others. The court distributes the debtor's property as far as it will go. The court then wipes out any remaining debts.

Bankruptcy is one way for debtors to get a fresh start. However, bankruptcy won't wipe out student loans and child support payments. The law also limits discharges of tax obligations.

In addition, debtors can't declare personal bankruptcy again for at least eight years. Home mortgage lenders and others are also more reluctant to make loans after people declare bankruptcy.

More importantly, a fresh financial start usually won't help unless financial habits change. For this reason, federal courts make everyone seeking personal bankruptcy go through credit counseling.

Of course, your best bet is to avoid trouble in the first place. Learn now how to budget and live within your means. That's the best way to avoid getting neck-deep in debt!

Be Smart About Credit

GOOD ¢

Resist people who urge you to "stretch" and incur extra debt for a pricier home, engagement ring, wedding, car, or other large purchases. You'll be paying the monthly bills—not them!

NON ¢

Don't let pride or denial delude you. Ignoring financial problems won't make them disappear. If you have a credit or debt problem, admit it and seek help.

Do the Math

● Refinancing is taking out a new loan to replace an older one. In the right cases, refinancing can produce big savings. Lower monthly payments may be more manageable, too.

● However, refinancing doesn't always make sense. Before making any deal, consider the costs.

● Assume Kerry and Edward took out a twenty-year home mortgage loan of $100,000 with a fixed rate of 6 percent a year. After three years of monthly payments of $716.43, the outstanding principal on the loan is $92,255.77.

● 1. Suppose interest rates drop to 5.3 percent. If Kerry and Edward refinance at that rate for seventeen years, their new monthly payments will be $687.09. Suppose refinancing will cost 2 points—2 percent of the amount being refinanced—plus another $2,000. Calculate the refinancing costs. Should Kerry and Edward refinance?

● 2. Now suppose Kerry and Edward could refinance the outstanding balance of $92,255.77 with a fifteen-year fixed rate mortgage at 3 percent. The monthly payment would drop to $637.10. Assume the refinancing costs would be the same: 2 percent of the amount being refinanced, plus another $2,000.

a. How much lower would the monthly payments be if they refinanced?
b. How long would it take to recoup the costs of refinancing?
c. What other benefit would refinancing have if Kerry and Edward plan to stay in their home for many years?

Troubleshooting Tools

Glossary

collateral—Property that secures someone's promise to repay a loan.

credit agreement—Contract in which one party agrees to advance money for another. Credit card agreements are a type of credit agreement.

credit history—Past performance under contracts for loans, credit cards, or other types of debt.

creditworthiness—Degree to which someone seems likely to pay creditors on time.

debit card account—Contract under which use of a debit card authorizes immediate bank account withdrawals.

foreclosure—Process by which a creditor may seize and gain title to property that secures a loan.

identity theft—Fraudulent use of someone else's personal information for gain.

interest—Payment or charge for the use of money, usually expressed as a percentage of the amount owed.

Be Smart About Credit

predatory practices—Abusive, unfair, or fraudulent business conduct.

principal—Amount of a loan or investment.

refinancing—Taking out a new loan to replace an older one.

revolving credit—Arrangement under which payments free up more of a credit limit for borrowing.

secured loan—Lending arrangement that lets a creditor seize property if the debtor doesn't pay on time.

term loan—Lending arrangement where someone must repay all amounts owed within a defined time.

usury—Unethical or immoral lending.

Learn More

Books

Butler, Tamsen. *The Complete Guide to Personal Finance: For Teenagers and College Students.* Ocala, Florida: Atlantic Publishing Group, 2010

Chatzky, Jean. *Not Your Parents' Money Book: Making, Saving, and Spending Your Own Money.* New York: Simon and Schuster Books for Young Readers, 2010.

La Bella, Laura. *How Consumer Credit and Debt Work.* New York: Rosen Publishing Group, 2013.

Lawless, Robert. *The Student's Guide to Financial Literacy.* Westport, Conn.: Greenwood, 2010.

Thompson, Helen. *Understanding Credit.* Broomall, Pa.: Mason Crest Publishers, 2011.

Internet Addresses

Bankrate.com: Educating Teens About Credit
<http://www.bankrate.com> Search for: "Teen" or "Teens"

CNN Money 101: Teaching Teens About Credit
<http://money.cnn.com> Search for: "Teen" or "Teens"

The Mint.org: Fun Financial Literacy Activities
<http://themint.org/>

Do the Math Answer Key

Chapter 1: Two Ways to Look at Debt

1. The shortfall is $5,843: $30,993–$25,150 = $5,843.
2. The principal amount of the loans would be $24,073.16: (3 × $5,843) + (1.12 × $5,843) = $24,073.16.

Chapter 2: Different Kinds of Credit and Debt

1. To calculate how much the total interest is as a percentage of the purchase price, divide $163.32 by the $500 purchase price, and then multiply the quotient by 100. So, ($163.32/$500) × 100 = 32.7 percent, rounded to the nearest tenth of a percent.
2. Subtract $54.39 from $163.32, and the remainder is $108.93.

Chapter 3: The Costs of Credit and Debt

1. The answer is 5/7. For the first year, payments are approximately $700 per month, and the interest portion of each payment is roughly $500. 500/700 equals 5/7.
2. Hold a straight edge parallel to the x-axis around where $358 would fall on the y-axis. The straight edge intersects the curve at a point above the x-axis about three-fourths of the way between 96 months and 108 months. Divide by 12 months for each year. The answer is 8.75, or almost 9 years.
3. Divide $71,943.69 by $100,000, and multiply the quotient by 100 to get the answer: 71.9 percent. This problem does not consider any fees or points Kerry and Edward may have paid to get the mortgage loan.

Chapter 4: Credit Ratings and Reports

1. Add the current balances for each credit card and loan: $5,899 + $49 + $4,000 + $4,400 + $4,800 + $2000 = $21,148
2. Advice will vary, but should include: (a) paying all bills on time; (b) reducing the outstanding credit card balances; and (c) waiting before applying for more loans or credit.

Chapter 5: Know Your Rights and Responsibilities

The letter should use a business format. It should include your name, address, the date, account number, and date of the disputed statement. Then it should briefly explain the reasons for the three disputed charges from Del's Deli. It should also note the credit of $29.46 for the returned video game. State that you're enclosing copies of relevant receipts. Also, note that you'll pay the undisputed amount of $606.10 by the due date to avoid finance charges.

Chapter 6: Troubleshooting Tools

1. Refinancing costs would be 2 percent of $92,255.77, plus $2000, for a total of $3,845.12. Monthly payments would be $29.34 lower, but divide $3,845.12 by $29.34, and you get 131 months. Divide by 12 to convert that time to years. Recouping the refinancing costs would take almost 11 years. Refinancing does not make sense.
2. a. Subtract $637.10 from $716.43. Monthly payments would be $79.33 less.
   b. Recouping $3,845.12 of refinancing costs would take 48.47 months—just over 4 years.
   c. The shorter loan term would save Kerry and Edward two years of monthly payments.

Index